T5-AVM-431
WITHDRAWN
University Libraries
University of Memphis

TECHNICAL and BUSINESS REPORT PREPARATION

Third Edition

ROBLEY WINFREY

Registered Professional Engineer
Formerly, Professor of Civil Engineering,
Iowa State University

The Iowa State University Press, *Ames,* Iowa, U.S.A.

ROBLEY WINFREY is Chief of the Economic Research Division, Office of Research, U.S. Bureau of Public Roads, an assignment he received in 1958. Prior to that, he was Chief of the Personnel and Training Division of the Bureau. Before joining the Bureau he was Professor of Civil Engineering at Iowa State University. In addition to teaching, he was engaged in research on valuation and highways from 1922 to 1952. He holds both his B.S. and his M.S. in Civil Engineering from Iowa State University. In 1961 he was guest professor at Stanford University in the Engineering Economic Planning Program, and has taught evening university courses in Washington, D.C. He has published almost a hundred professional papers and he is the coauthor of *Engineering Valuation and Depreciation.* He is a member of the American Society of Civil Engineers, American Society for Engineering Education, Institute of Traffic Engineers, and the Highway Research Board.

Composed and printed by the
Iowa State University Press,
Ames, Iowa, U.S.A.

Revised from *Report Preparation*
by Frank Kerekes and Robley Winfrey

First edition 1948
Second edition 1951
Third edition 1962
Second printing 1967

Library of Congress Catalog Card Number: 62-9119

Stock # 1670

Preface

Decision making in the professions, business, and government is the responsibility of many officials from the top level of command down through junior officials and assistant professionals. Most decisions are reached only after careful study and digestion of reports from a lower echelon or from a consultant. Thus technology, business, and government owe much of their progress and daily accomplishments to their system of internal reporting as well as to reports requested from the outside. Poor reports may be responsible for the wrong decision; the decision to do nothing may be the result of an unconvincing report.

The ability to write good reports is a valuable personal asset that leads to recognition and advancement as well as to personal satisfaction. Study and practice are needed to know how to shape this tool for particular application and how to use it effectively. This book is a guide to assist men in science, technology, business, and government to acquire skill and effectiveness in the preparation of their reports, and to help them avoid pitfalls.

Fortunately, for the sake of the art of communication, there is no uniform standard for reports. There are, however, generally accepted forms, techniques, and conventions. Business executives and technical men have evolved criteria by which the goodness of a report may be judged.

Effective reports have three good qualities: (1) a sound technical foundation, (2) good, readable, and understandable English, and (3) good physical appearance, appropriate for the purpose. These three qualities may be obtained by an author of a report if he sets out to do so. His greatest opportunities for improvement probably come in form, content, language, arrangement, and physical appearance. Too few authors of reports give sufficient critical attention to the underlying principles and basic techniques that serve as the ready tools with which reports are made to achieve their purpose effectively.

This book contains material, techniques, procedures, and suggestions by which the three key qualities may be attained. Those whose duty it is to prepare reports should not, however, regard the specific citations of this book to be the last or only word on the subject. Usually there are several acceptable ways to prepare a certain report or to handle the details within a report. Each author should make certain that he has adopted that treatment which will best serve his objective. Some organizations have carefully prepared guides, instructions, and formats for preparing their reports. Where these good standards exist, they should be followed; where they do not exist, study of this book will help.

The typewritten, handmade report is the original form of every written report whether or not it is later duplicated by other means. Above all else, the writer of a report needs to know how to prepare this first copy. Once this copy is completed, the additional work of duplication is largely mechanical. However, one who is familiar with the processes of duplication can facilitate the publication of his report by anticipating the needs of the duplicating process employed.

Although the author wishes to stress the importance of correct, clear, concise, and convincing expression, it is reasonable to assume that the individual already has acquired adequate skill in writing by the time he is assigned the responsibility for preparing a report. Therefore, a comprehensive treatment of English and composition is omitted. Skill of writing is but one of the basic tools.

Report preparation also uses important and specialized techniques in the collection of data, in the assimilation and analysis of the pertinent information, in the exercise of discriminating judgment, and in the expression of ideas by graphic and mathematical systems. Therefore, the emphasis is upon the complete process of *preparation* rather than upon the single skill of *writing*.

In preparing this third edition, the author has used the second edition as the working base. To Frank Kerekes, coauthor of the second edition, is extended a well-deserved, sincere, personal gratitude. His contributions of philosophy, expertness in writing, and counsel in the prior editions have carried over to this edition. This author is forever thankful for his help, his personal friendship, and inspiration as a great teacher.

To former students, associates, and to the field of report preparation in general, the author is thankful for the privilege of drawing upon their productions and experiences. Thanks is given to industrial organizations for furnishing illustrative specimens. Lastly, but importantly, to Verne C. Winfrey is given the author's most personal thanks for inspiration, tolerance, and editorial counsel, as well as for much of the statistical work on the section on readability.

Robley Winfrey

Table of Contents

Technical and Business Report Preparation

CHAPTER 1

Reports

As a form of literature, the report has gained an important and universally recognized place in the professions, business, industry, and government. Its form, arrangement, and content have acquired certain characteristics that distinguish it from other writings. Although the readers of reports look for these special characteristics, the written report still affords unlimited opportunity for creativeness, initiative, and individuality. Each report can (and should) be distinctive. This is one reason why the study of reports is an educational and professional requirement.

WHAT THE REPORT IS

A report is a document written in business, technical, or scientific prose for the purpose of conveying information to a higher echelon of the management of the organization. Although this definition is in terms of a written document in prose form, a report may be made orally or through a motion picture or other graphic device.

The features of the report that distinguish it from other forms of writings and business documents are:

1. A report is usually prepared at the request of a superior or a client; a report is seldom prepared by the author upon his own initiative.
2. A report is prepared and read not by free choice, but in the line of duty; reading of a report is for business or professional gain and not for entertainment or relaxation.
3. A report is prepared under a specific situation to meet the need of management officials for information or a basis of making a decision.
4. The intended readership of a report is limited to a single individual or a closely bound group, such as the president, manager, owner, chief engineer, a committee, a commission, a council, a board, or a legislative body.
5. A report is characterized by its liberal use of tabulations, graphics, mathematics, and technical and business phraseology and concept.
6. A report is factual; when opinion and conclusions are given they are labeled as such and their basis is made known to the reader.
7. A report will contain a complete description of the methodology used in getting together the information contained in the report, and in addition all relevant information in detail.
8. A report is a document not sold on the market and not in competition with other literature.

Truly, the report is a specialized form of business and professional literature designed as a tool to facilitate management decisions and management control of its activities – it is not fiction, not entertaining reading, not reading for just anyone who may come across the document, and is not written in popular style to gain readers.

PROMINENCE OF REPORTS

The report is the one means of communication by which the several levels of supervision and management can be kept posted on the situations under their responsibility and supplied with the facts upon which their decisions are to be based. The growth in the use of reports as a tool of management has been parallel with the growth of business, industry, and government. Only in the small one-man managed business or organization is there an absence of reports. The report is the eyes, ears, and legs of the manager in those organizations sufficiently large to prevent the manager from keeping daily personal contact with all activity.

There are two main uses of the report: first, internal, within an organization when one individual or department reports to another individual or department; and second, external, when a consultant reports to his client.

That the report is a prominent and important tool in business is illustrated by the fact that during 1959 and 1960 a partial search of the literature disclosed that 25 periodicals printed 36 articles on some phase of the technical report. In addition, 26 periodicals printed 44 articles on the annual report. Closely related to these published articles on reports were the 51 articles on technical writing published by 34 periodicals. There is such a close association of technical writing with report writing that the foregoing figures could be combined into one total to represent the whole picture — 85 periodicals and 131 articles.

Typical of the publications that printed articles on reports and technical writing in 1959 and 1960 are the following:

Journal of Accounting	*Iron Age*
Advertising Age	*Machine Design*
American Business	*Management Methods*
Chemical Engineering	*Mechanical Engineering*
Electronics	*Mill and Factory*
Gas Age	*Nation's Business*
Industrial Marketing	*Newsweek*
Office Management	*Public Relations Journal*
Oil and Gas Journal	*Sales Management*
Petroleum Engineering	*Supervision*
Product Engineering	

Typical titles of the articles published are:

How to write better reports; three ways to test your writing
Design and development of an engineering report
Technical reports; a new look
Color aids technical reports
Organizing and administering the reporting function
Basics of effective reporting
How to make your reports clear, concise, and effective
Reports which management can use for control
How to write a good technical article
How to encourage engineers to write
Professional man and the obligation of authorship
Planning illustrations first simplifies writing later
Six steps to effective engineering writing
Writing for the business press
Speed thoughts into words — business man's writing job
Effective communication; saying it simply gets it done fast
What is technical writing
How to be interesting, though factual
Preparing a prize-winning annual report
Annual reports — an effective public relation tool
Annual reports; changes in the making
Perking up annual reports
Annual report grows up at last
How to popularize your annual report
Blind spot in annual reports

When it is considered that the publishers of these articles on the report and technical writing must maintain a continuous readership or go out of business, the logical conclusions are: (1) The publishers must consider such articles profitable to publish, (2) the readers thereof must consider them helpful to their responsibilities, and (3) the authors thereof realize the importance to others of report and technical writing. All of which is sufficient to prove that a serious study of the report is profitable both for business and for the professional person.

The major book publishing companies have available some 40 or so books on report and technical writing.

Technical writing is recognized as a specialized profession. The *Society of Technical Writers and Publishers, Inc.*, with headquarters at Columbus 14, Ohio, has approximately 3,000 members in its more than 40 chapters. This society carries on an active technical program for its members in a manner similar to that followed by the other scientific and technical societies. It sponsors its own publication, the *STWE Review*.

Colleges and universities conduct conferences, institutes, and workshops on report and technical writing. These training courses, lasting 3 days to 2 weeks, are scheduled annually by 15 to 20 institutions. Fees per registrant range from $35 to $175. The courses attract executives, scientists, and engineers whose professional work in industry, business, government, and research require technical writing. Here is additional evidence that report preparation has achieved a place of top rank in business and industry.

TYPES OF REPORTS

The classification of reports into types enables the writer to orient his thoughts and work. As soon as he associates the report with a certain type he can organize the collection and treatment of material. The skills employed in preparing all types of reports are the same. The type of report is closely related to the function which the report is expected to perform. On the basis of function, reports may be classified as follows:

I. The periodic report — record of work accomplished in a stated time period
   A. Regular time intervals
      1. Daily, weekly, monthly
      2. Quarterly, semiannually
      3. Annually
   B. Intervals based on events or accomplishments

II. The inquiry report — specific assignment for inquiry
   A. Informational
   B. Action

Periodic reports at regular time intervals are generally used as a basis of control of operation in public and private enterprises. These reports present to management for immediate or future use quantitative and qualitative information on accomplishments, status of operations and conditions, and frequently some outlook to the future. These periodic reports may originate at any level of management, but top management is finally responsible for the major reports that go outside the operating organization. For instance, the board of directors would approve the annual report to stockholders. The top executive or administrator or commission would approve the annual report of a government agency. Many of these periodic reports contain detailed statistics covering material consumed, labor employed, units produced, work accomplished, and other data useful to management in comparing operations for different time periods and in planning future operations.

Typical procedure often builds up from the daily or job report to the annual report. Daily reports are made on prepared forms carefully designed to reflect the nature of the work and to yield desired summaries which are transferred to weekly or monthly reports. From these weekly or monthly reports, the heads of departments write their reports to their executives who in turn prepare annual reports to their boards of directors, stock holders, council members, and heads of government agencies.

When certain operations are underway, such as design or construction of major facilities, management may request that the progress be reported as of a date set by management or upon completion of a stage of the operation. Such progress reports may also be prepared by a consultant reporting to his client. Upon completion of these types of operations a final report is usually required, as a historical document. This final report and, to a lesser degree, the progress reports contain salient features valuable at a later date should a similar project be undertaken, or alterations made.

The inquiry report is written to supply information or advice on a specific question. Such reports may be prepared by employees within an organization or by consultants engaged for the specific purpose. Inquiry reports are of two broad classes: *Informational reports* which supply information of general or specific use but not in answer to a current question up for decision, and *action reports* which purport to answer the question by recommending a course of action, or furnishing the basis for the immediate decision of management. When the action is taken, the report has accomplished its purpose. The inquiry report may be made in two stages, also, the preliminary or progress report and the final report. The periodic progress report covers an operation underway as previously decided by management, while the inquiry progress report covers a possible course of action not yet decided. The production department would submit a periodic progress report to the general manager on its work of getting into production a new product — say a homecraft type of radial drill press. Yet months prior to starting production of the drill press the general manager would have submitted one or more progress inquiry reports and a final report to the board of directors as a basis for decision to manufacture the drill press.

Reports that present the findings of research demand slightly different treatment, for research may include hunting in the library for information, inventing or developing new gadgets, processes, materials, and application, or investigating the laws of nature and the universe. In general, however, a research report is a special adaptation of the inquiry report. With due regard for the subject matter and the readers, a report on research may be prepared by following the same procedures and steps applicable to all other technical reports.

Throughout this classification of reports care has been taken to use a simple classification, yet one embracing the range of reports found in business, engineering, science, and government. Lacking, and designedly so, is that long list of names for reports for special purposes. For example, the reader may find other writings on reports that describe the following types:

completion	laboratory
construction	operation
design	recommendation
experimental	research
examination	sales
failure	survey
interim	test
inspection	trip
investigation	

Within a given organization, such names for reports probably serve a local need. For a general, but basic treatise on the preparing of business and technical reports such special adjectives for reports have no purpose.

FORMS OF REPORTS

Depending upon to whom the report is to be addressed and the length and nature of his subject matter, the writer of a report has a number of possible physical forms from which to choose. These forms may be used for any of the types of reports mentioned. Yet certain forms lend themselves better to some types than to others. The usual classification of reports on the basis of appearance follows:

1. Form report	4. Short report
2. Memorandum report	5. Formal or long report
3. Letter report	6. Oral report

Form reports are those reports that are recorded on specially prepared forms. Form reports may be either periodic or inquiry. Form reports are important devices for recording original information about an operation, the progress of a manufacturing process, or a construction job. Form reports are also indispensable in the collection of original data through surveys, tests, and observations. The replies to well-planned questionnaires are returned on form reports. Forms have received insufficient consideration because authors hesitate to use them for, they say, it is too easy to fill them in without thought. The filling in of a form is only the second step in the cycle. The design of the form requires a thorough knowledge of the information needed, of the interpretation expected, and of the abilities of those persons who are to fill in the forms. A carelessly designed form will indeed yield insufficient, inadequate, and confusing information.

Memorandum reports are informal yet official statements of communication within an organization to supply information in answer to an inquiry or to supply periodic information on an operation. Memorandum reports are so-called because a special letterhead for internal correspondence is used in which the usual inside address, salutation, and complementary closure are eliminated. A simple arrangement of

To: ____________
From: ____________
Subject: ____________

is usual. Thus, the memorandum report may be identical in subject content to the letter report. The memorandum report is also used to make informal records of interdepartmental conferences between officials of a company and other members in their departments. These reports serve to record the salient statements, recommendations, and ideas discussed during a conference. Considerable discrimination needs to be exercised to retain the essential features and to discard the material that does not contribute to the purpose of the conference.

Letter reports are a form of business correspondence used externally in reporting upon a technical subject. Scope and content are of such magnitude that the letter, exclusive of enclosures, ranges from one to three pages. The supporting tables, illustrations, and computations are added as enclosures or exhibits. The letter report is an original composition written according to a generally accepted scheme for business letters, but permitting the exercise of individuality and resourcefulness. Subheadings are frequently used.

Short reports follow the general form of the formal or long report, but omit some of the preliminaries. Short reports are between the memorandum and letter reports and the formal or long report in length, but are composed as the formal report and sent with a separate letter of transmittal. Short reports find their best use in those instances when the subject, content, attachments, and situation are such that the memorandum or letter forms are not appropriate nor is the formal report.

Formal reports are used when the scope and contents are relatively comprehensive. In such instances a letter report would have little significance and the short report does not provide for all the needed preliminaries. A letter in these instances would place the salutation so far from the closure that the reader would not realize he was reading a letter. In the formal report each brief element of the letter is extended in treatment and becomes what is termed a "part." The letter of transmittal retains contact between writer and recipient.

Oral reports play an important role in presenting the gist of the written report to a client and to groups. The oral presentation of papers at technical society meetings indicates that most speakers would benefit from applying known techniques (see Chapter 15) to get their messages across clearly and effectively. Even a carefully prepared letter report does not equal the personal appeal that can be created by a well-prepared oral report, delivered in a dynamic and dignified manner.

TECHNICAL PAPERS

Many of the subjects written about in technical papers (see Chapter 14) are the same subjects for which reports are written. The subjects emanate from the operation of an organization, including its research and development department, and include all phases — design, construction, maintenance, production, sales, and management. These papers have for their purpose the informing of other persons who may be able to use the information to improve their own business or professional practice.

These papers differ from reports primarily in their readership and treatment of the subject. A technical paper is intended for hundreds to thousands of readers who are subscribers to the periodical, or members of the society or association publishing the article or sponsoring its oral presentation at a meeting. The technical paper, because of its widespread readership, omits many of the details, stresses results rather than how the results were obtained. It is written to attract readers, for no one is compelled to read the paper in line of duty as is true of the report. In physical form the technical paper is without the preliminary parts found in reports. The paper needs only a title, author's name, and author's identification to make it complete.

THE FUNDAMENTAL SKILLS

To approach the preparation of a report which seeks to find the solution to a management question or a technical problem, or to supply a fund of information for later use, the usual scientific method is applicable. The seven steps are as follows, usually in the order given:

1. *Recognition* of the need for the desired information or solution and a determination to take the required action. This step is usually taken by the officer superior to the person preparing the report or by the client of the consultant.
2. *Definition and limitation* of the assignment and subassignments, including authorizations to commit moneys and people to achieve the desired objective. Concrete statement of objectives is made jointly by the supervisor and his worker to whom he has given the assignment, or by the client and his consultant.
3. *Collection* of factual data, experience, ideas, opinions, and assumptions which may have a bearing upon the objectives sought or procedures in reaching the objectives.
4. *Analysis and assimilation* of the information gathered: correlation, comparison, sorting, arranging, and evaluation in terms of the objective.
5. *Synthesis* of the analysis to reach all possible specific solutions and presentations which would satisfy the objective.
6. *Evaluation* of results leading to positive decisions on the solution or selection of information, and the checking of the accuracy and soundness of facts and technical procedures.
7. *Organization and assembly* of the report to submit to the supervisor or client.

The above seven steps are fundamental to the solution of all problems — social, technical, personal — because they represent a logical method of thinking. Having them clearly in mind will aid the investigator and speed up his thinking. In the execution of these seven steps the investigator will be guided by all his skills.

Mastery in preparing reports lies in acquiring proficiency in the fundamental skills common to all types of reports. This emphasis on fundamental skills rather than on the content and arrangement of types of reports reduces the process of report preparation to a scientific basis. Each report is an opportunity to apply a limited number of fundamental skills to the extent and manner appropriate to the function. With a reasonable command of these fundamental skills the writer of reports can make an indefinite number of applications suitable to any required function.

By study and practice the writer of reports will acquire proficiency and confidence in:

1. Recognition of content, form, and classification of reports
2. Presentation of technical matter through correspondence and reports based upon personal experience, observation, and judgment
3. Ability to prepare a formal report in standard form, with all the preliminary and main parts in logical order
4. Collection, selection, analysis, and interpretation of data
5. Arrival at an answer to a technical prob-

lem through well-supported conclusions and recommendations
6. Achievement of exactness, directness, and soundness in style of technical writing in contrast to other forms of writing
7. Communication of ideas completely, concisely, convincingly, clearly, and correctly
8. Artistic arrangement of composition and associated illustrative materials
9. Graphical presentation
10. Tabular presentation

To the foregoing skills the writer of a report usually brings the following previously acquired skills:

1. Reasonable proficiency in English composition
2. Mastery of spelling, grammar, and punctuation
3. Knowledge of the essentials of business correspondence
4. Enough technical training so that he can write with authority on subjects within his assignment

The author's ability to write reports that command respect, approval, and action will be considerably improved by the critical study of many reports, especially those currently being produced. Further, current literature should be watched for papers on reports and technical writing. The selection of the reports to study should be based on the characteristics of good reports as presented in this book. Practice in the unit skills discussed in this book will enable one to write good reports consistent with accepted types and forms, yet distinctive in personal individuality.

THE LANGUAGE OF REPORTS

The technical or business report possesses characteristics that definitely distinguish it from other accepted styles of writing. The report is not a pure literary achievement such as the essay, short story, novel, or sonnet. The principal styles employed in report writing are exposition and description.

The preparation of a technical report requires first-hand knowledge, understanding, and contact with the subject. The collection and analysis of data involve discrimination that comes with a comprehensive acquaintance with the problem considered on a broad basis. The interpretation of the data and attaining of the objective require scientific reasoning, technical skill, theoretical comprehension, and practical experience. The arrival at conclusions and the presentation of recommendations draw upon judgment in evaluating the merits of several choices.

The preparation of a report draws upon a number of skills, among which the ability to communicate thought by the vehicle of words is one to be recognized and mastered if professional stature is to be attained.

English in the technical report is comparable to mathematics in the design of machines and structures as either is the single important link in the completed chain of thought.

The features that distinguish the report from other writings are:

1. Technical nature of the subject as exemplified by emphasis on the physical sciences and business practices even in their dealing with related social sciences and human relations.
2. Strict adherence to the outline form of presentation developed by direct approach achieved by writing that is complete, correct, concise, clear, and convincing.
3. Formal use of the third person style. Certain special considerations may warrant the use of the more familiar first and second person.
4. Emphasis upon the quantitative approach even though qualitative statements are frequently employed.
5. Established dependence upon accuracy, definiteness, and reasoned analysis, interpretation, and conclusion.
6. Use of mediums other than words for the conveyance of thought; namely, statistical methods, tabular arrangements, diagrammatic and photographic illustra-

tions, and mathematical treatment of scientific or technical matter.

7. Inclusion of the original source material upon which the solution, conclusions, and recommendations are based.
8. Direct personal relationship between reader and writer through the letter of transmittal and other supporting correspondence.
9. Use of a calm and judicial tone with distinctive individuality.
10. Over-all criterion that the report presents the facts desired, the answer to a question, the solution of a problem, the record of prevailing conditions, or other specific objectives as needed by the management or the client.

Although there is considerable opportunity for creative work and individual literary style, the form of the report follows well-established custom. When a formal report is written the author includes the preliminary sections, the body, and the terminal section. When a letter report is written, the parts of the formal report are condensed and presented according to accepted conventions of letter writing.

The language of the report is impersonal, calm, and moderate. There is no occasion to use extreme statements, superlatives, and emotional modifiers for they tend to weaken the prestige of the author. Every effort is made to write completely, concisely, correctly, clearly, and convincingly. The paragraphs in a report are characteristically short. The reader is guided through the report by the inclusion of main headings and their subdivisions. The typography of these headings is carefully planned and advantageously placed to be of most service to the reader.

The selection of words, the included subject matter, and the position of certain parts of the report are all determined in terms of the person or persons who will read the report. Furthermore, the report, in contrast with other literary works, will use illustrations, diagrams, charts, tabulations, and mathematical analyses in conjunction with writing. In most reports the writer needs skill in using narration, description, exposition, and argumentation. From the introduction, where the history of the subject may assume the narrative, through the development of the body where description of things and the exposition of processes and ideas are important, to the final preparation of the conclusions and recommendations where the argumentative form of writing may be required, the writer of reports draws upon every device that language offers for the communication of ideas. To these he brings his technical skill and knowledge, his ability to analyze and synthesize, his acquaintance with graphic and mathematical procedure, and his understanding of psychology.

The writer of a report communicates with a predetermined readership, frequently only one to a dozen or so individuals, having a self-established interest in, and usually a responsibility for the matter reported upon. This exclusiveness of readership demands a directness of writing not accorded the general writings of prose, including the usual scientific and technical papers.

CHAPTER 2

Planning the Investigation and Report

The preparation of a report on any technical, business, or professional question involves understanding the objectives and organizing the investigation. These steps require planning, of which outlining is an essential part. If a good plan and outline are made of the investigational phase, the work of outlining the report preparatory to writing is comparatively easy. Planning and outlining are, therefore, both considered in this chapter.

BASIS AND NATURE OF PLANNING

Planning is the process of determining the steps by which an objective may be attained. In the preparation of reports, planning enables the person in charge, the expert, to utilize talent, time, and money effectively. He needs to determine the nature and amount of work required to assemble the information upon which to base the solution to be developed. He needs to assemble an organization which will operate efficiently on a technical basis. The plan for the preliminary work will depend upon the character of the problem and time limitations. The nature of the problem will suggest the most suitable type of report for presenting the solution and its supporting data. The type of report will in turn suggest a suitable plan for the office and field work. The scope and magnitude of the problem will serve as a guide for choosing a suitable form for the written report. The oral report, when required, is prepared from the written report.

The character of the work is determined by the type of the report, that is, whether it is to be a periodic or inquiry report. For the periodic report, records have been compiled. The writer needs only to sort through the files for the information after he has blocked out the major and minor functions of the company's work. For the inquiry report, the type of information on which the solution is to be based needs to be ascertained; then the required information is assembled from existing sources or developed by surveys, experiments, or research.

The client, sponsor, or executive officer usually notifies or issues authorization to the person or agency selected to prepare a report. This notification may be verbal as a result of a conference, but, more often, it is written in order to provide a record of the appointment or selection, and to outline, in some instances, the nature of the problem and the scope of the work.

The scope and nature of a problem usually orient the writer, whether he represents a private organization, a governmental agency, or an administrative head of a company, to formulate a brief but comprehensive statement of the work to be done.

Every assignment to "investigate and report" brings with it the need for an accurate statement of the objectives of the report, background, special considerations, and scope. Agreement on these needs is reached at the outset by the parties involved — mainly the person or organization asking for the report and the person responsible for preparing it.

Few reports can be written without performing detailed study, investigation, and analysis preliminary to writing. All reports are better when they are the result of advance planning and outlining. This is true even for the simple, brief, relatively inexpensive studies reported upon daily in the course of commercial, industrial, and professional activities of technical and business men.

PLANNING THE WORK

As stated before, the nature and amount of planning and work required for the preparation of a report depend upon the classification of the report according to its functional type. Nevertheless, there are certain steps in the planning and in the accomplishment which are common to all reports.

By following some systematic procedure, the person in charge of preparing a report will assemble the required information with less effort and more discrimination than if he starts to work without definite plans and objectives.

First, he will study the assignment to determine the objectives and the uses of the report.

Second, he will itemize the information needed in order to accomplish the objectives.

Third, he will make an inventory of what information is readily available within his own organization, what information needs to be obtained from external sources, and what information needs to be developed by additional tests or research.

Fourth, he will outline the methods he will employ to get the necessary information.

Finally, he will estimate the time and the cost required to complete the report.

Planning for Periodic Reports

Periodic reports are issued at regular intervals by most private and public organizations. When new work, new processes, and new projects are involved, periodic reports, such as preliminary, progress, and final reports, are issued at special intervals.

The planning for the regular periodic report involves an analysis of the work of the organization and a classification of the procedures and departments required to conduct business in an effective and economical manner.

Planning an annual report for an organization resolves itself into two major considerations: first, decision of what activities to report, and second, what sequence to use in presenting the activities. The Port of New York Authority may be used to illustrate certain considerations of planning an annual report. The preliminary parts of the report are omitted from this discussion.

The objective of such an annual report is to inform the governors, the legislators, and the people about the major activities and accomplishments, and to account for all financial matters.

One plan would be to treat the activities on an internal functional basis as follows:

I. Introduction and general review
II. Long range plans and planning
III. Design
  1. New York port
  2. International Airport
  3. George Washington Bridge
IV. Construction
  1. New York port
    (by piers or terminals)
  2. New Jersey port
  3. George Washington Bridge bus terminal
  4. George Washington Bridge
V. Maintenance and repairs
  (by facilities)
VI. Operations
  (by facilities)
VII. Administration
  1. Financial
  2. Real estate
  3. Personnel
VIII. Accounts and statistics
  1. Accountant's certificate
  2. Financial reports
  3. Operational statistics

An alternate plan would be to arrange the report by individual facilities, grouped by function:

I. The Port Authority — its history and function
II. Air terminals
  1. Employment, traffic, investment
  2. Proposed airport
  3. New York International Airport
    A. Operations and traffic
    B. Unit terminals
    C. Hangars
    D. Runway development
    E. Fuel storage and service
    F. Other developments
  4. LaGuardia Airport
    Subitems
  5. Newark Airport
    Subitems
  6. Teterboro Airport
  7. Heliports
III. Terminals
  1. Bus terminal activity
  2. Bus terminal expansion
  3. George Washington Bridge bus terminal
  4. New York truck terminal
  5. Newark truck terminal
  6. Port Authority building and freight terminal
IV. Marine terminals
  1. Investment and tonnages
  2. Elizabeth Port Authority piers
  3. Etc. for about 20 facilities
V. Tunnels and bridges
  1. Traffic and general review
  2. George Washington Bridge, lower level
  3. Etc. for other facilities
VI. Arterial facilities
  (by each facility)
VII. Railroad equipment program
VIII. Port development plans
IX. Protection of the Port's competitive position
X. Administration
  1. Commissioners and officials
  2. Financial department
  3. Legal department
  4. Public relations department
  5. Administration department
    A. Personnel
    B. Medical
    C. Organization and procedures
    D. Community relations
    E. Purchase and administrative services
  6. Engineering department
  7. Operations services department
  8. Real estate department
XI. The staff
XII. Financial
  1. Financial review and summary
  2. Financial reports

Although lengthy and detailed, the plan for the annual report of The Port of New York Authority or other organizations is easy to prepare; essentially the plan follows the activities and functions and the organizational compartments.

Planning for Inquiry Reports

The inquiry report by its nature includes (1) the assembly of observations recorded in printed form or obtained as original field data in order to answer questions involving the behavior or thinking of people, or (2) the development of new information by experimental work to answer questions involving new processes and new materials.

On the basis of preliminary work, inquiry reports can be divided into those that involve the collection of facts and opinions readily available and those that require the development of new information by the agency responsible for making the report.

While periodic reports are planned largely around past activities, the inquiry report is planned around one's experience related to similar investigations. The needs in planning work for a preliminary report on a proposed activity may be analyzed and related to similar problems that have been solved in the past. The similar features are separated from the unsimilar features. The general nature of the series of steps that will lead to the final solution is determined from previous experience or after due study and reflection based upon known principles and newly obtained data.

These steps may be illustrated by an analysis of the planning for a civic project to develop the master plan for the city of Ames, Iowa. The general outline of a final report can be tentatively blocked out by an individual who possesses intimate, as well as thorough, knowledge of the underlying basic features and elements of a problem. A person with these qualifications can consider the problem and the steps required for its solution in its entirety. He knows the principal elements that will need to be studied. Furthermore, his professional background and training will enable him to plan the development of the individual items that contribute toward the solution. Thus, when one is directed to develop a master plan for a city, his mind associates the assignment with the intimate knowledge that he already possesses or may need to acquire.

First, the city planner lists the major elements that enter into the solution of the problem, in this case, the dynamic and physical aspects of city life. These are:

Future development of city	Recreation
Major streets	Municipal improvements
Transit	Civic developments
Transportation	Educational expansion
Parks	Zoning for land use

Each of these major parts is then analyzed with respect to its contributing sections. The future development of the city involves a study of census reports to establish population trends. Then, the extension of city limits needs to be carefully considered on the basis of residential, commercial, and industrial requirements. Finally, housing problems press for solution of slum clearances and low-cost housing developments. As shown by the accompanying outline, each of the other nine major parts can be subdivided into its subsections.

ORGANIZATION FOR PREPARING THE MASTER PLAN FOR THE CITY OF AMES

I. Future development of city
   A. Population trends
   B. Extension of city limits
      1. Residential
      2. Commercial
      3. Industrial
   C. Housing
      1. Slum clearance
      2. Low-cost housing
II. Major streets
   A. Designation of major streets within present city limits
   B. Provision for major highway routes
   C. Extension of street systems to unplatted sections within the present city limits
   D. Extension of street systems to adjacent areas
   E. Correction of street names and numbers
III. Transit, traffic, and parking
   A. Bus
   B. Taxi
   C. Parking
IV. Transportation
   A. Railroad
   B. Motor vehicle
   C. Air
V. Parks
   A. Neighborhood
   B. Recreational
   C. Parkways
VI. Recreation
   A. Athletic
      1. Observer
      2. Participant
   B. Educational
   C. Vocational
VII. Municipal improvements
   A. Sewage disposal plant
   B. Municipal light plant
   C. Fire stations
   D. Municipal incinerator or refuse collection and disposal
   E. Municipal hospital
VIII. Civic developments
   A. Civic center
   B. Auditorium
   C. Swimming pool
   D. Skating rink
   E. Civic art
   F. Community club buildings
   G. Art center
IX. Education
   A. Extension of school building requirements
   B. Playground facilities
X. Zoning
   A. Zoning ordinance
   B. Zoning map

With this outline as a guide, the related available information is inventoried and the additional required data and information determined. After having established the pertinent information to be obtained by field surveys or by reviewing the records, the work can be planned and qualified personnel employed. Few people realize that, in many cases, the table of contents of the report springs into existence in the early stages of planning because the person in charge has had sufficient experience to enable him to visualize the major phases as well as the details that will need to be studied, analyzed, and marshaled.

Planning an investigation to reach an objective and the outlining of the report of that investigation require separate considerations based upon the type of assignment. Unlike the periodic report of activities which is written around the functions and organizations, an inquiry report is wholly creative. Consider as an illustration a report upon the probable future growth and development of a specific city, especially one having had a recent rapid growth, such as many cities and towns had during the 1950's. This city will be called Valley View. It has been transformed from 6,000 to 35,000 population in recent years. The mayor and city council have contracted with a consulting firm to report upon Valley View's future physical, economic, and cultural development as a basis of forming policies and plans to control developments toward known objectives. Recent growth was without a plan and toward no certain objectives. The plan of the investigation and the outline of the report might be prepared as follows:

I. Introduction
  1. Situation
  2. Recent growth and developments
  3. Need for the study
  4. Objectives
  5. General procedure

II. Summary and conclusions
  1. Land use trends
  2. Population trends
  3. Economic development
  4. Public services
  5. Revenues and tax schedules

III. Land development in and adjoining Valley View
  1. Trend in land use
  2. Growth by annexation
  3. Residential development
  4. Zoning

IV. Population characteristics
  1. Population trends
  2. Factors attracting population
  3. Population densities
  4. Commuting

V. The economic base of Valley View
  1. Income characteristics
  2. Employment
    A. Occupations
    B. Total employment
  3. Industrial development
    A. Local plants
    B. Attractiveness to new industry
    C. Industrial parks
    D. Labor supply
  4. Commercial activity
    A. Retail sales
    B. Physical facilities

VI. Forecast of population and economic development
  1. Land use to 1980
  2. Population changes to 1980
  3. Economic development to 1980
    A. Nearby population centers
    B. Industrial development within Valley View
    C. Commercial development within Valley View

VII. Present finances and services of Valley View
  1. City revenues, general fund
    A. Property assessments
    B. Special fees and charges
  2. City expenditures, general fund
    A. Services
    B. Public works
    C. Government
  3. Employment
  4. Public school finances
  5. The city's public debt
  6. Services to adjacent unincorporated areas

VIII. Future requirements for public services and facilities
  1. Government functions and administration
  2. Public services
    A. Fire, police, and health
    B. Library and recreational
  3. Public works
    A. City streets
    B. Sewage disposal
    C. Storm drainage
    D. Public buildings

IX. Estimates of future city revenue

1. Property tax potential
2. Sales tax potential
3. Special fees and service charges
4. Borrowing for public works

X. Development of a master plan for city growth

XI. Appendix
1. Tabular data
2. Laws and ordinances
3. Definitions

Surveys, Observations, and Investigations. The usual procedures for gathering survey, observational, or investigational information on which to base a report involve interviews, correspondence, questionnaires, and field observations.

Experiments, Tests, and Research. For purposes of clarity, tests may be confined to the process of verifying the physical nature of materials and the mechanical operation of devices, both in conformity with established methods of procedure; experiments may be confined to the determination of the characteristic behavior of machines, processes, and structures under the influence of variable external conditions; research may be confined to the discovery of basic knowledge relating to human behavior, manufacturing and industrial processes, and scientific fundamentals.

The performance of standard tests is employed to give students intimate contact with fundamental characteristics of processes and materials, to provide experience in the conduct of experiments and research, to develop the technique of careful manipulation of instruments and machines, and to encourage accurate observation, analysis, interpretation, and reporting. The following sequence is a guide to the student in the compilation of data for making the test and writing the report:

A. Concise statement of the objective
B. Preparation of the specimen according to recognized standards
C. Review of pertinent and readily available references
D. Outline of major and minor determinations to be made
E. Procedure of the test
1. Preparation for the test
2. Preparation of the specimen
3. Performance of the test

F. The completion of the report
1. Graphs
2. Results

G. Discussion of supplementary questions based upon information obtained or deducted from the test

The primary responsibility of the person making tests is to become acquainted with the general requirements, the type of instruments, the equipment and machinery needed, the step-by-step procedure in making the test, and the forms to use in recording data.

The experimental determination of the factors that contribute to good construction of soil-cement roads was made possible only after extensive research revealed the fundamental scientific principles required to produce suitable soil-cement mixtures for light-traffic roads. Then a number of soil-cement experimental roads were built for observation. The variables applied to the road were the amount and type of traffic, the weather conditions during construction, the different methods of construction, the use of different equipment, and field control procedure. In Illinois, 6,000 feet of road were divided into eight sections varying from 500 to 900 feet in length. Each section was designed in accordance with the recently developed soil-cement mixture principles. Samples were designed and tested in the laboratory and then compared with the performance of comparable samples of similar specimens taken from the field. Thus, the procedure may rightfully be called an experimental soil-cement road because the final desired solution will be the one which meets the requirements on a comparative basis of parallel tests rather than on a predicted design based directly upon basic principles and theory.

The research which enabled the investigators to arrive at suitable experimental determinations of good soil-cement road designs required a comprehensive and intensive investigation to discover the principles that govern the properties and performance of soil-cement mixtures. The sequence of the work for this project is typical of research procedure in general even though important variations may be required in each specific project.

1. Economic need for a low-cost, stable, all-weather road stimulated some noteworthy experimentation.
2. Increased need for a solution gained the technical and financial support of talented men and well-equipped organizations to cope with the problem in proportion to its importance and difficulty.
3. Thorough study of existing literature was undertaken to collect and compile information on soils, including soil physics, mechanics, and chemistry.
4. Analysis of the information thus assembled indicated that there were possibilities of combining soil and cement to produce a low-cost, all-weather road for light traffic provided the relations of soil and cement could be evaluated and generalized.
5. Formulation of a general hypothesis based on available data. In this case, "If soil-cement mixtures followed the general moisture-density relations of raw soils, then the preparation of soil-cement specimens compacted to optimum moisture at maximum density would place the material in the most stable condition possible to obtain in the field."
6. Development of laboratory tests to simulate field conditions and to try many possible combinations in order to establish principles governing the fundamental factors.

The following outline for a proposed research project (*next page*) can serve with minor changes and additions in planning either extended private experiments or research. The completion of this outline will enable the person in charge of the preparation of a report to anticipate the scope and nature of the study, the most suitable personnel, the time required, and the probable cost of the project.

Planning and performance of the field and office work are to report writing what design and specifications are to a machine, structure, process, or organization. With the pertinent and related information completed in an orderly manner, the writer could hardly be restrained from the urge to commence the manuscript. By keeping closely in touch with all phases of the work, the writer's mind begins to evolve the solution of the problem and the most effective manner in which to present and substantiate that solution.

PLANNING THE MANUSCRIPT WORK

In conformity with the procedure of planning the collection of information, the writing likewise needs to be planned and organized. The extent and significance of the problem will be factors in determining the form in which to develop the written report. Detailed field observations, compilation of personal views and opinions, and data of individual tests are usually recorded on form reports. The results accumulated weekly, monthly or yearly are usually summarized in memorandum reports to keep those in various stations of responsibility in close contact with the progress and trend of the study. When the project is of limited scope, the final report may be presented as a letter report — even though several exhibits or enclosures may be included. When the subject involves considerable data and the analysis and solution are extensive, the formal report with conventional parts can be used to best advantage. All detailed development, analyses, tabulations and curves should be summarized vividly to create rapid understanding and lasting impressions. Oral reports should give only essential and significant phases of a study.

Planning the Outline

The principal purpose of outlining is to organize the material assembled in accordance with a suitable system of classification.

The writer of reports will gain knowledge and power by analyzing specific reports and, then, generalizing his observations for his personal use in the future. The examples and their analyses must, of necessity, be few and brief in a textbook treatment of the subject. The authors may consider their purpose to be achieved if they stimulate the reader to well-oriented action and systematic filing of his observations.

In drawing, the word outline is used to designate lack of detail or to show only the

OUTLINE OF PROPOSED RESEARCH PROJECT

A. Submitted by ______________________ Date ______________

B. Title of project
   1. General title
   2. Titles of subprojects, if any

C. Personnel
   1. In charge
   2. Co-operating
   3. Assisting
   4. Consulting

D. Co-operation or help desired from other agencies
   1. Departments within the organization
   2. Commercial firms, trade or manufacturing associations
   3. Technical organizations or committees of such

E. Estimated costs
   1. Current fiscal year
      a. Salary of staff
      b. Labor and other hourly hire
      c. Supplies, materials, etc.
      d. Equipment and permanent apparatus
   2. Same items for next fiscal year, if project is to carry over

F. Time required
   1. Project to be started ______________________ (date)
   2. Project to be completed ______________________ (date)

   Note: Items *G* to *J* should be developed fully, so that the director of research will have all information pertinent to his study of the proposal.

G. Review of literature on the subject
   1. Previous work by this organization
   2. Work of experiment stations
   3. Other American or foreign investigations

H. Purpose and object of the research: Results to be sought, stated in detail

I. Need for the investigation
   1. Reasons why the investigation is worth while, including the inadequacy of other researches
   2. Reasons why this organization should institute the research

J. Method of procedure: Complete outline of the proposed methods of attack, stating the various series of tests to be made, observations to be recorded, and description of materials, apparatus, and sources of information to be used.

outer boundaries or edges of an object. In thinking, the word outline is used to designate the major ideas in sequence and with brevity. In writing, *outline* designates a brief conventional form for presenting ideas, and *outlining* describes the process by which an outline is prepared.

The table of contents of any book, bulletin, report, or technical article is an excellent example of an outline. In this form, the outline, or table of contents, is usually prepared last, after all parts of the book, bulletin, or report are finished, even to the extent of establishing the paging. The preparation of the table of contents is discussed in Chapter 12.

Outlining is the process of planning the contents and sequence of a book, bulletin, article, or report. Outlining comes at the beginning of writing and after the collection, assimilation, and analysis are completed. Outlining is the process of creating the plan to be followed during the presentation, marshaling and interpretation of the usable data in order to attain logical conclusions, sound recommendations, and a satisfactory solution. Outlining is an essential and indispensable phase of orderly and logical thinking.

In this discussion four elements in outlining will be considered; they are systems, types, requirements, and preparation.

Systems of Outlining

One of the first decisions to be made by the writer is the choice of the system in which the subject of the report can be developed most conveniently and effectively. The principal available systems are:

1. Time sequence
2. Logical sequence
3. Processing, production, or manufacturing sequence
4. Management or organizational sequence

Specimen Outlines 2.1 through 2.5 at the end of this chapter are used to serve as examples of the manner in which outlines may be presented. The written outline is illustrated in Specimens 2.1, 2.2, 2.3, and 2.4, and the charted outline, in Specimen 2.5.

The time sequence is the basis for the presentation of *Oil's Transportation System* (Specimen 2.1). The first five main headings classify the sequence in which oil is transported from the time it is produced as crude oil until it reaches the service stations. The sixth heading summarizes the amount and kind of equipment required for each of the principal transportation types. Had the author desired to stress equipment, his title and outline might have been planned on the basis of a logical outline.

Equipment Used in Oil Transportation

1. Pipelines
2. Ocean-going tankers
3. Barges
4. Railroad tank cars
5. Tank trucks

The logical sequence is the basis for the presentation of the *Topic Outline With Functional Generalities* (Specimen 2.2) and *Topic Outline With Individuality* (Specimen 2.3). Both examples illustrate how the classification and the division of the subject were developed to obtain the principal purposes of the two reports.

Insulating Properties of Building Materials (Specimen 2.2) is an outline of a research report. The logical order of the study, the thoroughness of preparation, the willingness to make available the procedure employed, and the scope of the investigation in respect to the materials tested all give a view of the investigation as a whole and of the manner of proceeding with it. This outline is general and functional as well as logical. Therefore, it may be used as a pattern for research reports. Yet there are other schemes available to the writer of reports who wishes to display some initiative and individuality.

Causes of Failure in Bituminous Pavements (Specimen 2.3) is also logically arranged. The author chose the specific or individualized basis of classifying the results of a survey type of report. He helps his reader, in fact he puts his reader at ease, because he shows clearly that there are only three principal types of failure in bituminous pavements, namely, disintegration, instability, and failure of base or foundation. Each of the principal types of failure is recognizable by certain causes. Finally, each cause of failure is explained on the basis of scientific or technical reasoning. It is reasonable to assume that this author made a thorough search of published articles, records of city officials, and of experts in this special field of engineering.

Two possible approaches for planning the outline on a basis of logical classification are:

A	B
1. Introduction	1. Introduction
2. Review of literature	2. Types
3. Investigation	3. Causes
4. Method of procedure	4. Effects
5. Presentation of the main topic	5. Reasons
6. Results and findings	6. Conclusions
7. Conclusions	7. Recommendations
8. Recommendations	

Processes, methods of production or manufacturing sequences may be outlined in written form. Frequently the operations may be simultaneous. In some cases certain operations may even form a closed sequence. For these reasons, the outlining becomes more effective by using either the chart or diagram methods illustrated in Specimen 2.5.

The organization chart, *Civil Engineering* (Specimen 2.5), enables the author to show at a glance that a person in the profession of civil engineering embarks from the beginning along three channels of development; namely, field of work, functional activity in each field, and the responsibility he carries in either field or function. This organization shows that there are certain fields on the same level of individuality and others subordinate to a field. Thus, railways is subordinate to transportation systems, and irrigation to hydraulic projects. Also, in any field there are equally individual functions each with its group of subordinate operations.

Types of Outlines

An outline may be developed either as a topic or as a sentence outline. The topic outline consists of nouns or noun equivalents as headings. Noun equivalents are gerund phrases or relative clauses. Sentence outlines consist of complete but concise sentences at all planes of main and subordinate headings.

The topic outline permits generalized statements whereas, the sentence outline compels specific and accurate thinking.

The topic type of outline is illustrated in Specimens 2.2, 2.3, and 2.5. The sentence type of outline is illustrated in Specimen 2.1 for principal headings; the subheads in this case are topic type. The topic subheads are a part of the sentences commenced in the principal headings; they are itemized as topics in order to make it easier for the reader to visualize the kinds of transportation equipment.

Among the advantages of the sentence outline, which is used far less often than the topic outline, is the fact that the writer gains excellent experience in writing topic sentences. When the outline is completed the first sentence is available for every paragraph or, at least, for every section. Although carefully developed topic sentences are far from monotonous, some variety in construction can be introduced occasionally by opening a paragraph with a transition sentence or by withholding the topic sentence until the end of the paragraph.

Specimen 2.4 in sentence form was briefed from the article "Report on Engineering Design." The original report, printed in the *Journal of Engineering Education*, was prepared by a committee assigned to make the study. From this sentence outline the author readily expanded the material to his requirements. Each sentence, whether as the main heading or subheading, served the function of a topic sentence that was developed into a paragraph or chapter. The preparation of a comprehensive sentence outline can be of considerable value when the final report or technical article is written.

Formal Requirements for Outlines

The sequence of relative importance is conventionally represented by the use of symbols and indentations. Whether the topic or sentence type is used, brevity and directness are essential characteristics of an outline. The headings of the outline should not be general; rather, the headings should possess the individuality of the subject-matter content. Specific headings create more vivid images and hence arouse the interest of the reader and enhance the possibility for understanding the report.

The outline arrangement for *Causes of Failure in Bituminous Pavements* (Specimen 2.3) illustrates an effective arrangement for four levels of classification.

The outlines in Specimens 2.3 and 2.5 possess individuality because the headings are specific nouns closely related to the subject. These two outlines provide a framework for keeping the development of the report in mind and, at the same time, for supplying specific information.

In contrast, the topic outline in Specimen 2.2 consists of generalized statements. The reader would have no idea of the purpose of this report if the title were lost. Another way to put the same thought is to say that the outline lacks individuality because other titles could be supplied to the same outline. One example of another title will suffice to illustrate the point: *Structural Adaptations of Various Building Materials.* Nevertheless, the outline in Specimen 2.2 has merit in helping to organize material, at least in the early stages of writing.

Preparation of the Outline

The preparation of an outline depends upon thorough comprehension of the entire project. All of the work preliminary to writing should be finished, including the solution of the problem.

Although no two individuals use identical

Specimen 2.1.

Sentence outline developed on a time sequence basis from a pictorial flow chart

OIL'S TRANSPORTATION SYSTEM

1. The crude oil is produced at the well.
2. Short pipelines carry the crude oil to nearby storage tanks.
3. Three systems are used to transport the crude oil to refineries. They are:
   a. Pipelines
   b. Ocean-going tankers
   c. Barges
4. The refined products are distributed to terminal or bulk plants by means of:
   a. Pipelines
   b. Ocean-going tankers
   c. Barges
   d. Railroad tank cars
   e. Tank trucks
5. Distribution from terminals or bulk plants to service stations is achieved primarily by means of tank trucks.
6. This low-cost transportation system created by the American petroleum industry requires a considerable amount of equipment. It is contemplated that there will be in use for 24 hours a day:
   a. 140,000 miles of pipelines
   b. 650 ocean-going tankers
   c. 2,000 barges
   d. 142,000 railroad tank cars
   e. Thousands of tank motor trucks

procedures for preparing an outline, nevertheless, certain ideas are available to assist the beginner in this important phase of writing. An inventory of random facts and ideas may be placed on separate sheets or listed column fashion. During this operation and even from the beginning the mind formulates the purpose of the study. Thus, gradually the controlling ideas become clarified. By this time the assembled material begins to fall into definite and clear headings. Then, the main or principal headings loom up to form a natural and related system of division.

A concise statement of the objectives of the report is of prime importance because it focuses attention upon the contents and serves as the target toward which the entire discussion is aimed.

The principal factors supporting the main objectives of the report form the main headings, which are the only headings that may occur to the writer in the early stages of outlining. The first attempt at outlining a report utilizes the topic type. In planning the report on *Oil's Transportation System* the writer first writes down a few main items:

First trial	*Second trial*
1. Pipelines	1. Well to storage
2. Ocean-going tankers	2. Storage to refinery
3. Barges	3. Refinery to bulk plants
4. Railroad tank cars	4. Bulk plants to service stations
5. Tank trucks	

With the main items established, the writer is led to think of the supporting facts that serve to explain or validate the main headings. These ideas or concepts he writes down as subheadings. The writer then prepares the topic outline which he follows in writing the report:

Oil's Transportation System

1. Produced at well
2. Piped to storage tank
3. Transported to refineries
   a. Pipelines
   b. Ocean-going tankers
   c. Barges

etc.

Specimen 2.2.

Topic outline with functional generalities

INSULATING PROPERTIES OF BUILDING MATERIALS

A. Introduction
   1. Statement of the problem
   2. Purpose of the investigation
   3. Scope
B. Review of literature
   1. Bulletins
   2. Articles
   3. Foreign publications
C. Investigation
   1. Objectives
   2. Hypotheses
   3. Method of procedure
   4. Results
D. Materials
   1. Wood
   2. Clay tile
   3. Metals
   4. Concrete
   5. Plastics
E. Methods of procedure
F. Results and findings
G. Conclusions
H. Recommendations
I. Acknowledgments

The sentence outline compels the writer to think specifically and clearly about the organization of the report he plans to write. These sentences serve as excellent topic sentences to introduce the parts of the report. In fact, the topic sentences form generalized or summarized statements of the material the reader may expect to find in the report.

Oil's Transportation System

1. The crude oil is produced at the well.
2. Short pipelines carry the crude oil to nearby storage tanks.
3. Three systems are used to transport the crude oil to refineries. They are:
   a. Pipelines
   b. Ocean-going tankers
   c. Barges

Having established the various headings according to their planes of rank, the writer is ready to develop the outline into final form. Intimate contact with the facts and related investigations, experiments, and other source material will enable the writer to fill in the detailed discussion that converts the skeleton of the outline into a report with substance, life, and vigor.

The process of outlining may be summarized in the following main steps:

1. Jot down on paper each idea as it comes to mind, without regard to its importance or place in the outline.
2. Classify the ideas from step 1 by grouping them into major groups and subgroups.
3. Arrange the main groups into a logical order suitable to use in the report.
4. Arrange subsubjects in logical order under the main groups.
5. Check the completed outline on the following points, and rearrange as needed: sequence, equal ranking of equal subjects, duplications, omissions, wording and clarity of topics.

The development of an outline on this basis will accomplish a review of the investigation to the date of outlining and be the means of pointing out to the writer deficiencies in his plan or in the information at hand.

Specimen 2.3.

Topic outline with individuality

CAUSES OF FAILURE IN BITUMINOUS PAVEMENTS

I. Disintegration
   A. Hardening of asphalt film on aggregate
      1. Oxidation
      2. Polymerization
      3. Migration
      4. Evaporation
   B. Insufficient asphalt
      1. Poor design of mix
      2. Adsorption by aggregate
   C. Water action
      1. Aggregate surface affinity
      2. Asphalt adhesion
      3. Amount of asphalt

II. Instability
   A. Low friction
      1. Particle contact pressure
      2. Surface texture of particles
      3. Amount of lubricant
   B. Low cohesion
      1. Asphaltic binder
         a. Type of asphalt
         b. Amount of asphalt
      2. Mineral aggregate
         a. Surface area
         b. Size of voids
         c. Density

III. Base and foundation
   A. Insufficient compaction
   B. Insufficient drainage
   C. Soil type

Specimen 2.4.

Outline in sentence form.

REPORT ON ENGINEERING DESIGN

I. An increase in the number and complexity of problems facing engineers has resulted in a corresponding increase in the number and complexity of mathematical techniques used by engineers and taught in the engineering schools.
  A. The result has been to crowd engineering curricula to the point where it can include only a fraction of these techniques.
  B. Two aspects of this change have been:
    1. Increase in mathematical content of engineering subjects, and
    2. Displacement of subjects centered around devices with subjects centered around physical principles and mathematical techniques.
  C. Faculty members thought it well to study this change to
    1. Arrive at a common understanding of the meaning of words related to design,
    2. Find what elements are common in the process of design in various engineering fields,
    3. Study the problems of the practicing designer,
    4. Study analytical techniques adapted to solution of the designers' problems, and
    5. Consider the problem of teaching design in the M.I.T. School of Engineering.
  D. The word "design" was interpreted broadly, which led to consideration of the whole content of engineering education.
  E. The committee plan of study included the study of the semantics, special design tools, conferences with practicing engineers from ten technical fields, and conferences with faculty members and industrial leaders.

II. The first problem was to establish communication by agreeing upon a common language.
  A. One of the primary difficulties experienced in any effort of this kind is the tendency of every human being to use words as weapons to advance his own position rather than to reveal and clarify thought.
    1. Through this process words come to assume meaning and carry emotional content quite apart from their dictionary meaning.
    2. "Bad" words are useful chiefly as missiles to be guided to the enemy.
  B. A considerable semantic difficulty is offered by the failure of the general public to distinguish between science and engineering.
    1. Science implies a body of knowledge and a scientist is one who professes to a part of this knowledge.
    2. The goal of the engineer is to utilize knowledge of the physical world for social benefits.
    3. The scientist's problem is to discover truth, the engineer's to determine a course of action.
  C. Engineering design is the process of applying the various techniques and scientific principles for the purpose of defining a device, a process, or a system in sufficient detail to permit its physical realization.
    1. A design problem implies action and a final result which has physical reality, not a result which is only an idea or a report.
    2. Design is a conceptual process, one in which at least a fragment of a mental plan is necessary before the process can proceed.

Adapted from *Journal of Engineering Education.* 51: No. 8: 645–60. April 1961.

3. Accepting this definition of design, we may ask the question: What engineering activities, other than design, are there?
4. If we add the area the designer must be knowledgeable about to the area he must operate in, we see that it includes nearly if not all of what is called engineering.

III. One source of confusion in thinking about design is the tendency to identify design with one of its languages, drawing.
  A. Design, like musical composition, is done essentially in the mind, and the making of drawings or writing of notes is a recording process.
  B. Drawing should be taught not primarily to give the student facility in the use of tools, but to give him practice in pictorial extension of the mind.
  C. Pictorial language is especially well adapted to expressing particular physical form and physical space relationships.
  D. The particular language the designer uses depends upon the problem at hand and the training of the people involved.

IV. The representatives from industry who consulted on both design and engineering education came from essentially one-man firms to large corporations.
  A. A wide range of design problems was covered in the conferences with industrial men.
    1. All design problems made use of logic, physical principles, experience, judgment, intuition, numerical computation, drawing, symbolic diagrams, and experiments, but these ingredients were mixed in varying proportions.
    2. Some design problems lend themselves to the development process, others do not.
  B. New design problems refuse to fit any pat program for their solution; the consequent need for a fresh attack for each problem constitutes the challenge of design.
  C. Although coming from a diversity of organizations and technical problems, the industrial representatives had a remarkable uniformity of opinion on subjects related to engineering education.
    1. One area of agreement was that each person was essentially satisfied with his own educational experience.
    2. Each representative dwelt on the desirability of an engineer having a good grounding in fundamentals, but the fundamentals were not precisely defined.
    3. Recent engineering graduates were criticized for unwillingness and inability to consider a complete problem such as a design problem.
    4. The tendency of the young engineer to look upon himself as a specialist and to balk at tackling jobs outside of his specialty was noted.
    5. Young engineers feel at home in solving problems which have numerical answers — the kind of problem used in school for teaching analytical techniques.
    6. Another area of agreement was on the effectiveness of engineers who had had the benefit of an internship in one of the academic or peripheral laboratories where problems similar to those in industry are found.

V. In a design problem, synthesis must come first.
  A. In order to make the problem amenable to analysis, it is necessary to conceive a model having the essential characteristics of the actual device, but simplified to eliminate nonessential details.
  B. Numerical analysis must be used with judgment.
    1. The false assurance which engineers derive from an over-analyzed problem can have disastrous results.
    2. The most important use of analysis by the designer comes from his knowledge of general principles and the form of mathematical relationships rather than from actual computation.

C. The good designer avoids the trap of purely qualitative thinking.
   1. Good designers recognize the assurance that comes with numerical computation and they strive to increase its application when it will result in more reliable decisions.
      a. As a result, the design process tends to become stereotyped as the problem becomes older and a larger proportion of decisions can be made on the basis of numerical computation.
      b. An ingenious man, however, will be able to make valuable contributions to an old field.
   2. The designing engineer who remains on the frontiers of engineering finds himself making only a small fraction of his decisions on the basis of numerical analysis.
      a. When the problem becomes older, he moves on to the new and more difficult field.
      b. It is a shock to students entering practice to discover what a small percentage of the decisions made by a designer are made on the basis of the kind of calculation the student spent so much time learning in school.

VI. The ostensible content of an engineering education is a body of knowledge and a set of skills which should enable a student to solve engineering problems.
   A. But engineering education is much more; students acquire attitudes and habits as well as information and techniques.
      1. Important among these attitudes are:
         a. Willingness to proceed in the face of incomplete and often contradictory data and incomplete knowledge.
         b. Recognition of the necessity of developing and using engineering judgment.
         c. Questioning attitude toward every piece of information, every specification, every method, every result.
         d. Recognition of experiment as the ultimate arbiter.
         e. Willingness to assume final responsibility for a useful result.
      2. It is essential to inquire whether these attitudes are fostered by the kind of education we provide and to study the effect of the changing educational pattern.
   B. Unfortunately the physical sciences and engineering sciences as applied to mechanics, circuit theory, thermodynamics, etc., lend themselves to the single-answer problem in the teaching process.
      1. Single-answer problems include all those which can be answered with numbers or functional relationships.
      2. Obviously the closed-end, step by step problem is an effective teaching tool but it does not develop desirable attitudes.
      3. Examination of the effect of single-answer problems on engineering attitudes reveals:
         a. Incomplete or contradictory data have little place in single-answer problems.
         b. Engineering judgment is not required of either the student or the instructor.
         c. The existence of an objective standard puts the instructor in an impregnable position which only a few of the bright students will dare to challenge.
         d. The single-answer problem usually suggests the infallibility of logic rather than the ultimate word of experiment.
      4. The single-answer question has a strong negative effect on attitudes we hope to teach our students.
      5. Recognizing the shortcomings of the single-answer question, what alternatives have we?

C. Two alternates to the single-answer question, among others, may be illustrated.
  1. The comprehensive problem or analytical experiment which requires making an appropriate conceptual model of a physical situation and checking this model by experiment.
  2. Development of problems which require engineering judgment and imagination as aids in solving the problem, which may have many acceptable solutions.

VII. Use of comprehensive problems and problems requiring engineering judgment will not, however, be sufficient to bring our education into balance; other lines of attack are necessary.
A. The engineering classes should be small and taught by faculty with engineering experience.
  1. Recruiting a faculty primarily from newly made Ph.D.'s and Sc.D.'s leads to teaching analytical techniques to embryo analytical technicians.
    a. The need is to hire a percentage of experienced engineers as teachers.
    b. A second method is to see that teaching staffs have opportunities to gain engineering experience.
  2. Assembly of a faculty with engineering experience will require changes in recruiting policies and adjustments in budgets.
B. Because our science and engineering rests on a foundation of experiment we should include the experimental method in our fundamentals of engineering education.
  1. The competent engineer appreciates the power of the experimental method.
  2. Experimental research sponsored by government and industry contributes greatly to the education of graduate students.
  3. We must endeavor to see that the experimental method is an important part of the students' lives during their undergraduate years.
C. The extraordinary success of the internship procedure with graduate students suggests the desirability of its use in earlier years.
  1. Some undergraduate students could participate in the research program on which graduate students are used.
  2. The co-operative scheme is another way of giving the undergraduate an internship experience.
D. It seems essential to involve students, preferably starting early in their educational careers, in the decision-making process we call design.
  1. The ideal goal of education in the design area is a problem carried through construction, test, and evaluation.
  2. Design covers such a diversity of problems that it can best be taught by the case method, that is, by designing something.
  3. It has already been stated that design can be taught only by experienced designers.
    a. Faculty members should be encouraged to work on complete engineering problems in academic and peripheral laboratories, and by taking leave to work in industry.
    b. Endowed chairs should be established for the purpose of bringing qualified engineering designers from industry for limited periods to teach design in their special fields.

VIII. Design ability and analytical ability do not always occur in an individual in equal proportions.
A. Should we recognize two different types of students and provide two avenues leading to different occupations?

1. All students should have some exposure to both types of activity, that is, be involved in mathematical problems of analysis and conceptual and decision-making activities.
2. Provision should be made for students who show particular aptitude for design to spend more time in this area.

B. Every student intending to go into either science or engineering should be exposed in his freshman year to a conceptual, decision-making subject.

IX. The deliberations of the committee, its conferences with others, and careful analysis of the requirements of design and engineering education lead to the following recommendations:

A. That all students be involved in the design process beginning with the freshman year.
B. That engineering subjects be examined with a view to increasing the number of problems involving decision-making and experiment.
C. That engineering internships be encouraged and recognized with academic credit where appropriate.
D. That flexibly equipped and staffed laboratories be made freely available to faculty, graduate, and undergraduate students alike.
E. That chairs of engineering design be established to attract experienced designers from industry.
F. That the program of sabbatical leaves to increase scholarly attainment be broadened to provide the same opportunity for sharpening and focusing the engineering attainment of the faculty.

Specimen 2.5.
Topic outline in chart form

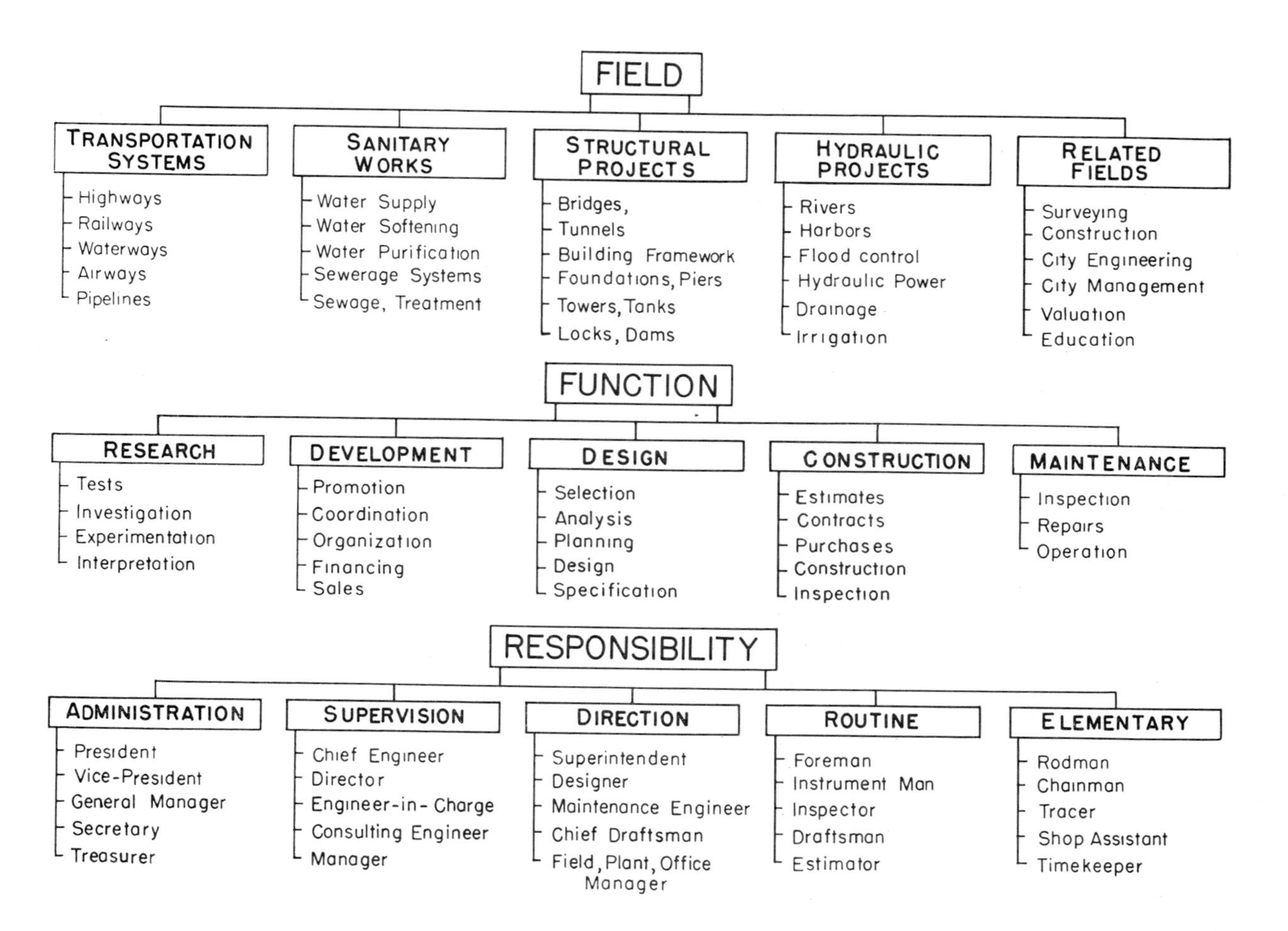

CHAPTER 3

Collection of Information

To write a report in which every word, number, idea, and illustration establishes the acceptability of the solution and the soundness of the conclusions and recommendations, requires a well-planned program for the collection of pertinent information.

PRELIMINARY CONSIDERATIONS

The ways and means of collecting information are of paramount importance to the writer of reports because few assignments are so simple that the author can solve them merely with the information he alone possesses.

The writer of an authoritative report should possess command of the subject matter and exercise skill in analysis, interpretation, and synthesis. To be well informed requires broad experience in technical as well as in administrative responsibilities. To be keen in analysis and interpretation requires demonstrated competence to observe, to classify, to judge, and to associate new problems and conditions in terms of previously acquired knowledge and experience. To be effective in synthesis requires creative skill in assembling and recombining ideas and facts into a new logical unit. At all stages of the procedure the writer is working with information in different forms and values.

Analysis of the Assignment

A clear statement of the assignment by the client or responsible officer and an accurate interpretation of the requirements by the writer are essential in determining the extent and quality of the information that needs to be assembled.

The uses to be made of the report are instrumental in the selection of the information to be collected. There may be endless information available on a subject, but the report writer needs to discriminate in the selection of only that which will serve to establish the value of his report. Personal integrity needs to be exercised both in the selection and in the presentation of information. Accuracy, soundness, and appropriateness should be the criteria on which selection is made. The prime attitude of the report writer is judicial; to have value to the reader, his report must be based upon favorable as well as unfavorable information. The reader, through the writer, can weigh relative merits of the conclusions and recommendations and base his action on his confidence in the judgment of the writer.

Organization for Collecting Information

After the principal elements of an assignment are determined and classified according to their relative importance and magnitude, the writer makes an inventory of the information he possesses and that which he needs to procure from outside sources. The methods available for the collection of information are based upon the major objectives to be achieved by the report. The sources of information may be classified as follows:

1. Existing information in possession of the writer
   a. Knowledge
   b. Experience
   c. Material in personal and office files
2. Existing information to be assembled from
   a. Publications
   b. Letters
   c. Questionnaires
   d. Interviews
3. New information to be developed by
   a. Surveys and observations
   b. Investigations
   c. Experiments and tests
   d. Research

In planning the collection of information the writer will utilize his knowledge of available sources and will apply this knowledge in terms of the type of report to be written. Broadly classified in Chapter 1, the types are periodic reports and inquiry reports.

For the usual periodic report personal and office files will furnish the bulk of the information. The source of information will be daily reports by workers, foremen, superintendents, and heads of departments as well as interoffice reports.

For the inquiry report the writer will draw heavily and importantly: first, upon surveys, observations and investigations of human activities, manufacturing processes, and technical performance or failure; and second, upon the results of experiments, tests, and research into comparative performances or new fundamental theories. The collection of information through surveys and investigations may be accomplished by questionnaires, interviews, existing information to be assembled, and observations and records made "on the spot." Information from experiments, tests, and research is usually obtained by a systematic use of equipment, materials, and processes and the recording of observations based on a series of controlled trials.

In the following pages several basic methods and procedures are developed for the systematic collection of information.

PUBLICATIONS

There are few, if any, entirely new fields of thought that are not very closely related to previously established knowledge, concepts, methods and experience. Thus, even though a report is to deal with a new problem, the solution will be mainly in terms of facts, theories, and applications previously established. Although a report should preferably be based on the assembly of newly developed information, the writer cannot ignore what others in his professional field have achieved and recorded. For these reasons, in addition to the existing information in possession of the writer or the agency he represents, publications related to the topic of the report will furnish breadth of view, background, and, in many instances, directly-applicable source material.

Importance of Published Material

From a practical point of view a person is asked to write a report for only one of two reasons or both. The person either has an established record for eminence in his professional field or he has demonstrated skill in studying a question and arriving at sound conclusions and practical recommendations which he can present effectively. On the other hand, eminence and experience like all other achievements need to have a beginning; therefore, a discussion of how to use publications, to conduct interviews, how to plan and distribute questionnaires are all important "know-hows" for the beginner in the art of report preparation.

There are known and proved methods for obtaining information effectively and efficiently from publications. The extent of the library search depends upon the scope of the report, the time available, the personnel available, and the money to be expended. These criteria apply to all other phases of collecting information and preparing the report.

The writer's background in the assigned task will prompt him to analyze his assignment by the aid of several trial topic outlines. Gradually, his mind will produce the major headings which will tentatively yield a possible means of developing the report. With this tentative outline in mind, he can list the pertinent publications to be examined.

Published Sources of Information

Where are references to good publications available? The following suggestions are partial but useful:

1. The Applied Science and Technology Index
2. The Business Periodicals Index
3. The Engineering Index
4. The New York Times Index
5. The Reader's Guide to Periodical Literature
6. The Engineering Societies' Libraries[1]

When these six important works of reference material are unavailable, which is the usual situation except in large libraries and organizations, the author can still draw upon the following sources:

1. Publications of technical societies, and the service that many render in the preparation of bibliographies
2. Publications of trade institutes and associations
3. Publications of experiment stations and research foundations
4. Technical and scientific magazines
5. References to authors and articles in all of the foregoing sources of information
6. Regularly published abstracts in various phases of science, engineering, finance, public affairs and government publications

Selection of Published References

As soon as references are found, they are recorded on sheets of paper or on cards. Although literature citations are frequently placed on cards 3 by 5 in., 4 by 6 in. or 5½ by 8½ in., the standard sheet 8½ by 11 in. has several advantages over the smaller cards:

1. The complete reference can be copied.
2. The notes can be more extensive with tabulations, curves and basic computations indicated.
3. The 8½- by 11-in. sheets are not bulky, are easy to file, and less likely to become misplaced.
4. A combination of the 8½- by 11-in. correspondence sheets with the complete reference and space for notes, and the 3- by 5-in. cards for single topic statements, provides the writer with a useful and flexible scheme for assembly of, classification of, and reference to information on which his report is to be based.

Small cards have the advantage of containing only one item on a card. This feature makes it possible to study several arrangements of the material to arrive at a logical and effective sequence.

This practice of listing the references on cards or sheets is valuable because the writer usually has numerous occasions for their use. They will serve later in the preparation of the list of references or bibliography.

It is good practice to make a complete record in the typographical form to be used in the report of the references at the time they are first consulted. This practice is discussed on page 36 in this chapter.

Review of References

Having compiled what appears to be all of the useful references, the writer is ready to investigate the original publications to determine their merit. In order to avoid copious note-taking, the writer should first review all of the publications and note on his records whether the references are excellent, good, fair, or unrelated. The published information associated with the references may be used to test and evaluate each reference.

1. *Author*

   Is the author an authority in the field? Does he participate in original survey and research projects, or does he have the skill to assemble and present effectively the work of others? Do other writers and research workers refer to his publications? Does he have influence in shaping the thinking in his profession? Has he had noteworthy practical experience?

2. *Title*

   Does the title indicate a contribution to the information required and does the table of

[1] A review of current periodical literature is printed monthly in each of the Founder Societies' magazines. Each magazine carries a classified list of abstracts for all phases of engineering activities, practices and theories. The material is selected from about 2,000 technical publications from 40 countries and 20 languages. Photoprints of any reference are available for a nominal charge per page.

contents or introductory abstract indicate a thorough and original treatment of the subject?

3. *Periodical, publisher* and *date*

   Is the periodical held in high respect professionally? Is the publisher discriminating in the choice of authors and articles? Is the date an indication of timeliness? Is the date old but the topic and treatment of fundamental significance?

An example of the foregoing criteria:

The scaling and disintegration of portland cement concrete with time in use is a phenomenon not fully understood, though extensively studied. An investigator wishing to perform research on the role of the performance of cement in concrete would certainly turn to the publications of the American Concrete Institute. Here he would find the name of Frank H. Jackson as author of a paper dealing with the *Long-time Study of Cement Performance in Concrete: Chapter 11 – Report on the Condition of Three Test Pavements After 15 Years in Service.*[2] To the investigator this paper looks good, but, who is Jackson? What are his professional attainments? Is he theoretical, practical, or both? Is he well-known and an accepted authority on concrete? The following are the editor's statements about Mr. Jackson as published in the *ACI News Letter* under the section "Who's Who This Month."

> Past president of ACI, Mr. Jackson is well known to Journal readers and has been active in Institute affairs since 1924. He was awarded, along with Harold Allen, the ACI Wason Medal for "the most meritorious paper" in 1948 for "Concrete Pavements on the German Autobahnen." Associated with the Bureau of Public Roads from 1905 until his retirement in 1953, he has received recognition from several organizations for his work in the highway field, including the Distinguished Service Award of the Highway Research Board in 1948 and the Meritorious Service Award of the U. S. Department of Commerce in 1950.
>
> Mr. Jackson is an honorary member of ACI and of the American Society for Testing Materials. He currently is serving on ACI Committee 201, Durability of Concrete in Service; Committee 212, Admixtures; and Committee 613, Recommended Practice for Proportioning Concrete Mixes.

Certainly an author of such noted and long-time career in cement and concrete materials is authority of highest level. But what about the *Journal* itself? How does it insure its contributions are timely, worth while, and technically sound? Also, from the *News Letter* is this statement:

> The Technical Activities Committee selects the papers, committee reports, discussions, and other contributions for JOURNAL publication. A volunteer corps of experts in various segments of the field assists in technical appraisal of the manuscripts. Technically speaking, acceptable contributions present original material for improvement of design, manufacturing, or construction; confirm, revise, or upset established ideas or practices; or review, digest, or arrange accumulated experience for more ready use.

Upon knowing that the author is highly qualified, and that the publication selects its papers with great care, certainly there is assurance that Jackson's paper on the performance of cement in concrete is fully reliable.

An additional check, particularly for articles in trade, class, and technical periodicals and special monographs, is to look into the motive for such article and publication. Although it is safe to assume ethical practice and professional honesty exists, nevertheless, many technical subjects have two or more sides and it is not always required that all facts and viewpoints be published.

In making notes on the original article, first read it quickly, and, if possible, detect and record the major headings of the outline. Then, select for actual recording only those items that have a bearing on the purpose of the report.

Important conclusions, recommendations, formulas and processes may be quoted verbatim. Care should be taken to be accurate and to give proper credit to the author.

Curves, tables, and diagrams should be

[2] Jackson, Frank H. Long-time Study of Cement Performance in Concrete: Chapter 11 – Report on the Condition of Three Test Pavements After 15 Years in Service. *Jour. American Concrete Institute.* 29: No. 12: 1017–32. June, 1958. See also the *ACI News Letter* published as a separate section of the journal, pages 1 and 45.

noted by title and page reference. Later the writer can readily return to the specific ones he may need in working up his report.

Less important matter can be abstracted in the writer's own words, but the author of the original source should be mentioned by name for the credit he deserves for his original ideas or time-consuming assembly of information.

During the search for and review of the literature it is essential to refer to the working outline prepared at the outset of the project and to file cards or sheets according to this outline at convenient intervals, often rather than seldom.

USING BIBLIOGRAPHICAL MATERIAL

It is traditional in writing to make specific reference to the source material selected from the works of others. In technical and scientific writing it is especially desirable to give exact and complete references to all works that are mentioned or quoted. This practice is fair to the original author, the writer, and the reader.

Citations and references are given principally for the following reasons:

1. To avoid plagiarism, or suspicion of plagiarism;
2. To be of assistance to the reader who may wish to read further on the subject or to look up additional details of the work cited;
3. To extend professional courtesy to prior authors by acknowledging their writings; and
4. To establish prestige and confidence in one's work by showing that the literature of the field has been studied.

Technical, business, and scientific works are made available to all who may wish to use the information, either in the form of applied knowledge or in connection with additional writing on the subject. An author is usually pleased that a subsequent writer has made reference to his work, and, in fact, quoted parts of it, but at the same time he is greatly provoked when acknowledgment of his work is not given. Citations are easy to include in one's own writing and including them is an easy means of extending thanks to other writers for use of their material.

Copyrighted Material

The Constitution of the United States provides in Article 1, Section 8, that Congress is empowered *to promote the progress of science and useful arts, by securing for limited times to authors and inventors the exclusive right to their respective writings and discoveries.* The law grants copyright for 28 years with the right to renew for another 28 years. A copyright is obtained upon publishing the work with the copyright notice printed on the title page or back thereof and then sending to the Copyright Office two copies of the publication, an application, and $4 registration fee. The copyright is granted in the name of the owner, i.e. the author, or the publisher when the author has transferred title of the work to a publisher.

During the fiscal year 1959–60 there were 222,533 registrations and 21,393 renewals of copyrighted works. New registrations included 60,034 books, 3,306 contributions to newspapers and periodicals, 64,204 periodicals, and 65,558 musical compositions. Most books and a reasonable percentage of periodicals are copyrighted, but few newspapers are. Practically every work published for the purpose of making a profit from its sale is copyrighted.

When there is little opportunity to gain financially from sales of a publication, there is little reason to copyright it. Scientific publications usually are not copyrighted and neither are technical bulletins, pamphlets, and circulars published to make information available to those interested. Once a work is issued in mimeograph, offset, or other form, and not copyrighted, the right to copyright is lost.

Proper procedure in using copyrighted works is often a question. The copyright owner, among other things, has the exclusive right to print, reprint, publish, copy, and vend the copyrighted work, and to translate, dramatize, arrange, or adapt it. The copyright statute does not provide for the use of copyrighted material in any of these manners without the permission of the copyright owner. Copyright protection covers the particular way an author has expressed himself, but does not extend to any ideas, systems, or factual information his work may convey.

The courts have recognized certain limited uses of copyrighted material as "fair use." In the broadest terms, the doctrine of "fair use" means that copyrighted material may be used to a limited extent, without obtaining permission, in some circumstances where the use is reasonable and not harmful to the copyright owner's rights. Under this doctrine, scholars and critics have been held free to publish short extracts or quotations from copyrighted works without permission of the copyright owner, for the purpose of illustration or comment.

The line between "fair use" and infringement is not clear or easily defined. There is no specific number of words, lines or notes that can safely be taken without permission. Acknowledging the source of the copyrighted material does not avoid infringement.

Every writer or publisher should be extra careful to obtain permission to use the works of others. A writer should be both ethical and courteous. If he has any doubt as to the propriety of his using the material from another source, he should first obtain permission from the author, if uncopyrighted, and from the copyright owner if copyrighted.

Methods of Referencing Bibliographical Material

The reader may be given the exact references to the literature by either one of two methods. Footnotes may be supplied throughout the text or a listing of the references may be given at the end of the report. In works of extended character a combination of these two methods is sometimes used. Footnote references are restricted to those works that are specifically cited in the text, while a list of references or a bibliography will most likely contain many references not specifically cited. A listing of citations or references is usually placed at the end of the report following the terminal section, but preceding the appendix. In long reports of many chapters a listing of references at the end of chapters is frequently helpful to the reader. A bibliography not essential to the reading of the report may be placed in an appendix.

When only a few citations need to be given, the footnote form is desirable. When the report contains a bibliography or references which are not cited, a listing of them is preferred to the use of footnotes.

The term "bibliography" should be used as the title when the listing is an exhaustive compilation of the available works on the subject. Except for highly scientific and research type of reports, the listing is usually a "list of references," or "selected references." The term "citations" may be used when the listing contains only works specifically cited in the text.

A bibliography which is mainly a listing of the important works on a subject rather than of specific works cited in the report, may state the number of pages, tables, and illustrations contained in the work. Also, a sentence or two abstract may be given. This additional information enables a prospective reader to form a more enlightened valuation of the reference than he can from reading only the title and facts of publication.

When a list of references is given for general use of the reader with comparatively few of them being cited in the text, the citation may also be given in footnotes. Although a duplication of certain material, this practice has the advantage of placing the reference directly before the reader at the place mentioned and of providing a ready means for page citations.

The list of references is usually arranged alphabetically by author, though in certain historical reports, a chronological listing may be used. Each reference is assigned a number in sequence from the first to last. References within the body of the report are indicated by giving these numbers in parentheses following the word or sentence indicating the need for a reference. Thus, (15, p. 6) would indicate that the material mentioned is to be found on page 6 of reference number 15 in the list of references given.

In a listing of references alphabetically by author, those without stated authorship (anonymous), principally staff-written articles in periodicals, may be listed alphabetically under their titles. This practice is preferred to listing them under "anonymous" which form is sometimes used. Publications without author, but issued by a society, bureau, department or association are listed alphabetically under the name of the issuing organization.

Publications of joint authors, regardless of the number of authors, are listed under the name of the first-named author. The names of the other authors may or may not be inverted. When there are more than three authors, the names of all but the first may be omitted and in their place the words "and others" are used.

A chapter or part in one book which may have been written by another author is listed under the author of the particular chapter, followed with the author and title of the publication in which it is included.

When footnotes are used rather than an alphabetically arranged list of references, the author's name need not be inverted. In footnotes, many publications follow the style of listing the title first, then the author's name. This plan is also acceptable, though listing the author first is perhaps more usable to the reader, who may wish to consult the original work.

In the interests of simplicity, ease of preparation, and pleasing typography, there is reason for not using quotation marks and underlining in references in typewritten copy. Many printed bibliographies and references, either as footnotes or as listings, set the title of the work and the publication name in distinguishing type, such as small capitals or italics. Titles set in roman type may be set off from the other material by the use of quotation marks. These special features, while perhaps desirable in printer's type, cannot be deemed necessary in typewritten copy. References, properly written and punctuated, create no confusion among their several elements, and, therefore, all parts of the reference may be typed in ordinary type without underlining and without quotation marks. In lists of references or bibliographies, the titles may be written in lower case, rather than capitals and lower case, without resulting in confusion.

Street addresses are necessary for all but the well-known publishers. Likewise, street addresses for associations, agencies, and organizations not readily known to the reader are usually given.

A reference is not complete without the date of publication. Should no date be given in the original, an approximate date should be supplied and enclosed in brackets. If an approximate date cannot be supplied, insert in brackets "no date" or "n.d." at the point where the date is normally given.

Elements of a Citation

The mechanical form and order of parts of a complete reference to a specific work in the literature is subject to variable practice, according to the particular likes of the writer or according to the standards of the particular publication. The essential parts, however, are well established and consist of (1) the author, (2) the title, and (3) the facts of publication. A good list of references will provide these essentials in an accurate, complete, and consistent manner. Mechanical form in the use of capital letters, abbreviations and punctuation will be kept uniform.

As between books, periodicals, public documents, monographs, newspapers and other forms of published and unpublished sources, the exact form of citation varies. The suggested forms for the several types of references given herein represent good, standard practice, though there are other forms equally good. In general, the highly abbreviated forms found in the *Business Periodicals Index*, *Engineering Index*, *Reader's Guide to Periodical Literature*, and other reference mediums

Specific Examples of Reference Forms

Order of Elements — Examples

1. Books

Author
Title of book
Edition, if other than first
Volume, if more than one
Page
Place of publication
Publisher
Date

Bonbright, James C. Valuation of Property, vol. II, pp. 976–1018. New York, McGraw-Hill Book Co. 1937.

Bullinger, Clarence E. Engineering Economy, 3rd ed., pp. 81–99. New York, McGraw-Hill Book Co. 1958.

Terborgh, George. Business Investment Policy, pp. 39–48. Washington, D.C., Machinery and Allied Products Institute and Council for Technological Advancement. 1958.

2. Periodicals

Author, if given
Title of article
Name of publication
Volume
Series number if paging is not continuous within volume
Page
Date

Camilli, G. Gaseous Insulation Goes to Work. Power. 103: No. 7: 62–66. July 1959.

How Photos Help Trim Damage. Railway Age. 146: No. 17: 35–36. April 27, 1959.

Solow, Herbert. Delrin: du Pont's Challenge to Metals. Fortune. 50: No. 2: 116–19, 160–64. August 1959.

Stable Steel Prices – A Basic False Premise (Editorial). The Iron Age. 184: No. 2: 7. July 9, 1959.

3. Journals and Proceedings

Author
Title of paper
Publication and publisher
Volume
Series number if needed
Page
Date

Barnes, Kenneth. The Place of the Junior College in Engineering Education. Jour. of Engineering Education, American Society for Engineering Education. 49: No. 3:214–16. December 1958.

Engel, Olive G. Erosion Damage to Solids Caused by High-Speed Collision With Rain. Jour. of Research, U.S. National Bureau of Standards. 61:No. 1:47–52. Research Paper 2882. U.S. Government Printing Office, Washington. 1958.

Younger, D. G., Jr. A Fatigue Failure Hypothesis Based Upon Stabilized Unidirectional Slip. Proc., American Society for Testing Materials. 58:576-95. 1958.

4. Bulletins, circulars, and monographs

Author, or publisher if no author is stated
Title of work
Page
Name of publisher
Address if necessary
Series number
Date

Evaluating Your Personnel Management, pp. 23-36. U.S. Civil Service Commission, Personnel Management Series No. 6. Washington. October 1954.

S. D. Warren Company. Guide for Selecting Printing Papers, pp. 3-4. Boston, Mass. 1961.

Rao, M. V. R. Pressure Losses Through Forced-Air Perimeter Fittings and Supply Outlets. University of Illinois, Engineering Experiment Station. Bulletin 449, p. 17. May 1958.

5. Public documents

Author, or publisher if no author is stated
Title of work
Volume
Page
Name of issuing department, bureau, etc.
Series
Address if necessary
Date

Hartford, Conn. Department of Finance. Report for Fiscal Year Ended March 31, 1959, pp. 38-39. City of Hartford, Conn. 1959.

Iowa State Highway Commission. 51st Annual Report, 1959-60, pp. 14-22. Ames, Iowa.

Piqua, Ohio. New Industry Planning Committee. An Industrial, Economical, and Recreational Guide to Piqua, Ohio. Piqua Chamber of Commerce. Piqua, Ohio. October 1957.

U.S. Treasury Department, Internal Revenue Service. Bulletin F, Tables of Useful Lives of Depreciable Property. (IRS Publication No. 173) U.S. Government Printing Office, Washington. Revised, January 1942. Reprinted 1955.

6. Newspapers

City of publication Name of newspaper Title of article Volume and series number Page and column Date	Arlington, Va. Northern Virginia Sun. Steady Rise Reported in Home Loan Interest. 22:No. 263:8, Col. 1. August 8, 1959. New York, N.Y. The New York Times. A Test for Con Edison (Editorial). 108:No.37,075:26, Col. 1. July 28, 1959.

7. Unpublished and private material

Author or name of issuing organization Title of work or description Page Source Date	American Appraisal Company, Milwaukee, Wis. Information on Building Cost Trends. (Private communication.) January 1961. Berry, C. Radford (Pennsylvania Public Utility Commission). Evaluation of Depreciation Practices by the Professions (from the Commission Viewpoint). The Columbia Gas System, Inc., Depreciation Seminar. Gannett, Fleming, Corddry and Carpenter, Inc., Harrisburg, Pa., September 1955. Renshaw, Richard W. An Analysis of Highway Benefit-Cost Analyses. Unpublished M.S. Thesis (Civil Engineering). Library, Northwestern University, Evanston, Ill., August 1959.

8. Trade catalogs and promotional material

Name of issuing company Address Title of Publication Series number Page Date	Bethlehem Steel Co., Bethlehem, Pa. Industrial Fasteners, Catalog 405, p. 84. 1955. Universal Form Clamp Co., 1238 N. Kostner Ave., Chicago 51, Ill. Products for Concrete Construction, Catalog No. 759, p. 53. 1957. Reprinted 1959.

should not be used in reports or other writings because the reader is not likely to be acquainted with the shortened forms. Moderate abbreviation is desirable in the interest of saving space and affording rapid readability.

Many citations on a page sometimes produce extensive footnotes, particularly if each note were to be written out in full. The following abbreviations are usable in lieu of repeating the full citation. The abbreviation *ibid.* (*ibidem,* the same place) may be used in place of as much of the immediately preceding reference as applies. Where a reference is made to matter previously cited but other references follow the previous citation, *loc. cit.* (*loco citato,* the place cited) or *op. cit.* (*opere citato,* the work cited) may be used according to the meaning.

[1] Mossman, Frank H., and Morton, Newton. Principles of Transportation, pp. 211–18. New York, The Ronald Press Co. 1957.

[2] *Ibid.* p. 195.

[3] Cady, Edwin Laird. Developing Executive Capacity, pp. 62–69. Englewood Cliffs, N.J., Prentice-Hall, Inc. 1958.

[4] Mossman and Morton, *op. cit.,* p. 430.

[5] Taff, Charles A. Traffic Management, rev. ed., pp. 564–77. Homewood, Ill., Richard D. Irwin, Inc. 1959.

[6] Cady, *loc. cit.*

Most publications and scientific and professional societies prescribe the typographical form for footnote citations and bibliographical reference lists. The writer should always ascertain whether such form is prescribed and, if so, follow it exactly when writing for publication. The forms herein illustrated may be used in the absence of a prescribed form to the contrary.

A few acceptable forms other than those previously given follow:

Business Information (book), *Marian C. Manley,* pp. 63–74. Harper & Brothers, New York, N.Y., 1955.

Henry G. Burger, The Need for Marketing Engineering. *Jour. of Marketing,* 23: No. 3: 244–252. Marketing Assn., 27 East Monroe Street, Chicago 3. January 1959.

Roll Extrusion — A New Metal-forming Technique, Adolph W. Ernestus. *American Machinist,* June 29, 1959. pp. 84–86.

QUESTIONNAIRES

A questionnaire is a special form of correspondence developed to procure authoritative information from a number of persons through the medium of well-directed questions.

The questionnaire is a legitimate method for obtaining information in those instances where other procedures either will not yield as good results or will involve too much time, effort, or cost. The indiscriminate use of the questionnaire, especially for unimportant objectives, has developed some justifiable prejudice against this useful and, in some instances, unique scheme for collecting information.

As a rule, the questionnaire is welcomed only by one who is specially interested in the subject of inquiry. In fact, the recipient of a questionnaire should be one who recognizes the importance of the subject and the merit of the questions as factors leading to the desired information. Questionnaires should be directed only to those persons known to have a definite connection with the subject through their position or through their contributions to technical discussions and literature.

The person preparing a questionnaire should study the subject thoroughly in order to separate the information he can obtain by his own efforts from the information which, in his judgment, can be supplied only by the recipient. This careful survey of the subject will reveal the facts essential for reaching the objectives. If the recipient of the questionnaire recognizes the importance of the topics he will usually cooperate by responding.

The recipient will judge the professional status of the sender by the quality and character of the questions. Good questions gain the respect and support of the person to whom the questions are addressed.

The suggestions included in this discussion are based upon the requirements for a comprehensive survey by the questionnaire method. Experience will provide the judgment to simplify the procedure in less involved applications.

Form of the Questionnaire

The arrangement of the questionnaire determines its acceptability on the basis of first impression made by a pleasing appearance. Neatness, readability, and typography are factors which contribute to a favorable first impression. Brevity should prevail as compared with comprehensiveness. If these qualities are further supported by well-conceived, intelligent questions, the recipient is likely to supply the answers willingly, carefully, and promptly.

The form of a questionnaire should not be stereotyped; each questionnaire should be designed to fit the needs of the occasion. There are times when a simple letter accompanied by a few well-chosen questions is an adequate means of getting the desired information.

For each element of a questionnaire, experience has evoked an accepted form which is helpful in the preparation of the questionnaire and which assures a reasonably good return. The essential elements will be discussed in the following sequence:

1. Questions
2. Instructions
3. Covering Letter
4. Identification

Questions

Persuasiveness in the character and tone of the questions is desirable. Thoughtful consideration should be given to the time and effort required to answer questions. The questions which are so planned that the work of searching for information and of writing the answers requires the minimum expenditure of effort will command a satisfactory return.

Nature of the Questions. Questions should be stated so that only definite opinions and unqualified facts will be given in straightforward answers which lend themselves to a predetermined classification.

Wording of the questions so that it is difficult for the recipient to make more than one interpretation is important. Stating the questions in terms that are consistent with the vocabulary of the recipient is one measure that helps prevent misinterpretation.

Specimen Questionnaire 3.1 illustrates well-worded questions. See page 45.

Question: On the basis of your experience, should there be a common freshman and sophomore year for all engineering students?

A.	Favor common freshman year	10
B.	Common freshman year, except shop, surveying, etc.	5
C.	Common sophomore year for the greater part	4

This question was one of six directed to 19 engineering educators who have achieved a high degree of responsibility. Their replies were controlled in terms of the desired information, but they had a free choice. Therefore, with 10 votes for "A" and only 5 votes for "B" it is reasonable to conclude that a common freshman year should receive serious consideration. With 4 votes for "C" it is reasonable to conclude that a certain portion of the sophomore year should be common to all courses.

If this question had been stated, "What is your opinion about the desirability of a common freshman year?" the 19 answers would have been difficult to evaluate.

Arrangement of the Questions. Questions and their subdivisions should be so arranged that the information desired will follow a planned development leading toward a logical conclusion.

The questions should be critically chosen and logically arranged to guide the thought of the recipient into a channel which will lead directly to the results to be obtained. The desired questions may be listed on separate slips, studied carefully, and then arranged in a suitable sequence.

The grouping of questions is important for at least two reasons. Good grouping and clear thinking are synonymous; a proper grouping of questions on the basis of their relationship will enable the recipient to associate the subject presented to him with the facts at his disposal; the sender can then arrange the information he receives more effectively for interpretation. Thus, arrange subordinate questions under main headings. There are occasions when the subject is sufficiently involved to warrant the preparation of a separate set of questions to each of several groups. When the answers arrive from all the solicited groups, they are assembled to form a composite background on which to develop the report.

The principal responsibility of an editor of a magazine or newspaper is to select articles that will sustain the interest and desire of his subscribers. From time to time he gives his readers the opportunity to tell him how his publication can be of greater service to them. Specimen 3.2 illustrates how Kenneth K. Stowell, editor of the *Architectural Record,* appeals for the cooperation of his readers through the medium of a "covering letter."

Mr. Stowell starts with the catchy old phrase, "The wheel that squeaks the loudest is the one that gets the grease." He employs the direct "you" approach throughout the letter. Finally, resistance to compliance is minimized by, "I am enclosing a self-addressed envelope for your convenience. It requires no postage." The questionnaire, Specimen 3.2, is well-designed because the main questions are subdivided into elements that smoothly guide the thinking of the recipient. The opinion and judgment of the recipient are controlled by a series of qualitative terms as illustrated in questions 1 and 2.

Number of Questions. Main questions should be as few in number as are necessary to bring the required information to a logical conclusion.

Specimen 3.1 was developed to secure the judgment of 19 heads of departments on the improvement of the curriculum in engineering. These men carry important responsibility and their days are crowded with work. The questions had to appeal to them on the basis of merit and timeliness. The designer of the questionnaire had to analyze the trends of the time and anticipate the classification of replies in terms of multiple choices. Therefore, the entire study was condensed to six principal questions with two or three subdivisions for each. A 100 per cent return is convincing indication that the recipients considered the study important.

Use of Factual Questions. The factual question is useful while the opinionated question is hard to answer. In Specimen 3.3 the answers require judgment rather than quantitative statements. Yet, to eliminate opinionated answers in general terms the designer of the questionnaire supplied the "degree" of judgment. By this scheme the answers can be classified and interpreted to good advantage. Specimen 3.5 is designed entirely for factual answers which can be readily supplied by the secretary of the recipient.

Avoid Biased Questions. The biased question involving health, physical defects, personal habits, professional advantages or disadvantages, religious or political associations yields poor results. These types of questions are to be avoided except when such questions are the main purpose of the questionnaire, which is seldom the case in the field of business, science, or engineering.

Instructions

The instructions are given to define the nature and scope of the questionnaire. The purpose of the investigation should be clearly stated as well as the time when the answers are expected to be returned. In general, the better the instructions in a well-prepared questionnaire, the better the ensuing results.

A statement appealing to the recipients' co-operative spirit as well as professional interest in the young engineer introduces Specimen 3.3. Simple instructions are given for the answering of the tabulated form in Specimen 3.4.

Covering Letter

Few letters are as important as the letter that transmits a questionnaire. This statement is particularly true because there exists a strong prejudice against questionnaires of the usual type. The main purpose of the covering letter is to gain the confidence and co-operation of the recipient. Dignified and ethical persuasion is necessary because the recipient does not expect the questionnaire, often contributes valuable and even confidential information, and generally receives little substantial reward for the talent, energy, and time he gives to the study. It is true, however, that there is personal satisfaction in co-operating with a responsible person who is engaged in the study of significant questions that confront business and the professions and who assembles answers which will benefit society as a whole.

Salesmanship may be the keyword for the tone of a letter transmitting a questionnaire. When the importance of the subject warrants, the letter should be carefully prepared as a form letter but individualized sufficiently so that the recipient will consider the letter as having been written especially to him. The recipient deserves this consideration because he is asked to supply information without compensation.

Although the covering letter needs to be brief, it is expected to perform the primary function of salesmanship by giving attention to the following items:

1. Interest of the recipient may be gained by indicating why he was chosen, why the information is essential, and why he was taken into the confidence of the investigator.
2. Reward may be offered in terms of a digest of the report, of freedom from further solicitation, and of guaranteed secrecy of the information and personal identification.
3. Tone of the letter should be sincere, original, courteous, direct, and persuasive.
4. Recipient should be assured that the information requested is not extensive and that the time required to furnish the information is not great.
5. Letter preferably should be typed; however, when large numbers are involved, the letter may be neatly duplicated by one of the many available processes.
6. Letter should be on good quality paper, free from ornamentation and easy to read. A personal signature is an indication of the sender's respect for the recipient.

The covering letter for Specimen 3.5 informs the recipient of the importance of sending his reply promptly. This questionnaire was sent to 214 persons, and 170 responded immediately. Since it was desirable to receive answers from the entire group of 214, a follow-up letter, included in Specimen 3.5, was sent; this letter brought in 29 more responses.

As illustrated in Specimen 3.4, the direct "YOU" appeal is tactfully introduced in the covering letter written by the editor of *Better Homes and Gardens*. An appeal for co-operation and an expression of faith winds up the letter with a brief but effective paragraph: "Your answer will help us make *Better Homes and Gardens* a better magazine. We know you won't fail us. Thank you very much."

The questions on the reverse side of the covering letter are well organized. They lead the addressee along a definite path and remind him of items which he might easily omit. The completion of the questionnaire is made easy by providing little squares for "check marks." An appeal to pride of ownership will yield many answers to the questions, "Brand name or name of manufacturer" and "In about what year did you buy it?" Notice too, how easy the work of mailing becomes by the statements ". . . reply in the envelope provided," and "It needs no postage and you need not sign your name."

Identification

Identification of the questionnaire is important to both the sender and recipient. The essential items to appear on the questionnaire are title, sponsor's full name and address, return address, and date. Certain questionnaires need to indicate the groups to which they are sent.

When there needs to be a check on the persons replying or when such information will be helpful in interpretation of the results, definite space should be set aside for the name and address of the person and organization replying as well as the date of reply.

Mailing List

A satisfactory mailing list will include only those who are known to be well versed in the field encompassed by the questions. It is reasonable to assume that the recipient of the questionnaire may even desire to obtain a copy of the report, or at least a summary of the findings. The sender should select a well-distributed representation of participants. Perhaps the list of organizations or persons from whom answers could be obtained may be too long for practical mailing. If so, the list may be abridged through approved statistical sample selection procedure. In general, the sender will find it advisable to test the workability of the questionnaire by sending out a few to persons whom he knows well and who are representative of the group to whom the questionnaire is to be sent. When the mailing list is not fixed by the restricted purpose of the study, profitable sources for a mailing list are yearbooks and current publications to which those persons closely related to the subject belong or contribute.

A notation of those who answer and those who do not answer will be helpful in determining the value and accuracy of the information received.

Specimen 3.1.

Questionnaire

TABULATION OF REPLIES TO QUESTIONS RELATING TO THE ENGINEERING CURRICULUM

Note: Boxes for check marks were used in this questionnaire where the tabular replies are now shown.

1. Have you made any significant changes in your curriculum recently, or are you contemplating any such changes in the near future?
   a. No changes 10
   b. Minor changes 8
   c. Important changes 1
2. Do you favor a common freshman and a common sophomore year for all engineering students?
   a. Favor common freshman year 10
   b. Favor common freshman year, except shop and surveying 5
   c. Favor common sophomore year for the greater part 4
3. What is your opinion regarding the offering of group electives which enable the student to specialize and concentrate on major interests? Do you favor a prescribed course with little opportunity for elective work?
   a. Do not favor specialization 13
   b. Favor offering electives 6
4. Do you believe that a sound curriculum may be built by emphasizing those phases in engineering which stand out most prominently in an analysis of the employment records of the graduates?
   a. Do not favor such consideration 14
   b. Favor it if basic training is not sacrificed 5
5. Is it your impression that a five-year engineering course is a closed question as far as your school is concerned? That is, are members of your staff supporting such a plan?
   a. Favor or use fifth year 8
   b. Do not favor fifth year 11
6. Do you require summer camp or industrial experience of your students?
   a. Have summer requirement 13
   b. Do not have summer requirement 6

Return to:	Information furnished by:
(Name and title)	School __________
(Organization)	By __________
(Address)	Date __________

A R C H I T E C T U R A L

R E C O R D

PUBLISHED BY F. W. DODGE CORPORATION — 119 WEST 40th STREET, NEW YORK 18, N. Y.

August 16, 19..

"THE WHEEL THAT SQUEAKS THE LOUDEST
IS THE ONE THAT GETS THE GREASE."

It seems to be true that those who make known their needs and desires are most likely to be served best. This holds in all fields, including architecture and publishing. Therefore, we are writing to give you an opportunity to tell us how we can be of greater service to you and your office.

Since it is our purpose to be of maximum service to all of our readers, I take this occasion to ask what you like about the Record, what you don't like, and what you feel is the most useful and most interesting in your work. Your opinions and suggestions are of the utmost importance to us in making the Record an indispensable source of information and an inspiration to the profession.

I would greatly appreciate your checking the enclosed questionnaire as the expression of your own opinion. Of course, any additional comments and suggestions would be most welcome. By hearing directly from you about your own needs and desires, we can continue to make the Record increasingly useful to you. I am enclosing a self-addressed envelope for your convenience. It requires no postage.

Sincerely yours,

Kenneth K. Stowell

Kenneth K. Stowell

KKS:il
ENC

Specimen 3.2.

Questionnaire: Covering letter from *Architectural Record,* F. W. Dodge Corp.

Other Dodge Services: Dodge Reports and Statistical Research Service — Home Owners' Catalogs — Sweet's Catalog Files — Real Estate & Builders' Guide

Specimen 3.2.
Questionnaire

THIS IS MY OPINION OF ARCHITECTURAL RECORD

1. How does ARCHITECTURAL RECORD compare with other magazines in the same field with respect to:

		The Best	Good	Average	Needs Improvement
(a) Conciseness and clarity of text	(a)	___	___	___	___
(b) Completeness of material presented	(b)	___	___	___	___
(c) Accuracy of technical data	(c)	___	___	___	___
(d) Layout and appearance	(d)	___	___	___	___
(e) Variety of subjects of direct interest to architects and architect-engineers	(e)	___	___	___	___

My special comments are ____

____

2. How useful or interesting do you find the following features:

		Use Constantly	Use Seldom	Read Often	Don't Read	Want More	Want Less
(a) Building Type Studies	(a)	___	___	___	___	___	___
(b) Architectural Engineering (technical articles)	(b)	___	___	___	___	___	___
(c) Time Saver Standards	(c)	___	___	___	___	___	___
(d) For Better Building (news of materials, equipment and techniques)	(d)	___	___	___	___	___	___
(e) Dodge Data--economics, cost and other statistics in article form	(e)	___	___	___	___	___	___
(f) Editorial	(f)	___	___	___	___	___	___
(g) The Record Reports (news from the field)	(g)	___	___	___	___	___	___
(h) Recent buildings in pictures, plans and details	(h)	___	___	___	___	___	___
(i) Required Reading (reviews of new books)	(i)	___	___	___	___	___	___

My special comments are ____

____

Specimen 3.2 (continued)

3. What subjects would you like to see covered in greater detail? (You may double check those you feel most emphatic about)

___Innovations in design
___City planning
___Industrial design
___Architectural details
___Color schemes
___Structural methods and materials
___Finish methods and materials
___Mechanical plant of buildings:
  ___Electrical
  ___Heating
  ___Ventilating
  ___Air conditioning
  ___Sanitation
___Allied arts: sculpture, murals, etc.
___Interior design, furniture
___Office practice
___Business administration
___Financing techniques
___Prices and costs
___Cost estimating
___Legal decisions and aspects
___Current legislative measures
___Labor relations
___Architectural education
___News of architectural organizations
___Personal anecdotes

4. What do you like most about ARCHITECTURAL RECORD?

____

____

5. What don't you like about ARCHITECTURAL RECORD?

____

____

6. For future reference, do you file:
___The entire magazine? ___Pages cut from magazine?
___In a permanent binding?

7. Do you prefer a page size that permits filing of material for reference in standard file cabinets?
___Yes ___No

We would welcome any additional suggestions you may have for making the RECORD even more useful to you in your practice.______________________________

____

It will aid us in tabulating this information if you will fill in the lines below. However, if for any reason you prefer to remain anonymous, you may leave the space blank.

Name______________________ Registered Architect____Engineer______

Firm______________________ Position______________________

Street____________Zone________ City____________State__________

ARCHITECTURAL RECORD . . . . 119 West 40th Street, New York 18
August 19..

Specimen 3.3.
Questionnaire

TRAINING ENGINEERS FOR CAREERS

This questionnaire is submitted to you and others in the hope that the answers to its questions will suggest methods whereby the colleges can better fit young men for engineering careers.

Name (optional) ______________ Title ________________ Date _______

Department ________________________ Address ___________________

Please check answers as indicated.

I. The engineer's cultural standing

1. To what extent is it important for an engineer to be able to meet and converse with cultured and intellectual people?

   not at all ( )   slightly ( )   moderately ( )   very ( )

2. To what extent are the following present in the average engineering graduate?

	limitedly	moderately	extensively
(a) Respect toward women	( )	( )	( )
(b) Refinement of mind	( )	( )	( )
(c) Good taste	( )	( )	( )
(d) Wholesome morals	( )	( )	( )
(e) Truth and honor	( )	( )	( )

II. Stress and importance placed upon technical skill and knowledge during an engineer's college life

1. Which of the following should be stressed to the student engineer?
   (a) An underlying philosophy of life ( )
   (b) A true sense of right and wrong ( )
   (c) A sense of duty toward mankind ( )

2. Check any of the following which are more important to a man's life than technical considerations.
   (a) An underlying philosophy of life ( )
   (b) A true sense of right and wrong ( )
   (c) A sense of duty toward mankind ( )

III. Basis for the valuation of one's life

1. To what extent is the possession of material goods useful as a basis for the valuation of one's life?

   slightly ( )   moderately ( )   very ( )   only basis ( )

Specimen 3.3 (continued)

2. To what extent will the average engineering graduate depend upon his possession of material goods for valuation of his life?

   slightly ( )   moderately ( )   wholly ( )

IV. Engineering curriculums with respect to other than technical subjects

1. To what extent do you believe the following subjects important to a man's career and personal happiness?

	not at all	slightly	moderately	very
(a) Written and spoken English	( )	( )	( )	( )
(b) The social sciences	( )	( )	( )	( )
(c) Art	( )	( )	( )	( )
(d) Philosophy	( )	( )	( )	( )
(e) Psychology	( )	( )	( )	( )

2. How many semester credits of classroom instruction should be given in the following subjects in an engineering curriculum?

	none	2 to 3	4 to 6	7 to 10
(a) Written and spoken English	( )	( )	( )	( )
(b) The social sciences	( )	( )	( )	( )
(c) Art	( )	( )	( )	( )
(d) Philosophy	( )	( )	( )	( )
(e) Psychology	( )	( )	( )	( )

3. To what extent do you feel that a doctorate degree would be useful in the field of engineering that you represent?

   not at all ( )   slightly ( )   moderately ( )   very ( )

4. Which arrangement of course do you deem best suited for the proper training of an individual in preparation for an engineering career?

   (a) Four years for a degree ( )
   (b) Four years plus one year graduate work ( )
   (c) Five years for a degree ( )
   (d) Four years plus two years graduate work ( )

Return questionnaire to:

Name: ______________________ Title: ______________

Address: ______________________________________

May 14, 19____

BETTER HOMES AND GARDENS

MEREDITH PUBLISHING COMPANY • DES MOINES 3, IOWA

February 20, 19..

Dear Reader:

In publishing Better Homes & Gardens, our job is to make the magazine fit your needs and those of all our readers.

I wish we could visit all of you personally--we can't of course, but as a substitute won't you give us a little help by mail?

In planning editorial features we need a variety of background information about our readers. Your answers to the questions on the back of this letter will provide such information.

In a study of this kind, you represent several thousand readers. So you see how important it is that we have your answer. Won't you please answer as many of the questions as you can and mail your reply in the envelope provided. It needs no postage and you need not sign your name.

Your answer will help us make BETTER HOMES & GARDENS a better magazine. We know you won't fail us. Thank you very much.

Sincerely,

BETTER HOMES & GARDENS

F. W. McDonough

Editor

Frank McDonough
bet

Specimen 3.4.
Questionnaire: Covering letter

EW YORK CHICAGO PHILADELPHIA CLEVELAND DETROIT ATLANTA LOS ANGELES SAN FRANCISCO

Specimen 3.4.
Questionnaire

BACKGROUND INFORMATION ABOUT READERS

Please check below each of the items which you own; write in the brand name or the name of the manufacturer, and (as nearly as you can remember) the year in which you bought it.

	Now Own	Brand Name (or name of manufacturer)	In about what year did you buy it?
KITCHEN EQUIPMENT			
Refrigerator (electric)	☐		
Refrigerator (gas)	☐		
Refrigerator (ice)	☐		
Food freezer	☐		
Garbage disposal unit (in sink). .	☐		
Dish washer	☐		
Electric toaster.	☐		
Electric roaster.	☐		
Electric waffle iron	☐		
Electric food mixer.	☐		
LAUNDRY EQUIPMENT			
Washing machine (automatic)	☐		
Washing machine (wringer type) . .	☐		
Clothes dryer.	☐		
Ironer (electric mangle)	☐		
Water softener	☐		
LAWN AND GARDEN EQUIPMENT			
Lawnmower (hand type)	☐		
Lawnmower (gasoline powered). . .	☐		
Lawnmower (electric powered). . .	☐		
Garden tractor	☐		
Garden plow (hand type)	☐		
Hedge trimmer (electric)	☐		
Hedge trimmer (hand type).	☐		
FANS AND VENTILATORS			
Kitchen ventilating fan	☐		
Attic fan	☐		
Desk or table fan	☐		
Window fan.	☐		
Room air conditioner	☐		
RADIOS, PHONOGRAPHS, TELEVISION			
Radio-phonograph combination . . .	☐		
Separate record player.	☐		
Television receiver - radio comb. .	☐		
Television receiver (not comb.). .	☐		
Table model radio	☐		

Do you own your home or rent it? ☐ Own ☐ Rent

In what type of home do you live?

☐ Single family
☐ Duplex (or double house)
☐ Apartment (2 to 4 family)
☐ Apartment (5 family or more)

Your town ____________________

State ____________________

Date ____________________

IOWA STATE UNIVERSITY
OF SCIENCE AND TECHNOLOGY
Ames, Iowa

November 7, 19..

COLLEGE OF ENGINEERING
OFFICE OF THE DEAN

Ernest A. Prehm
Superintendent of Schools
Northwood, Iowa

Dear Mr. Prehm:

The attached tabulation has been arranged so that you may supply the information quickly and conveniently. Your cooperation in this study will contribute materially toward the completion of a study on enrollment and availability of courses in Iowa high schools.

Sincerely yours,

Dean of Engineering

HRC:ea
Enclosure

Specimen 3.5.
Questionnaire: Covering letter

Specimen 3.5.
Questionnaire

ENROLLMENT AND AVAILABILITY OF COURSES IN IOWA HIGH SCHOOLS

Name of school ______________________ Address ______________________

Superintendent ______________________ Principal ______________________

Consolidated ______________ Not consolidated ______________ Date ______________

Enrollment: 9th yr. __________ 10th yr. __________ 11th yr. __________ 12th yr. __________

Please place an X opposite each subject to indicate if the subject is (1) *Required*, (2) *Elective*, (3) *Not Available* at present, or (4) *Plan to introduce* in the near future (give probable date) in your high school curriculum. Also give the number of units of high school credit devoted to each subject if it differs from those listed below.

Units and Subject	Required (1)	Elective (2)	Not Available (3)	Plan to Introduce (4)
A. Mathematics				
a. ½-unit, High School Algebra				
b. ½-unit, Intermediate Algebra				
c. ½-unit, Advanced Algebra				
d. 1-unit, Plane Geometry				
e. ½-unit, Solid Geometry				
f. ½-unit, Plane Trigonometry				
B. Science				
a. 1-unit, General Science				
b. 1-unit, Biology				
c. 1-unit, Chemistry				
d. 1-unit, Physics				
C. English (Insert course title)				
a. 1-unit, 9th year				
b. 1-unit, 10th year				
c. 1-unit, 11th year				
d. 1-unit, 12th year				
D. History (Social Studies)				
a. 1-unit, Old World Background				
b. 1-unit, The Modern World				
c. 1-unit, Am. History & Gov't				
d. 1-unit, Modern Problems				
E. Drawing				
a. ½-unit, Freehand Sketching				
b. ½-unit, Mechanical Techniques				

Return to: Dean of Engineering
Iowa State University
Ames, Iowa

Information supplied by:

____
Signature

IOWA STATE UNIVERSITY
OF SCIENCE AND TECHNOLOGY
Ames, Iowa

December 11, 19..

COLLEGE OF ENGINEERING
OFFICE OF THE DEAN

Cortie A. Vernon
Superintendent of Schools
Villisca, Iowa

Dear Mr. Vernon:

We are still anxious to receive the information requested in the attached tabulation. Will you, therefore, do us the special favor of returning the completed questionnaire at your earliest convenience. Your prompt cooperation will be appreciated. Already 170 out of 225 persons have returned their answers. May we have this information for your high school. A self-addressed envelope is enclosed for your convenience.

Sincerely yours,

Dean of Engineering

HRC:ea
Enclosure

Specimen 3.5.
Questionnaire: Follow-up letter

INTERVIEWS

There are certain phases of collecting information that require personal contacts. This approach is particularly useful when some phase of the information is difficult to explain, when the answer should not be made public, or when correspondence has broken down and a personal touch is required to establish mutual confidence.

Purpose and Function

Interviews may be conducted person to person or by telephone. When the telephone is used the questions should require answers which can be supplied spontaneously from memory and without extended reference to source material. The telephone should not be used to obtain information of value when the two persons involved are strangers.

Interviews are used widely in everyday business. Newspapers and periodicals perhaps make the widest use of this technique in gathering information, but it is used widely also in the assembly of technical information for publication or for use in the ordinary operation of an office.

The success of interviews is more dependent upon the interviewer than upon the one giving the information. The interviewer should be frank in his explanation of the purpose of the interview, thoroughly prepared in his knowledge of the subject, willing to impart information as well as to receive it, and co-operative and sympathetic with the interviewed. Months of training are required to develop interviewers for professional positions in business or with periodicals.

Planning and Conducting Interviews

Surveys and investigations invariably require interviews on the part of the person in charge. When questions are simple and asked merely to gain information, the interviewed will speak freely; but when he is asked to give his opinion on a matter that is controversial or where the outcome of an undertaking may not be certain, the interviewed will answer cautiously and conditionally. In any case, the interviewed frequently requests that his remarks not be quoted verbatim. A great deal of tact, patience, and skill is required to bring out the essential information. All too often the interviewed consciously or unconsciously gets off the subject. The interviewer needs to be courteous and resourceful on all occasions, especially when he reintroduces the main topic of the interview.

Even though it is impossible to anticipate the exact course of an interview, it is the responsibility of the interviewer to plan the interview carefully. The following ten specific suggestions included in a course in Industrial Publishing of the New York Business Publishers Association will prove helpful:

1. Make a definite appointment with the man to be interviewed, and keep it to the minute.
2. Learn as much as possible about him before you go to the interview. Consult the morgue [file of information on personalities], "Who's Who," and other directories that may be available.
3. Know the subject of the interview. The best interviewer is one with whom the interviewed can talk on something like equal terms and not have to explain every little thing in ABC language.
4. Do not expect the interviewed to volunteer information or to take the lead in conducting the interview; that is your job.
5. Frame in advance some pertinent questions that get at the heart of the subject.
6. Do only as much talking as is necessary to keep the person interviewed talking.
7. Observe the courtesies of your position. Don't argue, don't contradict, don't insist. Discuss the points that require some comeback in order to bring out their meaning, or to bring up the other side of the question, or to keep the interview moving.
8. Keep some leading questions up your sleeve with which to bring the interview back to its subject matter if the interviewed becomes discursive.
9. If the information quoted is of an important character, or involves many statistical references, figures, mathematical formulas, or other exact statements requiring careful checking, it is generally best to submit a written record of the interview for approval before printing it.
10. Do not overstay your time. Leave while the going is good.

The person interviewed should be selected on the basis of his intimate and authoritative knowledge of the subject. If possible, an introduction is desirable from a person who knows both the interviewer and the interviewed.

A carefully prepared letter accompanied by the statement of a few principal questions will enable the person to be interviewed to think the matter through in advance and to make arrangements for a definite appointment. The questions may be arranged in outline form with sufficient space between each one for notes by the interviewed as well as the interviewer. Specifically, the letter should state briefly:

1. Reason for the interview
2. Purpose and significance of the questions to be discussed
3. Arrangements for the time and place of the interview to be made at the convenience of the interviewed. These arrangements can be dealt with most satisfactorily by telephone.

Immediately after the interview, a complete memorandum should be prepared, including a copy of the letter requesting the interview, the list of preliminary questions and answers; other questions, answers and statements that developed during the interview; and general notes of items that may be useful in the report. A businesslike record of the interview will eliminate the possibility of forgetting or confusing the data and opinions supplied by the interviewed.

Specimen Interview

Specimen Interview 3.6 was planned by Wesley W. Teich, a student in electrical engineering. The subject under consideration was "The Use of Gaseous Discharge Tubes in High-Speed Photography." The specimen includes copies of the letters requesting the privilege of an interview, the list of questions that accompanied the letter, and summaries of three interviews.

2811 Lincoln Way
Ames, Iowa
August 2, 19..

Dr. W. B. Boast
201 Electrical Engineering Building
Iowa State University
Ames, Iowa

Dear Dr. Boast:

I am preparing a written report this term on high-speed flash units used in photography and would appreciate receiving certain information from you.

Enclosed is a list of questions which I would like to discuss with you at your convenience. I will telephone you in a day or two to ask if an interview can be arranged.

Yours very truly,

Wesley W. Teich
Senior Electrical
Engineering Student

Specimen 3.6.
Interview: Letter of request

2811 Lincoln Way
Ames, Iowa
September 18, 19..

Prof. Harold E. Edgerton
Department of Electrical Engineering
Massachusetts Institute of Technology
Cambridge, Massachusetts

Dear Professor Edgerton:

From Mr. Mentch of Eastman Kodak Company I have been forwarded your answers to my questions about the Kodatron Flash Unit. I greatly appreciate your attention to my request.

My report on the use of condenser-discharge tubes in high-speed photography is nearing completion. I would like to see you to ask a few final questions and to check briefly the work done so far.

I will be in Boston next week and would like to meet with you on the afternoon of Thursday, September 27. I will telephone you on Wednesday to make definite arrangements.

Very truly yours,

Wesley W. Teich
Senior Electrical
Engineering Student

Specimen 3.6A.
Interview: Letter of request

Specimen 3.6.
Interview: Questions

USE OF GASEOUS DISCHARGE TUBES IN
HIGH-SPEED PHOTOGRAPHY

What methods can be used to determine the magnitude and duration of the transient discharge current?

How is the flash stopped after breakdown occurs?

How does the duration of the flash affect the maximum energy input the tube will stand?

How can the size of the charging equipment needed be determined?

What types of condensers can be used to supply the 20 to 100 mfd necessary at 2000 volts dc?

Wesley W. Teich
August 2, 19. . . .

Specimen 3.6.

Interview: Summaries

SUMMARIES OF INTERVIEWS

Dr. W. B. Boast, Department of Electrical Engineering,
Iowa State University, August 9, 19....

A discharge tube probably has a maximum energy rating which cannot be exceeded without damaging the tube. The time of discharge is so short that no appreciable dissipation of heat occurs while the tube is carrying current. The energy input, therefore, is independent of time.

There also is a limit to the maximum current that can be carried without excessive vaporization of the electrodes or damage to the tube seal caused by sudden heating.

The current limit sets the maximum voltage that may be applied to the tube, and the energy limit determines the maximum capacity permissible with this voltage.

The size of the charging equipment used in high-speed flash units will fix the length of time needed to charge the condenser and therefore the time between flashes. Parts of even nominal size would not be damaged by the high currents drawn when the charging cycle begins because the overload is of such a short duration. It is the charging time rather than heating that must be taken into account in designing charging equipment.

The condensers used to store the discharge energy should be of a type having low losses so that short-circuit discharge will not cause excessive heating. Paper- or oil-impregnated paper condensers, such as General Electric Pyranol or Westinghouse Inerteen, could be used. An ac rating of 660 volts, or perhaps 230 volts, would be sufficient for operation at 2000 volts dc. A typical Pyranol condenser rated at 120 mfd at 230 volts ac would weigh about 52 lb.

If a flash unit were used as a stroboscope at frequencies near line value, the rectifying system would have to be filtered and other precautions taken to insure that the condenser is charged to the same energy level during each cycle of operation. Charging equipment in this case would have to be designed for continuous operation.

* * *

Dr. P. H. Carr, Department of Physics, Iowa State
University, August 16, 19....

Some loss of efficiency will be encountered in the use of high-speed lamps because of the failure of the reciprocity law at high intensities. Most pictures are taken in the range of light intensities where the photographic emulsion is most efficient. When exposures have to be made either at low intensities, as in astronomical records, or at high intensities, as in this case, the product *It* must be increased to obtain a comparable density. This may be as much as 5 to 10 times, if the exposure is short.

Standard photographic texts contain the plot of light intensity against the *It* required for a standard density, usually as the logarithms of these quantities, and explain the physical theory accounting for the shape of this curve.

Specimen 3.6 (continued)

The color characteristics of a condenser-discharge flash cannot be predicted on the basis of a steady-state discharge of the same tube. During the flash, high currents will flow resulting in high temperature and pressure within the tube. Under these conditions higher states of ionization appear and consequently an increased number of color lines.

At these high pressures there is considerable continuous background in any spectrum. Thus, the light of the flash is more like the light of an ordinary tungsten lamp and less like the line spectrum of a steady-state discharge.

The light from the discharge tube is of a general cool quality and high in actinic value. The visible emission is accompanied by considerable ultra-violet radiation. This is not objectionable in black and white photography, but may cause trouble in the use of Kodachrome and in other color processes. The use of a Wratten No. 1 or a CC 15-color filter is suggested to reduce the effect of this radiation.

* * *

Dr. Harold E. Edgerton, professor of electrical engineering, Massachusetts Institute of Technology, Cambridge, September 27, 19. . . .

Almost all of the inert gases have been tested in condenser-discharge tubes. Each has its own characteristics, but cost prevents the commercial use of the rarer ones. Argon was used in the original tubes because of its low price. Mercury-vapor also has been used in some tubes, but it gives a red-deficient light and is more difficult to handle than the inert gases.

In experiments now being conducted on tubes, an integrating exposure meter is used to measure the output. This meter measures the integral of the intensity of the light over the discharge time as a voltage built up on a condenser charged with a current that is proportional to the intensity.

The grid method of flash control incurs a slight delay because of the inductive nature of the transformer used. The use of a thyratron in series with the lamp for control eliminates this delay, but limits the peak current to that which the thyratron will safely carry. This objection is reduced by modern hydrogen-filled thyratrons whose current ratings are higher because the gas reduces cathode destruction from positive ion bombardment.

Edgerton has been working on a project of taking aerial photographs at night. Large flash tubes receive the discharge of a 3000-mfd condenser bank charged to 4000 volts for this purpose.

The condensers are built in cases about the size of demolition bombs and are carried in the bomb rack of the plane. Power for the units is supplied from 12-volt generators. The charging rate is fast enough to permit a slight overlap in the pictures taken from the desired height and speed. Duration of the flash is approximately 1/100 second.

The widespread use of condenser-discharge tubes by amateur and professional photographers was not anticipated when the tubes were first developed. A unit was used first in the photographic studio at M.I.T. when ordinary techniques failed to stop the motion of a young boy. Since that time many experimental units have been tested and used in that studio.

CHAPTER 4

Mechanics of Style

Style possesses two distinct meanings: literary style and mechanics of style.

The *literary style* of a writer is determined by those characteristics that result from sentence structure, sentence length and arrangement, and diction. Mood, interest, enthusiasm, and decision on the part of the reader follow largely from the literary style employed by the author.

The *mechanics of style* of a writer is established by his characteristic use of capital letters, abbreviations, numbers, symbols, and, to a certain extent, punctuation, spelling, and italics. Although these mechanics have a bearing upon the ease of reading and understanding, they contribute only minutely to the development of a particular attitude toward the subject.

Literary style allows each author a free hand in expressing his individuality in writing. Mechanics of style provides a standard which is applied uniformly to the publication of all manuscripts processed by the organization setting forth the standard.

In everyday writing and reading, the student, the scientist, and the layman are seldom conscious of the mechanics of style. But editors, typesetters, typists, and authors are. In the areas of journalistic and technical writing as well as report writing, mechanics of style plays an important role.

SCOPE OF MECHANICS OF STYLE

Within the province of mechanics of style is included that physical treatment of words over which the writer has some choice. There is no universal agreement on when to capitalize certain words, when to use numerals instead of words, and when and how to abbreviate. These items have not become fixed rules of writing. Similarly, punctuation, spelling, and treatment of compound words are questions of style because there are several choices available to the writer.

Accuracy of meaning, desirable emphasis, economy of words and space, ease of reading and pleasing typographical appearance are achieved through good styling. Within a given publication and within a given technical field, a uniform mechanics of style should be followed consistently. These uniform practices must be decided upon by the author, or by the editor if the report is to be published. These are not questions of right or wrong which can be answered by reference to the dictionary or an English text. They are matters of precedent and usage. For instance, the following forms will be understood by the readers of technical publications as well as general publications, but the form to use is a matter of choice in each instance.

six per centum	6 per centum
six percent.	6 percent.
six per cent	6 per cent
six percent	6 percent
	6%

Per centum is no longer used in English composition, though all other of these forms are in current use. The form *per cent.* is now rarely used though 50 years ago it was used probably more frequently than any of the other forms.

Another case of many variations of the same expression which illustrates the need for a standard style is:

lb. per sq. in.	lb psi
lbs. per sq. in.	psi
lb per sq in	lb./sq. in.
lb. per in.^{2}	#/sq. in.
lb–in.^{2}	lb./in^2
lb. p.s.i.	#/in.^{2}

By using capital letters and different spacing between letters, other variations can be developed for pounds per square inch, for which psi is now the generally used form in technical publications.

Because accepted usage of capitals, abbreviations, and numerals can be found for many variations of a given case, each publisher has found it advisable to formulate his own rules of style which he expects his authors, editors, typesetters, and proofreaders to follow. Many a publishing firm has issued its own manual on style. Even though these manuals are standard for the publishers issuing them, the standards differ on many matters. That these authorities disagree is not a serious matter, because many of the differences result from serving different readerships. Service to the reader should be the first objective of any style. The second objective is to be consistent within a selected style system.

An examination of textbooks, periodicals, and publications of technical societies will reveal many differences in styling, particularly between different scientific fields. Because of these differences, the student who sets out to learn standard practice in style may become confused. He will find that the publications of the older established publishers are good examples of acceptable styles in their respective fields and that in principle they are not far apart.

IMPORTANCE OF MECHANICS OF STYLE

While mechanics of styling is a standard element in all writing, whether technical or nontechnical, the subject is of greater importance in the technical and scientific fields. Here there is a greater opportunity to gain by the advantages which good styling offers to both publisher and reader. The judicious use of capitals, abbreviations, and numerals results in definite savings in writing time, in writing space, and in reading time. In addition to economy, these items are worthy goals because a well-chosen style promotes comprehension on the part of the reader, who should always be given first consideration. The emphasis produced by capitals, italics, and numerals draws the attention of the reader to these items and enables him to locate easily the items so written. For instance, use of the form, Fig. 12, makes it easier to locate a passage in the text referring to Fig. 12 than if the form, figure twelve, is used.

Mechanics of style is a standard of practice that contributes to good typography, either with typescript or printer's type. Frequent use of capitals detracts from good-appearing typography as may also excessive abbreviations.

PRACTICAL RULES OF STYLE

The essentials of good practice in the uses of mechanics of style can be stated rather simply:

1. Make the practices such that the reader will readily grasp the meaning intended, especially in the use of abbreviations.
2. Follow a reasonable and logical style commonly used in the particular subject field of the report and, therefore, one likely to be easily recognized by the readers.
3. Make the style one which results in pleasing typography and economical typing and typesetting.
4. Follow consistently throughout the report, paper, or manuscript the style adopted.

The following general practice usually applies in the writing of technical works. In case of doubt, use:

1. Lower-case letters rather than capitals
2. Numerals rather than words for numbers

3. The word spelled out rather than its abbreviation
4. Words or abbreviations rather than signs or symbols (%, ″, ′, @, ¢, #, &)
5. The comma, rather than omit it.

Good, consistent styling promotes acceptance of written work just as does the use of excellent English. Variations in the use of style slow up the reader by causing him to hesitate and to lose the chain of thought. A report or article well styled for its class of readers may be read without making the reader conscious of the style.

SPECIFIC ELEMENTS OF STYLE

A complete treatise on style would make a small book in itself, but it is essential to the purpose of this book on preparation of reports to present a brief explanation and discussion of capitals, abbreviations, numerals, and punctuation.

Capital Letters

Even in an extensive manual of style it would be difficult to mention every rule and give specific illustrations on the use of capital and lower-case letters. For general usage, however, the chief objectives of style in the use of capitals can be achieved by following the main rules and keeping in mind that, as with other forms of styling, the purpose is to serve the reader.

Capitals are used for emphasis—for making certain words stand out from others. When capitals are used sparingly they perform their main function of helping the reader to understand; when overused, the result is poor typography and confusion for the reader. To a certain extent, capitals perform the same function as do italic and bold face letters.

The trend in usage is away from capitals. If a particular case is debatable, the safest decision is to use lower case. Letters of the alphabet are read in lower case with less effort than when in capitals. However, lower-case words may pass unnoticed by the reader. If capitalized, they are more likely to receive special attention.

Capital letters, usually as initial letters of words, are used in two general ways. First, for proper nouns within the body of a composition, and second, for words in headings, topic statements, tabulations and at the beginning of a sentence. Here are some style suggestions for capitalization:

1. Capitalize names of people, places, and things when they are used in a proper sense.

Henry Brown	Ford automobile
Missouri River	General Electric Company
Fifth Street	Ohio State Department of Health
Chicago, Illinois	Marston Hall

2. Adjectives and derivatives of proper names are capitalized except when their usage has become so general that the name has been reduced to a common noun.

Arabic numerals	babbitt (metal)
English language	bessemer steel
German silver	bunsen burner
Imhoff tank	diesel motor
Southern pine	manila rope
Spanish history	morocco leather
	paris green
	portland cement
	prussian blue
	roman type

3. Capitalize proprietary (trademark) names, except when the name is commonly used by good authority in the lower case.

Bakelite (plastic)	caterpillar (type of tread)
Caterpillar (tractor)	cellophane (transparent cellulose)
Celotex (fiber board)	carborundum (abrasive)

Duco (enamel)	dictaphone (sound recorder)
Frigidaire (refrigerator)	duralumin (metal)
Kodak (camera)	mimeograph (duplicating process)
Koroseal (synthetic rubber)	monel (metal)
Lucite (plastic)	nylon (plastic)
Mazda (lamp)	pyrex (glass)
Polaroid (glass)	stainless (steel)
Stellite (metal)	
Vinylite (plastic)	

4. Capitalize the full names of distinguished organizations and their shortened names. However, if the shortened form is used frequently within the report, preferred practice is to use lower case.

Bureau of Internal Revenue	Interstate Commerce Commission
the Bureau	the Commission
Committe on Planning	State Board of Education
the Committee	the Board
University of California	Committee on Public Relations
the University	the Committee

5. When points of the compass are used to designate areas of the United States or the world they are capitalized; as directions they are not capitalized.

Middle Atlantic states	Middle Western states
Pacific Northwest	western Michigan
the East (the area of the eastern United States)	northwest (direction)
the Far East	east, north, west, south
Western customs	east by northeast
Middle West	
Midwest	

6. Capitalize words similar to the following when they are preceded by the identifying name, but not when used alone. Example: The Missouri River is the longest in the state.

bay	highway	park	river
bridge	island	point	street
creek	mountain	railroad	tunnel
forest	ocean	range	valley

7. Political divisions, when preceded by specific names are capitalized, but not when used alone or preceding the identifying name.

Fourth Ward	city of Atlanta
Tenth Congressional District	county of York
Story County	state of Idaho

8. Official and professional titles are capitalized when preceding a person's name, but when immediately following the name the lower case is preferred.

Pres. Harold K. Miller	Harold K. Miller, president, Miller and Company
Prof. H. F. Swenson	H. F. Swenson, professor of English
Doctor Budge	Henry P. Budge, doctor in charge
Superintendent Smith	H. Earl Smith, general superintendent

9. In the body of the report capitalize the nouns, chapter, article, experiment, plan, and other often used designations when followed by a numeral.

Book 10	Appendix B	Plan B
Volume 9	Experiment 8	Fig. 10
Chapter 11	Model M-1	Table 7
		Method A

Exceptions to the foregoing use of capitals are page 17, column 6, line 10, which are usually written lower case.

10. The first word following a colon is capitalized when it introduces a complete and independent sentence; do not capitalize following the colon when the material is a mere itemization or when it is dependent upon the preceding clause.

> The reasons for following Plan 6 are two: (1) The probability of being completed on time is high, and (2) the unit cost of operation is more favorable.
>
> The resolving power depends on three factors: wave length, refraction index, and angle of the cone of light.

11. Capitalize the first word of topic lines in outlines, headings, tables, and columnar listings.

> Items on the list were:
>
> Lumber
> Cement
> Hardware
>
> Cost of construction
> Investigation of resources
> Payroll deductions

Abbreviations

The use of abbreviations today is a continuation of a practice begun by the ancients to save labor in the carving of manuscripts in stone or in the copying of manuscripts by hand. As a time-saving practice, the copyists omitted letters from words which they thought would be understood by the reader in the shortened form. This practice developed until in the Latin there were some 5,000 shortened forms in use. To read either Greek or Latin, it was necessary to be familiar with these short forms.

Abbreviations are generally avoided in text matter, except in connection with technical terms and quantities. Their use is governed by what the reader is accustomed to and what he will understand. When used consistently and in forms familiar to the reader, abbreviations save space and promote ease and quickness of reading. In tabulations and engineering drawing, abbreviations are of their greatest value because here space is at a premium. For these special purposes, abbreviations may be condensed beyond what is considered good practice in composition, and words, not usually abbreviated, may be abbreviated.

In business correspondence and general writing few abbreviations should be used. In scientific writing their use is usually limited to technical terms which follow numerals. There is no specific set of rules to follow, except as rules are made by various publishers for their own specific purposes. Though the form of abbreviation does not vary widely, some words have several accepted abbreviations.

The latest major development in abbreviations came in 1941 when the American Standards Association published standards (Z 10.1—1941) for abbreviation of scientific and technical terms. These provide for the omission of the period except where omission would cause confusion. This form is coming into use gradually within the engineering publications, particularly in official publications of the engineering societies. However, the period should be omitted only in technical publications.

Abbreviations for scientific and engineering terms recommended by the American Standards Association are reproduced in full on pages 71-74. In addition, the following general rules apply to technical reports and general scientific writings:

1. The periods following abbreviations should be omitted in accordance with the American Standards Association form when applied to technical terms denoting units of measurement which follow numerals. Elsewhere the period should be used.

2. Use abbreviations for names of units only when following numerals.

3. Other than following a numeral, abbreviations should be used sparingly in the text matter. Use them only when it is certain that at least three-fourths of the readers will be fully acquainted with the abbreviations used. In tabular matter, on drawings and wherever space must be saved, abbreviations may be used to a greater extent than is considered good practice in text matter.

4. Usually all words of four letters and less are spelled out. Exceptions are feet, hour, and inch. Never abbreviate a three-letter word.

5. Abbreviations should not be used following numbers that are spelled out, as at the beginning of a sentence.

6. The plural of the word usually takes the same abbreviated form as is used for the singular. Exceptions to this general rule are: Nos., Profs., Drs., Sts., and Aves.

7. It is not considered good form in text matter to use the symbols and signs: /, #, ¢, @, lb/ft.[2] The per cent sign, %, is being used in text matter, and of course the dollar sign, $, is generally used. Other text forms 100 C, 210 F, and 60° 30′ 45″ may be used when appropriate. The foot and inch marks are not used in text matter.

8. The space and periods between letters are omitted in such abbreviations as TVA, ASA, and ASEE, and the space is also omitted when periods are used: A.S.A. or T.V.A.

9. In recent years there has been a growth in the practice of using capital letters without periods and spaces for the names of government organizations and associations, such as CAA, REA, ICC, AIEE, and AAA. This practice is convenient for the reader and author alike, and, where no confusion or misunderstanding will result, it should be followed. In technical papers when it is necessary to make frequent use of the name of a given organization, even though it is not well-known to the reader, the initial letters may be used if the full name of the organization is given with the first use of the initials. Example: ESMWT (Engineering Science and Management War Training).

10. The use of capital letters should be restricted in abbreviations to those cases where the words when spelled out would be capitalized.

11. The name United States may be abbreviated when followed by the name of a government department, bureau, or administration, but not when used alone.

U.S. Weather Bureau
the United States will send delegates

12. With the exception of titles (Dr., Mr., Pres., Prof.) spell out the first word of sentences.

13. If the readers are familiar with the forms and if the words are used frequently throughout the report the following abbreviations may be used in the text after first being spelled out:

FM (frequency modulation)
AM (amplitude modulation)
dc (direct current)
ac (alternating current)
bod (biochemical oxygen demand)
mgd (million gallons per day)
rpm (revolutions per minute)

14. The parts of compound abbreviations take the hyphen if the words spelled out would.

14 ft-lb   d-c generator   6-in. pipe

Numbers and Numerals

Whether to write numbers as numerals or as words remains an unsettled question. The fact that authorities, if there be any, follow anything but a uniform practice is evidence that the question is not fundamental. So long as the practice results in clarity to the reader, economical use of space, and pleasing typography, it matters little about many of the details in the handling of numbers.

Thus, the problem can be resolved into considerations related to ease of reading, exactness of understanding, typesetting efficiency, economy in the use of space, and typography. There is practically no writing, technical or general, which sanctions the use of "three thousand, nine hundred and eleven" in the place of 3,911. The former is cumbersome to read and time and space consuming to write. But somewhere between large numbers and zero, many styles break over to the use of words rather than numerals, excepting, perhaps, when dealing with exact quantities or measurements. This break is made at 10, 11, 12, 20, 50, or 100 by various publications. Considering the objectives and the main reason why numerals are used for large numbers, it is logical to use numerals throughout in technical writing. The trend in both scientific and general writing is in this direction. Perhaps the traditional adherence to the use of words rather than numerals will some day be abolished. Typographical appearance is perhaps the reason that spelling out numbers is not being given up faster than it is. Numerals, like capital letters, spot the typography and perhaps result in undue emphasis on small numbers.

The following recommendations for the use of numbers are based upon general practice in technical writing and the essential rules of good styling. Only the major usages are presented, since to include a complete treatment would go beyond the objective of this book.

1. For abstract numbers, and enumerations, words are preferred for numbers if under 10.

He was successful four out of five times.
There were nine houses on the street.
The load is 10 times that of last year.
The box contains six cans of 1 gal each.

2. Approximations should be written in numerals, if the same number in exact quantity would, though usage tends to words for the smaller, shorter, expressions; if approximations are to be spelled out, the problem of determining what is an approximate number must then be solved.

The load must have been at least 50 lb.
Perhaps 10 men attended the meeting.
The cost will be approximately $10,000 (or 10,000 dollars).

3. In all cases where abbreviations are used following the numerical quantity, numerals should be used.

1 gal is preferred to the form "one gal."

4. In an expression of a series of numbers in which strict adherence to a rule of style will cause part of the numbers to be in numerals and part in words, use numerals throughout.

The tools on the job include 24 shovels, 11 picks, 4 spades, and 1 wheelbarrow.

5. Use words for the ordinals of numbered street names. Always use numerals for house numbers.

627 Fifth Avenue	11476 Seventy-eighth Street
47 Second Street	4488 Sixty-third Street, NW
	3619 West Sixty-third Street

6. Mixed numbers, fractions, and decimals should be expressed in numerals, though some styles recommend the spelling out of small simple fractions.

5½ weeks	¾ of 1 per cent	⅕-hp motor
9¼ cents	1/60 sec	15/64 of the distance

Four-fifths of the members were present

7. Decimal forms should not be written with zeros to the right of the last significant figure greater than zero, unless the accuracy indicated exists. A zero should be placed to the left of the decimal point when the number lacks an integer.

The form 4.5 is preferred to 4.500 unless accuracy to the third decimal has been achieved.
Write 0.678 instead of .678.
Write $16,000 instead of $16,000.00 except when necessary to indicate exactness to the cent.

8. Numbers above three digits are pointed off in groups of three digits with commas, except for street numbers, model numbers, and numerals to the right of the decimal point, or four-digit numbers to be read in pairs. The space instead of the comma may be used to separate the groups of three digits. The space is used regularly in tabulations.

4,614 miles	$4 655 000
46,000 tons	1.67456 grams
1,200,000 volts	Model K-69867

9. Numbers in the millions and above are written as a combination of numerals and words.

6 million dollars	$6 million
2.65 million	2 million cu ft of excavation

10. A sentence should not begin with a numeral. If spelling out the number results in a cumbersome beginning, rewrite the sentence so that the numeral may be used later in the sentence.

11. Avoid the use of two numerals in succession. If one, usually the first or smaller one, cannot be spelled out, recast the sentence. When necessary to follow one number with another, separate them with a comma.

There were sixteen 200-lb steam gages available.
Twelve miles of track were abandoned in 1947.
January 16, 1951.

American Standard

Abbreviations for Scientific and Engineering Terms

Approved by

American Standards Association

70 East 45th Street New York 17, N. Y.

Introductory Notes

SCOPE AND PURPOSE

1. The Executive Committee of the Sectional Committee on Scientific and Engineering Symbols and Abbreviations has made the following distinction between symbols and abbreviations: Letter symbols are letters used to represent magnitudes of physical quantities in equations and mathematical formulas. Abbreviations are shortened forms of names or expressions employed in texts and tabulations, and should not be used in equations.

FUNDAMENTAL RULES

2. Abbreviations should be used sparingly in text and with due regard to the context and to the training of the reader. Terms denoting units of measurement should be abbreviated in the text only when preceded by the amounts indicated in numerals; thus "several inches," "one inch," "12 in." In tabular matter, specifications, maps, drawings, and texts for special purposes, the use of abbreviations should be governed only by the desirability of conserving space.

3. Short words such as ton, day, and mile should be spelled out.

4. Abbreviations should not be used where the meaning will not be clear. In case of doubt, spell out.

5. The same abbreviation is used for both singular and plural, as "bbl" for barrel and barrels.

6. The use of conventional signs for abbreviations in text is not recommended; thus "per," not /; "lb," not #; "in.," not ″. Such signs may be used sparingly in tables and similar places for conserving space.

7. The period should be omitted except in cases where the omission would result in confusion.

8. The letters of such abbreviations as ASA should not be spaced (not A S A).

9. The use in text of exponents for the abbreviations of square and cube and of the negative exponents for terms involving "per" is not recommended. The superior figures are usually not available on the keyboards of typesetting and linotype machines and composition is therefore delayed. There is also the likelihood of confusion with footnote reference numbers. These shorter forms are permissible in tables and are sometimes difficult to avoid in text.

10. A sentence should not begin with a numeral followed by an abbreviation. Abbreviations for names of units are to be used only after numerical values, such as 25 ft or 110 v.

Abbreviations*

absolute	abs
acre	spell out
acre-foot	acre-ft
air horsepower	air hp
alternating-current (as adjective)	a-c
ampere	amp
ampere-hour	amp-hr
amplitude, an elliptic function	am.
Angstrom unit	A
antilogarithm	antilog
atmosphere	atm
atomic weight	at. wt
average	avg
avoirdupois	avdp
azimuth	az or α
barometer	bar.
barrel	bbl
Baumé	Bé
board feet (feet board measure)	fbm
boiler pressure	spell out
boiling point	bp
brake horsepower	bhp
brake horsepower-hour	bhp-hr
Brinell hardness number	Bhn
British thermal unit[1]	Btu or B
bushel	bu
calorie	cal
candle	c
candle-hour	c-hr
candlepower	cp
cent	c or ¢
center to center	c to c
centigram	cg
centiliter	cl
centimeter	cm
centimeter-gram-second (system)	cgs
chemical	chem
chemically pure	cp
circular	cir
circular mils	cir mils
coefficient	coef
cologarithm	colog
concentrate	conc
conductivity	cond
constant	const
continental horsepower	cont hp
cord	cd
cosecant	csc
cosine	cos
cosine of the amplitude, an elliptic function	cn
cost, insurance, and freight	cif
cotangent	cot
coulomb	spell out
counter electromotive force	cemf
cubic	cu
cubic centimeter	cu cm, cm^3 (liquid, meaning milliliter, ml)
cubic foot	cu ft
cubic feet per minute	cfm
cubic feet per second	cfs
cubic inch	cu in.
cubic meter	cu m or m^3
cubic micron	cu μ or cu mu or μ^3
cubic millimeter	cu mm or mm^3
cubic yard	cu yd
current density	spell out
cycles per second	spell out or c
cylinder	cyl
day	spell out
decibel	db
degree[2]	deg or °
degree centigrade	C
degree Fahrenheit	F
degree Kelvin	K
degree Réaumur	R
delta amplitude, an elliptic function	dn
diameter	diam
direct-current (as adjective)	d-c
dollar	$
dozen	doz
dram	dr
efficiency	eff
electric	elec
electromotive force	emf
elevation	el
equation	eq
external	ext

* These forms are recommended for readers whose familiarity with the terms used makes possible a maximum of abbreviations. For other classes of readers editors may wish to use less contracted combinations made up from this list. For example, the list gives the abbreviation of the term "feet per second" as "fps." To some readers ft per sec will be more easily understood.

[1] Abbreviation recommended by the A.S.M.E. Power Test Codes Committee. B = 1 Btu, kB = 1,000 Btu, mB = 1,000,000 Btu. The A.S.H.R.A.E. recommends the use of Mb = 1,000 Btu and Mbh = 1,000 Btu per hr.

[2] There are circumstances under which one or the other of these forms is preferred. In general the sign ° is used where space conditions make it necessary, as in tabular matter, and when abbreviations are cumbersome, as in some angular measurements, i.e., 59° 23′ 42″. In the interest of simplicity and clarity the Committee has recommended that the abbreviation for the temperature scale, F, C, K, etc., always be included in expressions for numerical temperatures, but, wherever feasible, the abbreviation for "degree" be omitted; as 69 F.

farad	spell out or f
feet board measure (board feet)	fbm
feet per minute	fpm
feet per second	fps
fluid	fl
foot	ft
foot-candle	ft-c
foot-Lambert	ft-L
foot-pound	ft-lb
foot-pound-second (system)	fps
foot-second (see cubic feet per second)	
franc	fr
free aboard ship	spell out
free alongside ship	spell out
free on board	fob
freezing point	fp
frequency	spell out
fusion point	fnp
gallon	gal
gallons per minute	gpm
gallon per second	gps
grain	spell out
gram	g
gram-calorie	g-cal
greatest common divisor	gcd
haversine	hav
hectare	ha
henry	h
high-pressure (adjective)	h-p
hogshead	hhd
horsepower	hp
horsepower-hour	hp-hr
hour	hr
hour (in astronomical tables)	h
hundred	C
hundredweight (112 lb)	cwt
hyperbolic cosine	cosh
hyperbolic sine	sinh
hyperbolic tangent	tanh
inch	in.
inch-pound	in-lb
inches per second	ips
indicated horsepower	ihp
indicated horsepower-hour	ihp-hr
inside diameter	ID
intermediate-pressure (adjective)	i-p
internal	int
joule	j
kilocalorie	kcal
kilocycles per second	kc
kilogram	kg
kilogram-calorie	kg-cal
kilogram-meter	kg-m
kilograms per cubic meter	kg per cu m or kg/m^3
kilograms per second	kgps
kiloliter	kl
kilometer	km
kilometers per second	kmps
kilovolt	kv
kilovolt-ampere	kva
kilowatt	kw
kilowatt-hour	kwhr
lambert	L
latitude	lat or ϕ
least common multiple	lcm
linear foot	lin ft
liquid	liq
lira	spell out
liter	l
logarithm (common)	log
logarithm (natural)	$\log_e$ or ln
longitude	long. or λ
low-pressure (as adjective)	l-p
lumen	l*
lumen-hour	l-hr*
lumens per watt	lpw
mass	spell out
mathematics (ical)	math
maximum	max
mean effective pressure	mep
mean horizontal candlepower	mhcp
megacycle	spell out
megohm	spell out
melting point	mp
meter	m
meter-kilogram	m-kg
mho	spell out
microampere	μa or mu a
microfarad	μf
microinch	μin.
micromicrofarad	μμf
micromicron	μμ or mu mu
micron	μ or mu
microvolt	μv
microwatt	μw or mu w
mile	spell out
miles per hour	mph
miles per hour per second	mphps
milliampere	ma
milligram	mg
millihenry	mh
millilambert	mL
milliliter	ml
millimeter	mm
millimicron	mμ or m mu
million	spell out
million gallons per day	mgd
millivolt	mv
minimum	min
minute	min
minute (angular measure)	′

minute (time) (in astronomical table) ... m
mole ... spell out
molecular weight ... mol. wt
month ... spell out

National Electrical Code ... NEC

ohm ... spell out or Ω
ohm-centimeter ... ohm-cm
ounce ... oz
ounce-foot ... oz-ft
ounce-inch ... oz-in.
outside diameter ... OD

parts per million ... ppm
peck ... pk
penny (pence) ... d
pennyweight ... dwt
per ... (See Fundamental Rules)
peso ... spell out
pint ... pt
potential ... spell out
potential difference ... spell out
pound ... lb
pound-foot ... lb-ft
pound-inch ... lb-in.
pound sterling ... £
pounds per brake horse-power-hour ... lb per bhp-hr
pounds per cubic foot ... lb per cu ft
pounds per square foot ... psf
pounds per square inch ... psi
pounds per square inch absolute ... psia
power factor ... spell out or pf

quart ... qt

radian ... spell out
reactive kilovolt-ampere ... kvar
reactive volt-ampere ... var
revolutions per minute ... rpm
revolutions per second ... rps
rod ... spell out
root mean square ... rms

secant ... sec
second ... sec
second (angular measure) ... ″
second-foot (see cubic feet per second)
second (time) (in astronomical tables) ... s
shaft horsepower ... shp
shilling ... s
sine ... sin
sine of the amplitude, an elliptic function ... sn
specific gravity ... sp gr
specific heat ... sp ht
spherical candlepower ... scp
square ... sq
square centimeter ... sq cm or cm^2
square foot ... sq ft
square inch ... sq in.
square kilometer ... sq km or km^2
square meter ... sq m or m^2
square micron ... sq μ or sq mu or μ^2
square millimeter ... sq mm or mm^2
square root of mean square ... rms
standard ... std
stere ... s

tangent ... tan
temperature ... temp
tensile strength ... ts
thousand ... M
thousand foot-pounds ... kip-ft
thousand pound ... kip
ton ... spell out
ton-mile ... spell out

versed sine ... vers
volt ... v
volt-ampere ... va
volt-coulomb ... spell out

watt ... w
watt-hour ... whr
watts per candle ... wpc
week ... spell out
weight ... wt

yard ... yd
year ... yr

PUNCTUATION

All sentences depend upon punctuation for their meaning. Deletion of all punctuation marks from a composition leaves a string of words that do not express a single thought or group of thoughts. Punctuation is the device by which the author gives organization, emphasis, clarity and exactness to his expressions. Punctuation performs in writing what tone of voice, delivery, and facial expression perform in oral expression. Speech, without change in volume, tone, pause and rate of flow of words, is unintelligible and monotonous.

The two main purposes of punctuation are to give clarity to the author's statements and to make reading easy. The writer needs to keep in mind that the rules of punctuation are flexible but easily misused. Any rereading of a passage to gain its correct understanding is a signal that punctuation is poorly applied or that the sentence structure is cumbersome.

Less punctuation is required in well constructed sentences than in poorly constructed ones.

Punctuation marks should be omitted if they do not clarify the meaning, but used rather than omitted in all doubtful applications. It is now acceptable to omit commas in many places where they were mandatory 50 to 75 years ago. The semicolon is giving way to the period. Correctness and accuracy of meaning are achieved by careful use of punctuation marks, and they should not be omitted merely for simplicity.

The following discussion of punctuation covers the main uses and basic styling which apply in technical writings. For greater detail and specific rules the reader should consult authoritative books on English composition.

Apostrophe (')

The apostrophe is used to indicate (a) contraction (elision), (b) possession (possessive case), and (c) the plurals of letters, words, symbols and numerals.

(a) don't, M'Arthur, '62
(b) Miller's ship, machine's gears
(c) A's, and's, *'s, 2 by 8's, 30's

Brackets ([ ])

Brackets are used in pairs to indicate material supplied by someone other than the original author. (a) Editorial interpolation, (b) the correction of errors in quoted material or (c) additional information supplied is indicated by brackets. Brackets are used interchangeably with parentheses only when parentheses are within parentheses.

(a) "This machine [turret lathe] was purchased last year."
(b) "The water will be drawn from the Cheyenne [Sheyenne] River."
(c) "Cost rather than *value* is given." [Italics supplied.]
"Here [pointing to exhibit F] is shown the area affected by the proposed plant."

Colon (:)

The uses of the colon are somewhat arbitrary. Common usage places the colon (a) after the salutation in a letter, (b) between numerals denoting time of day and elements of time, (c) between volume and page number in bibliographical references, (d) between the numerals expressing ratios and proportions, (e) after certain introductory words or phrases preceding a series of itemized statements, and (f) before a final clause summarizing preceding material.

(a) Gentlemen:, Dear Mr. Jones:
(b) The time is 7:10 P.M. The race was run in 0:58:13.6.
(c) *Power Plant Engineering* 17:74-77
(d) The ratio is 2:3. A mix of 1:2.4:4.6 was used.
(e) The following equipment was ordered:
This location has three advantages: (1) plentiful water supply; (2) stable foundation material; and (3) adequate transportation facilities.
The question under consideration is: What working pressure should be used?
(f) Make thorough preparation; write swiftly and continuously; revise again and again with painstaking care: all these are requisites of good technical writing.

Comma (,)

Commas are used more by instinct than by rule. They are used to indicate pauses in the reading and to show separate words and parts of speech. Periods indicate full stops and complete separations, whereas commas are at the opposite end of the punctuation scale. Because commas offer greater latitude of use than other punctuation, the rules for their use are less fixed.

(a) The conjunction in a compound sentence is preceded by a comma if the second sentence is complete.

The personnel department is hiring additional men this week, and the new shop will open Monday.

(b) A defining or restrictive clause or phrase is not set off by commas, and the nondefining or nonrestrictive clause or phrase is. The restrictive clause is essential to the meaning, whereas the nonrestrictive clause is merely supplementary information.

Peak loads which last more than half an hour are supplied by extra generators.

Peak loads, which do not occur often, are supplied by extra generators.

The degree-days in the two regions studied varied from 80 to 120 per cent of the 10-year average.

The degree-days, which were about normal, varied from 80 to 120 per cent of the 10-year average.

The engineer who is directing the work has been in charge for six months.

Johnson and Company, who furnished the steel, have their offices in Illinois.

(c) A subordinate clause or introductory phrase placed ahead of the principal clause is followed by a comma. The comma may be omitted if the subordinate clause or phrase is simple and of few words.

If the committee had considered the subject earlier, the misunderstanding would have been prevented.

Discouraged by the rain, the foreman stopped the work.

When the signal sounded the men began to load the car. (Comma unnecessary.)

(d) Parenthetical words, phrases, clauses, conjunctions, adverbs and phrases that break the continuity, are set off by commas.

It was concluded, therefore, to abandon the project.

Cost accounting, generally speaking, is not practiced by agencies of government.

Atomic power, highly desirable as it is, will require some years to become universally available.

Nevertheless, the plan was submitted.

On the other hand, he followed prevailing practice.

(e) Alternatives and appositives require commas.

This is an increase of 95,468 cars, or 12.9 per cent, above the previous week.

The straight line, or zero interest, method may be used. (Two names for the same method.)

The straight line or present worth method may be used. (Two methods, either of which may be used.)

The men found that they could either start at once, or delay for several days.

Failure to prevent vibration is likely to result in damage, even collapse, of the machine.

The other two components, the power supply and the audio amplifier, may be purchased.

Mr. Howell, the factory representative, arrived on the job today.

(f) A frequent use of commas is to separate material which if not separated would lead to confusion or misunderstanding.

The contract was awarded January 10, 1961.

In 1961, 472 kw was the average load. (To avoid having numerals in succession it is preferable to recast the sentence.)

The average load in 1961 was 472 kw.

To Jack, Jones and Harris was the top ranking supply firm.

During the period of drilling, the equipment is realigned frequently.

(g) Enumerations and series expressions are punctuated with the comma to separate the several parts. Good authority may be found for both omitting and retaining the comma before the conjunction "and" or "or" preceding the last item in the series. Conservative writers and editors use the comma. The rule is to strive for clearness first and simplicity second; retain the comma if it is needed for clarity, otherwise omit it.

The box car shortage is affecting deliveries of clay products, fertilizer and phosphate. (Comma unnecessary.)

The cab fixtures include pneumatic window wipers, fire extinguisher, cab lights, headlight and engine compartment light controls, bell, horn, and sander operating control. (Comma necessary.)

(h) Set off absolute expressions with commas.

The directors having approved the budget, the general manager submitted a plan for expansion.

Two years later, the traffic being double its expected volume, the engineer approved a new route.

(i) Separate co-ordinate adjectives with a comma. One means of checking doubtful cases is to rewrite to see if sense is made when the adjectives are placed after the noun.

The cylinders are fitted with chrome-plated, cast-iron liners.

The locomotive is carried on two six-wheel, swing bolster, high-speed, pedestal-type swivel trucks.

A costly hammer mill was installed. (No commas used because "costly" and "hammer" are not co-ordinate as proved by the awkward rearrangement: "The mill installed was costly and hammer.")

(j) Consequently, furthermore, hence, however, moreover, nevertheless, and therefore are conjunctive adverbs which are set off by commas when used within a clause. When used, however, as a conjunctive adverb between the main clauses of a compound sentence, a semicolon precedes them and a comma follows. These words are usually followed by a comma when they begin a sentence. When these words are used as simple adverbs, commas are not required.

Furnace walls, however, can be built strong enough to withstand the pressure.

Consequently, a triode is preferable when the higher amplification of the pentode is not required.

The maximum output, therefore, does not mean maximum undistorted output.

Shortage of manpower was reported by all divisions; nevertheless, the upward trend in contract awards continues.

However this plan is carried out, it will be costly.

The introductory words "namely," "for example," "for instance," and "that is" are followed by a comma unless the succeeding material involves one or more complete clauses, when a colon is used. When these words are used within a sentence, commas precede them unless an enumeration is introduced which calls for a colon or dash.

Several of the figures are in error. For instance, 896 should be 899.

Many methods may be used. For example: The sand may be transported on an endless belt or pumped through pipe.

The important requirement, namely, keeping cost below $1500, was adhered to.

Dash (—)

In typewritten manuscript the dash is formed by joining two hyphens. The printer's dash is about three times the length of the hyphen.

(a) An abrupt interruption of the sense, a sudden shift in construction, or a faltering in speech is indicated by the dash. It should be used sparingly, mainly for pronounced breaks in sentence structure. In other cases the semicolon or comma is correct.

When water got into the cylinder during bad priming — the operator forgot to close the water-feeding valve — we found it difficult to start the engine.

To be sure of a job after 40 — a good job, that is — an engineer must study unremittingly.

Pressure loss not only reduces thermal efficiency, but — and frequently this is of greater importance — it also reduces maximum power output.

The tube sheets at each end of the condenser — the sheets support the tubes — are the largest bronze plates ever rolled.

(b) A dash is used to show incompleteness of a sentence, to introduce a repetitive phrase, or to introduce a summing up.

What was wanted was —

This plan is permanent — permanent during the present management — and, therefore, the one to propose.

For this application aluminum has two advantages — viz., lightness and availability.

(c) The addition of an enumerating or defining element to a sentence preferably is marked with dashes.

All of the equipment — tractor, blader, dozer, and truck — was sent to the job.

Other uses of the dash include (d) marking the separation of the end of a quotation and the author or title, (e) substitution for "to and including" between a spread of numbers or dates, (f) indicating an ending to be supplied, and (g) showing the omission of letters.

(d) ". . . manual dexterity in carrying out the plans." — Engineering as a Career, by Harold Holland.

(e) The distance was 6 – 8 ft.
During 1932 – 36 the company . . .

Note: It is better styling to use the word "to" for showing range of numbers when used in text material, particularly in typewritten material where the en dash is not available. The en dash is longer than the hyphen, yet shorter than the em dash, which is the standard dash in printing. The en dash is preferable to the word "to" in a combination of dates where the period of time rather than the range of values is indicated.

(f) The period 1910 —— was . . .

(g) The firm of Hennesy and S—— would submit bids.

Note: In (f) and (g) a 2-em dash is used.

Ellipsis (. . . or * * *)

Material not essential to the immediate purpose may be omitted from quoted material, and the omission is indicated by ellipsis marks. Three periods, (sometimes asterisks) are used for this purpose. The first one is one space from the preceding word. If the ellipsis ends a complete sentence, four periods are used, the first one being in its normal position to end the sentence.

"All speech and music . . . are made up of a combination of these audio-frequencies. . . . It follows that for good amplification these frequencies must be amplified to the same degree."

Omission of a whole paragraph is indicated by one full line of periods.

Exclamation Point (!)

The exclamation point is used to indicate (a) surprise, (b) strong emotion, (c) outcry, or (d) emphatic comment or command. The exclamation point is seldom used in technical writings because these writings are objective and impersonal rather than subjective.

The professor acknowledged the error!
Is the engineer to become the slave of labor!
Stop! The bearings are hot.
"Don't take chances!" is the key to accident reduction.

Hyphen (-)

The hyphen is more a mark of spelling than of punctuation. It is used primarily to join two or more words and to indicate the separation of a word into two parts at the end of a line. Compounds may be written solid, separated as two or more words, or joined with the hyphen. The following material is a brief description of the main uses of the hyphen; consult a dictionary, a book on compounding of words, or an authoritative style book for further material.

(a) Compound numerals from twenty-one to ninety-nine are joined with the hyphen. Fractions are also joined.

thirty-four, sixty-six
Two-thirds of the contract was completed.
A three-fourths majority is required.

(b) The following types of adjectives are hyphenated:

broken-down machine
cross-hatched area
d-c motor
double-edged knife
four-speed shift
house-to-house canvass
oil-burning locomotive
open-pit mine
snow-shedded railway
stem-winding clock
three-phase, four-speed motor
well-known make
2- by 4-in. board
50-ton mill
30-hp, 440-volt, 60-cycle motor
4,000-ton-per-day crushing plant

(c) The hyphen is omitted in the above expressions when the words are used so as not to form the adjective:

The mine was a large open pit.
The board was 2 by 4 in.
The motor operated on direct current.

(d) The following are typical compound nouns that are written with the hyphen:

engineer-director
city-state
cure-all
know-nothing
light-years
foot-pounds
car-miles
kilowatt-hour
kw-hr
bull's-eye

(e) Compounds of the following type are hyphenated:

all-American
pro-British
ex-governor
moth-eaten
off-key noise
co-operate
semi-independent
super-high speed
re-forming process
on-the-shelf aging
carry-all carts
X-ray
self-starter
re-enter

Interrogation Point (Question Mark) (?)

Direct questions are followed by the interrogation point, or question mark. This point should not be used following indirect questions. It is sometimes used to express doubt when there is a question about the accuracy of a statement. Use a period with a request stated as a question for the sake of courtesy.

The foreman asked, "How many tons of steel have we?"

The foreman asked how many tons of steel we have.

The workman reported that 11 (?) tons were on hand.

Will you please fill out and return this questionnaire.

Parentheses ( )

Parentheses are used to enclose parenthetical material written by the original author, but brackets are used to enclose material added later by an editor or writer quoting from the original. The punctuation required by the sentence is placed following the second parenthesis. But if the parenthetical statement is a complete sentence it carries its own punctuation within the parentheses.

This relationship (Fig. 6) is not unusual.

Authority to abandon tracks between Carrollton (formerly Hilltop Junction) and Westover, Missouri, was requested.

The outstanding feature of these five reservoirs is their storage capacities (See Table 6.).

The 6,888 who voted on the dues amendment (44 more than voted on the enfranchisement-of-juniors amendment), therefore, represent 46.5 per cent of the eligible voters.

Period (.)

The period is a full stop point used at the end of all sentences which do not require the exclamation point or question mark. Elsewhere, the period is used after an abbreviation (except as the style permits their omission), after a heading or title that is run-in on the same line with the sentence, and as a separating device in numbered or lettered enumerations.

For years there has been an increasing belief by well-informed persons that the construction industry should be knit into one effective group.

May we ask for a prompt reply.

Pres. A. H. Miller was formerly with Johnson and Co., Springfield, Mass., manufacturers of hardware.

Table 6. Summary of Depth Measurements

The following items were considered:

A. Cost of the improvement

B. Probable public opinion

Periods are not used at the ends of title page lines, display lines, side and center headings, box heads in tables, and at the ends of words or incomplete statements listed in column or outline form.

Quotation Marks (" ")

The main use of quotation marks is to indicate that the words they enclose are not those of the author. This usage includes direct quotations of speech and material taken from printed sources. Quotation marks are also used to indicate words or phrases used in other than their normal sense, slang expressions, misnomers, and technical terms likely to be new to the reader.

The company president added: "Similarly, we believe a compromise plan could be effected in the reorganization of the railroad company."

In his book, *Sales Engineering,* Lester states his objective ". . . to place before the younger sales engineer in simple terms, without sales promotion adornment, the principles of sales engineering, to indicate to him the importance of his burden, and to suggest the opportunities for him in present-day society."

Under advisement was a brief of the Ganey Corporation filed as a "friend of the court" opposing the plan of reorganization.

Some believe that managerial organization is a form of "human engineering," and that a group of "experts" can come into a company and establish by rigid logic an ironclad organization for it.

The brick mason called for more "mud."

Quotation marks are omitted at the ends of quoted paragraphs in series except for the last paragraph.

Both sets of marks are omitted when the quoted material is set in type smaller than the text or short measure lines.

Periods and commas are enclosed by the closing quotation mark; colons and semicolons are placed outside. Exclamation and interrogation points are placed inside the quotation mark when they are a part of the material quoted; in other instances they are placed outside the closing quotation mark.

Semicolon (;)

For pauses which are longer than can be indicated by a comma and yet less than the full stop of the period, the semicolon is used. Its major use is between the main clauses of a compound sentence in the absence of a connective and where the connective is a conjunctive adverb. In a series which is not sufficiently separated by the comma, the semicolon is used.

No, we do not know where we are going; we do not even know where we are.

We are like Columbus in one stage of his voyage to America: When he sailed from Spain, he did not know where he was going; when he got here he did not know where he was; and when he returned home, he did not know where he had been.

One value of the 10-minute quiz is that it enables the student to learn by doing; to find out what he has missed in his studying.

We instinctively know that a solution exists; moreover, we can justify such belief if we wish to set up and solve a set of simultaneous equations.

These percentages are: for freshmen, 53.8 per cent; for sophomores, 64.7 per cent; and for juniors, 71.8 per cent.

CHAPTER 5

Format and Arrangement

Reports should be correct in their scientific and technical aspects, and they should be composed in concise, clear, and flawless English. They should adhere mechanically and physically to good make-up and format. Good physical design is important starting with the outside cover and extending to the end of the report. High standard in appearance is achieved through paper quality, sheet size, binding, page design (margins, length of line, dimensions, and proportions), typography, design and location of headings, and all other physical aspects. These elements of a report should receive the same careful attention that the writer gives to his technical analysis and English composition.

PHYSICAL APPEARANCE OF REPORTS

Good appearance in a typed report is as essential and valuable as are neatness and attractiveness in industrial design and package containers for the retail trade. Pleasing physical appearance in reports is obtained by careful handling of white space and type areas, and by the arrangement of all details so that they contribute to ease of reading and understanding. In a well-arranged report, the attention of the reader is not consciously drawn to details of typography, page layout, and the mechanics of typing. When skillfully executed, these details blend into an artistic design of which the reader is unaware. Although the chief function of report format and arrangement is to achieve readability and understanding, reports of excellent physical make-up command a respect and confidence not accorded reports lacking in these desirable characteristics.

Before the first draft of a report is begun, the writer should determine the format and make-up desired for the final copy. Size of type page, margins, headline schedule, placement of tables and illustrations, and other specifications of the mechanical appearance are matters to be decided. It is important to give the typist instructions and specifications in addition to having everything marked on the draft so that all details will be in the form desired. In formulating these specifications it is necessary to know whether the report is to be duplicated by printing or other process.

When the manuscript is to be published in a previously selected periodical, proceedings, or series, the typed manuscript should conform to the standards of that publication. Reports to be duplicated by a process other than letterpress printing should follow the special requirements of the process.

DESIGN OF TYPE PAGE

Of the several aspects of the physical appearance of a report, the type page layout is basic because upon it depends how tables, illustrations, headings and typing are to be handled. Use of the report, method of binding, and number of copies to be prepared, along with the standards and policies of the organization responsible for the report, usually control the selection of the sheet quality and size.

Margins and Size of Type Page

Commonly used typing paper is of two sizes: 8½ by 11 and 8 by 10½ in. The legal-cap size of 8½ by 13 in. and the foolscap 8½ by 14 in. are also in use. The size 8½ by 11 in. is used more frequently and is preferred for report work where another size is not specified. United States government agencies use 8- by 10½-in. sheets.

The type area on the page should be approximately the same proportion of width to length as is the paper sheet, when allowance is made for binding at the left. The ratio of width to length of the 8½- by 11-in. sheet is 0.77. With a ½-in. binding margin allowed at the left, the ratio is 0.73 and with a ¾-in. binding the ratio is 0.70. These ratios are near to 0.707 which is the ratio of $1:\sqrt{2}$, a ratio of pleasing proportions and approximately that used in book publishing practice. For satisfactory appearance on standard paper 8½ by 11 in., the ratio of width of type page to length of type page should be between 0.67 and 0.77, and with such margins that this ratio is about equal to that of the effective size of sheet. The effective size of sheet is the full dimensions less that hidden from view by the binding. The type page of this book has a ratio of 0.760; the effective ratio of the sheet is 0.736.

For the 8½- by 11-in. sheet, when printing is placed only on the right-hand page, favorable appearance is achieved with a left margin of 1¾ in. including ¾ in. for binding, a top margin of 1 1/6 in. including page number, a right margin of 1 in., and a bottom margin of 1¾ in. Deluxe page layouts call for margins such that 50 per cent of the exposed page is in type and 50 per cent is in white space. For general-purpose reports and books, less margin may be used, so that the type page is about 55 to 60 per cent of the area of the sheet, exclusive of binding strip.

When reports are printed on both the left and right pages, the center margin is considered to be the sum of the two inner margins. This combined margin is made about equal to twice the outside margin. For all types of bindings, the effective margin at the binding edge is that which appears to the eye to be the net space. This net space should be equal to the outer margin when only the right-hand page is used for reading material.

The ranges of satisfactory margins for various lengths of lines of type are illustrated in Figs. 5.1 to 5.4. These diagrams may be used in determining the dimensions of the type page and its position on the sheet. Although time and thought and care are required to lay out a sheet, it needs only to be done once; thereafter the typist or printer can follow the layouts.

The preliminary parts such as table of contents, letter of transmittal, preface, and abstract should have a length of line such that the area of type results in a pleasing ratio to the whole page. When the material is less than the amount required to fill a standard page, the lines may be shortened and the margins increased to create a pleasing effect. These preliminary parts are independent units and may be typed without regard to the length of line and the margins used in the body of the report.

Line Spacing

The body of reports in typescript may be single- or double-spaced with indented paragraphs. Single spacing is used only when it is desirable to conserve space. Because the length of line is usually about 6 in. (the approximate maximum length of typescript line the eye can follow easily and accurately), single-spaced pages are more difficult to read than double-spaced pages. Usually, only the right-hand page is used. If the report is to be printed through a process of type setting, it is typed double space on only the right-hand page.

Quoted material is set in single-spaced, short-measure lines, with double space between paragraphs. The quoted material should be set in from each end of the standard text line. When material is set in this manner, quotation marks need not be used because the contrast in typography is sufficient to set off the quotation from the text matter. The shortening of the type line on the left should be more or less than the standard paragraph indentation so that the quoted matter will contrast with the first line of the paragraph which follows.

Footnotes are set single space, but full line width in indented paragraph form. When more than one footnote is at the bottom of the page, the footnotes are separated with one blank line. The footnote is separated from the body type by two blank lines (triple space typescript). A horizontal line 1 to 2 in. in length and placed above the left end of the footnote may also be used.

Tables and illustrations which are placed on the page with text material are separated from the adjacent lines of text above or below by two blank lines in both single- and double-spaced texts.

Page Numbers

Page numbers are placed at the top of the page, either centered over the type page or placed at the right side and directly above the end of the type line, just to the left of the right-hand margin. On pages with full-centered headings at the top of the page, the page numbers should be placed in parentheses at the bottom of the page in the center. Two blank lines should be left between the page number and the first line of type, either top or bottom. Although page numbers in some reports and books are placed at the bottom of the page, this position is not as convenient to the reader as is the top location.

Page 1 may be assigned to the inside title page, but the number is not printed, or to the first page of the body, usually the first page of the introduction. The pages of preliminaries following the inside title and before the introduction are usually numbered at the bottom for the reason that such preliminary pages generally start with centered headings. A second practice is to assign small Roman numeral page numbers to the preliminaries, making the introduction page 1 in the Arabic series. In this case the page numbers are also placed at the bottom of each page having a main heading. The appendix is numbered in sequence and in the same type style as the body of the report.

Headings

Short lines of topical headings inserted at points where the subject changes serve two purposes. They break up the type mass to achieve pleasing typography, and they serve as guideposts to the subject matter. The headings are distinguished from the body composition by their position, the surrounding white space, and by their type face and size.

The headings are directly related to the outline of the report in wording and topic form. They are therefore graded down in prominence from the heads indicating chapters to those indicating minor subdivisions or paragraphs of the report. In printer's type there is ample variety of size and face of type from which to select a suitable head schedule, but with the typewriter there is only one size with capitals and lower case.

Head schedules for typewritten manuscripts usually rank the order of importance of heads first by position, second by use of capital or lower-case letters, and third by underlining.

Importance of heads ranks down from the centered position, to the side position and finally to the paragraph or run-in head. An all-capital line ranks above the head that is written with only the important words capitalized, and the lowest in order is the head with only the first letter of the first word of the head in capitals, all other words beginning with lower case. Underlining the words raises the rank above the same position and face of letter when not underlined. In selecting a head schedule, underlining should be avoided when possible because of the extra time consumed in the typing of underlines. Excessive underlining defeats the main purpose of creating emphasis and becomes confusing in appearance.

The types of heads illustrated at the bottom of this page are suitable for typewritten reports.

Additional emphasis is given to headings by the proper use of white space above and below them. Space above the head and below the last line of the preceding paragraph should be one line greater than the space between the head and the first line of the paragraph following it. In exceptional situations the upper space may be equal to the space below, but it should never be less than the space below the head. Effectiveness of the heading depends upon proper spacing relative to the text, wording, and length.

In double-spaced typescripts (one blank line between each line of type), centered heads should be spaced with three blank lines above and two below. Side heads may be spaced likewise. Most run-in heads should be underlined in an indented paragraph, and with this arrangement the space above may be the normal blank line in double-spaced writing, though an additional line or half line of space is helpful. The spacing of heads is illustrated throughout this book and in the specimen report in the Appendix.

When using centered heads for chapters and starting chapters with a new page, it is good form to drop the heading about 1 in. below the normal top margin. However, if chapters do not start new pages, the headings which appear at the top of the page should

A. Centered on type page
   1. CAPITALS, CENTERED AND UNDERLINED
   2. CAPITALS, CENTERED AND NOT UNDERLINED
   3. Capitals and Lower Case, Centered and Underlined
   4. Capitals and Lower Case, Centered and Not Underlined
B. Side, flush with left edge of type page
   5. CAPITALS, SIDE HEAD AND UNDERLINED
   6. CAPITALS, SIDE HEAD AND NOT UNDERLINED
   7. Capitals and Lower Case, Side Head and Underlined
   8. Capitals and Lower Case, Side Head and Not Underlined
   9. Lower case, side head and underlined
C. Paragraph, or run-in on first line of paragraph
   10. CAPITALS, PARAGRAPH HEAD AND UNDERLINED
   11. Capitals and Lower Case, Paragraph Head and Underlined
   12. Lower case, paragraph head and underlined

An important factor to consider in the selection of a head schedule is the number of separate heads needed to indicate the relations of the various sections. One of the following schedules of heads usually will be found satisfactory:

Number of different types of heads needed	Head Schedule (numbers refer to foregoing list)		
	First choice	*Second choice*	*Third choice*
2	2, 6	2, 8	2, 7, or 1, 6
3	2, 6, 11	2, 7, 11	1, 6, 11
4	2, 4, 6, 11	2, 6, 7, 11	1, 3, 7, 11
5	2, 4, 6, 7, 11	2, 4, 6, 8, 11	1, 3, 5, 7, 11
6	2, 4, 6, 7, 10, 12	2, 4, 6, 8, 10, 12	1, 3, 5, 7, 10, 12

be typed on position of the normal line. When a main or centered head is the first line of the page, the page number should be placed at the bottom in parentheses.

The use of two successive heads without some reading material between them is to be avoided. However, do not write a useless paragraph of introduction or transition merely to avoid consecutive heads, even though they do not always make for the best typographical appearance.

Headings may or may not be identified by numbers or letters to indicate their sequence in the outline. For reports having many subdivisions and 50 or more pages in length of four or more orders of heads, numbered headings may be a convenience to the reader, especially when there is considerable reference to sections. A suitable series is: I, A, 1, a, (1), and (a).

POSITION OF TABLES AND ILLUSTRATIONS

Tables and illustrations in a typewritten report may be placed in either of two positions with respect to the text material. They may be incorporated on the page with reading matter or they may be on separate pages. The choice of these two positions is dependent upon the character of the report, the number of copies to be prepared, the available methods of duplication, the complexity of the tables or illustrations, and ultimate use of the report. A few general considerations can be discussed, though the position of this material is a matter to be decided for each individual report at the time it is under preparation.

When typing only on the right-hand page, an occasional illustration or table on the left-hand page is not good practice, because of the resulting difficulty in typing on both sides of the sheet. Furthermore, page numbering is awkward with such arrangement.

When the report is to be printed by a process of type setting it is essential to prepare each table and each illustration on separate sheets because they require different handling in the printing process. When the report is to be printed by one of the photographic-offset methods the tables and figures may be arranged in the photographic copy along with text and photographed together. Line work may be used with text in the mimeograph process by drawing the illustration on the stencil.

Tables and figures require special study of their final size, proportions, arrangement, spacing, and wording. Also, extra labor is required in typing, drafting, and mounting. This labor may be held to a minimum by early planning of the position of the tables and figures so that they can be put in final form with the least copying.

Tables and Illustrations on Page With Text

There are two distinct advantages in having tables and figures on the page along with the associated text material; this placement saves in over-all number of pages necessary for the report and the reader can see before him the material while reading the text pertaining to it. These advantages are difficult to achieve because of the necessity of following special procedures in preparing the tables and figures, and in laying out the typing to allow adequate room for them.

Tables are much easier to prepare on the same page with text than are illustrations because tables are typed. Text tables and the simple, formal tables of a half page and less in length may be conveniently and advantageously typed on the page along with text. The chief difficulty in this arrangement is that frequently there is not room on the page for the table in its normal sequence with the text. Also, it is necessary to plan ahead for the table to insure that adequate space is to be had. Another disadvantage is that, should revisions be made in the text, the table would need to be retyped also, usually an expensive and a tedious task.

Small photographs, simple sketches which can be prepared in original form for each copy of the report to be typed, and charts that can be printed in sufficient number of copies and mounted on the page in correct position constitute most of the illustrations that can be placed on the page with text material. In these instances the size of the illustration should be limited to about half the page depth so that sufficient reading material can be placed on the page to achieve a pleasing layout. To achieve satisfactory results when placing illustrations on the page with text, the exact dimensions, including legend, are determined before the typing is started, so that the proper amount of space may be left.

Because all illustrations and formal tables are assigned a reference number, they may be placed immediately above the reference when they appear on the page with composition, but they should not be placed on a previous page unless it be a facing page of a report printed on both sides of the sheet. When short tables or small illustrations are to be placed on the page with text, care should be taken to produce a pleasing layout. Four positions are possible: (1) At the top of the page, (2) within the central portion of the page with reading material above and below, (3) at the bottom of the page, and (4) cut into the left or right side of the lines so that short type lines appear at the side of the illustration. All four positions may be handled with effectiveness if consideration is given to the center of balance, unity, and mass. A small illustration having an open top or bottom should not be placed at the top or bottom of the page and neither should a narrow table or illustration. More lines of reading material should be placed below the illustration than above, and the center of the table or figure should be slightly above the center of the page when not at the top or bottom. Typical layouts are given in Chapters 6 and 7.

Because of the many difficulties encountered in placing illustrations on the page with text material it will generally be found a better plan to place them on separate pages. If more than three or four copies of the report are to be typed, separate pages will be found the better arrangement for all but the short simple tables and small photographs. When only two or three typed copies are needed for reports to be duplicated photographically or by copy machines so that only one original need be prepared there are greater opportunities for placing simple illustrations on the page with text.

Tables and Illustrations on Separate Pages

Tables and illustrations are ordinarily placed immediately following their reference in the text. This practice holds whether illustrations are placed on the same page with text material or on separate pages. Difficulties in make-up caused by several consecutive references to tables and illustrations and references which occur near the bottom of the page frequently preclude the placing of the table or illustration at its preferable position. When there is a high ratio of pages of tables and illustrations to pages of text it is inconvenient to the reader to turn several pages in order to find the continuation of a sentence which breaks at the bottom of a page. It is desirable, nevertheless, to place the tables and illustrations throughout the report in the sequence in which they are discussed and immediately following the discussion. When this is impracticable, they may be placed at the end of the chapter or section, at the end of the report but before the appendix, or, if particularly voluminous, in a separately bound volume of the report.

As stated in Chapter 12, tables, illustrations or other materials essential to the reading and understanding of the body of the report, are placed within the body. When it is elected to place tables or illustrations in the appendix they should be those which the reader may need only for reference rather than for understanding of the report. Also, tables for the appendix may be those which include extensive basic source data essential for substantiating the development of the report but not to the general discussion in the body of the report. The more important or smaller tables and illustrations may be placed forward with the discussion and others of less importance placed at the end of the section.

Folded Sheets

Sheets larger than the standard 8½ by 11 in. — or larger than the sheet in use — may be used for large tables and illustrations when their presentation cannot be made to advantage on the standard sheet. These larger sheets, usually folded in from the right-hand side, are placed in their regular sequence. The fold should be positioned so that it comes about 1/4 in. inside the right-hand edge of the sheet. By folding the sheet short, the fold will not be cut off if the report is trimmed and further, it will not be unduly worn when fingering the edges of the bound report.

Folds at both the right and top edges are necessary for a sheet which is larger than the standard sheet in each dimension. In folding a sheet on both dimensions the top is folded down first. The side is then folded in from the right so that the cut edge of the sheet may be taken hold of to extend the sheet first to the right then upward.

A table or illustration which is referred to continuously while reading the text may be placed on the right half of a double-sized sheet (the left half being blank) which is folded in. Thus, when this type of folded sheet is placed at the end of a report or chapter it may be left unfolded for ready reference while reading other parts of the report.

With all folds it is essential to clear the binding so that the sheet can be taken hold of and extended easily with one hand.

DETAILS OF TYPING

The full effectiveness of a well-chosen format cannot be achieved unless the typing is correspondingly well done. Besides the usual requirement of clean and even typing, the typist should strive for good breaks at the ends of the lines and at the bottom of pages, and a good balance in the spacing of headings and lists.

Unlike the evenness of the right end of lines to be found in printer's composition, typescript is uneven. The appearance of the right margin can be improved by holding the variation of line endings to the minimum. A desirable standard is not to extend a line more than one character beyond the assumed vertical margin line, and to leave not more than four blank spaces to the left of the margin line. This standard provides a variation of five characters in line length which will result in about 60 per cent of the lines being shorter than the standard and 15 per cent of the lines extending one character into the margin.

In hyphenating words at syllables at the ends of the line, good typing calls for retaining at least three characters at the end of the line and carrying over three or more. Further, there should not be three or more consecutive hyphenated lines. Although these refinements are desirable, they may be waived when difficult to achieve without retyping.

The carry-over from the bottom of one page to the top of the next page should be not less than a full line of type of the paragraph. If adhering to the standard length of page would result in carrying over only a fraction of a line, it is better to place the fractional line at the bottom of the preceding page, even though this page is made a line longer than standard. Similarly, the first line of a paragraph should not be the last line on the page; rather, make the page a line short.

Where center or side headings come so near to the bottom of the page that at least two lines of the paragraph cannot be placed on the page below the head, it is preferred practice to allow the short page, and to place the head at the top of the following page.

Center heads longer than three-fourths of a standard line should be typed in two lines, centering the shorter one beneath the first line. Side heads longer than one-half of a standard line should be broken, making the second line the longer and indented from the left margin.

Captions and legends are always centered on the table or illustration they describe.

Listings and text tables should be balanced on the page and condensed or expanded horizontally to achieve a pleasing spacing and centering. They may be single or double spaced if necessary to shorten or lengthen them to desirable proportions.

All materials such as quotations, listings,

and outlines which are typed in short measure need to have indentations on the left of at least one or two characters more or less than the standard paragraph indentation of the adjacent text lines; otherwise, the short measure material is not always sufficiently distinguished from the lines of normal length.

DUPLICATION OF REPORTS

The person preparing a report is required to prepare his material and to design his page format as well as to compose tables and figures so that the desired number of copies can be produced readily. Methods to be used in producing these copies vary according to the time element, number of copies wanted, facilities available, and the process requirements. The process to be used is partially controlled by whether color is to be used, whether physical dimensions of the pages are to be reduced, and whether photographs are to be included. Thus, one of the early steps of preparing a report is to decide the number of copies wanted and the process by which the copies are to be produced.

When only two to eight copies are required the typed portions may be produced by use of carbon paper and typewriter. When more than about eight copies are required, one resorts to a dry or wet chemical contact process, a photographic process with or without reduction in size, or one of the standard printing processes such as letterpress, offset, or mimeograph. Available in most offices are one or more of several excellent processes of duplicating by "fast copy" machines. Some processes require a stencil to be cut; some typing on any ordinary white paper, and others typing on a specially processed paper. See Chapter 16 for discussion of duplicating processes.

Those duplicating processes which transfer the original copy, with or without reduction in size, by use of chemicals or photography directly or through a printing process, require original copy in exact layout, wording, and detail, page for page. When such a process is to be used, all persons responsible for preparation of any part of the report are required to understand the finality of their work. For such reports, advance planning of every physical detail of the report is highly important.

Fig. 5.1. (opposite page) Diagram for laying out pages typed right-hand side only and bound at the left. Illustration is three-fourths size for 8½- by 11-in. sheets with a ¾-in. binding allowance.

The larger type page shown has a ¾-in. binding allowance and a right margin of 1 in., a satisfactory layout for reports. Fixing the binding allowance and the right margin controls all other dimensions. Typical layouts are:

	Binding allowance of	
	½ in.	¾ in.
Right margin, inches	1.00	1.00
Left margin without binding allowance, inches	1.00	1.00
Left margin with binding allowance, inches	1.50	1.75
Top margin, inches	1.10	1.14
Bottom margin, inches	1.65	1.70
Type page width, inches	6.00	5.75
Type page depth (height or length), inches	8.25	8.16
Ratio, width to depth of type page	0.73	0.70
Type area, percentage of effective area	56%	55%

A small type area, as illustrated, may be used for preliminary pages, tables and listings needing a short line to produce a pleasing layout.

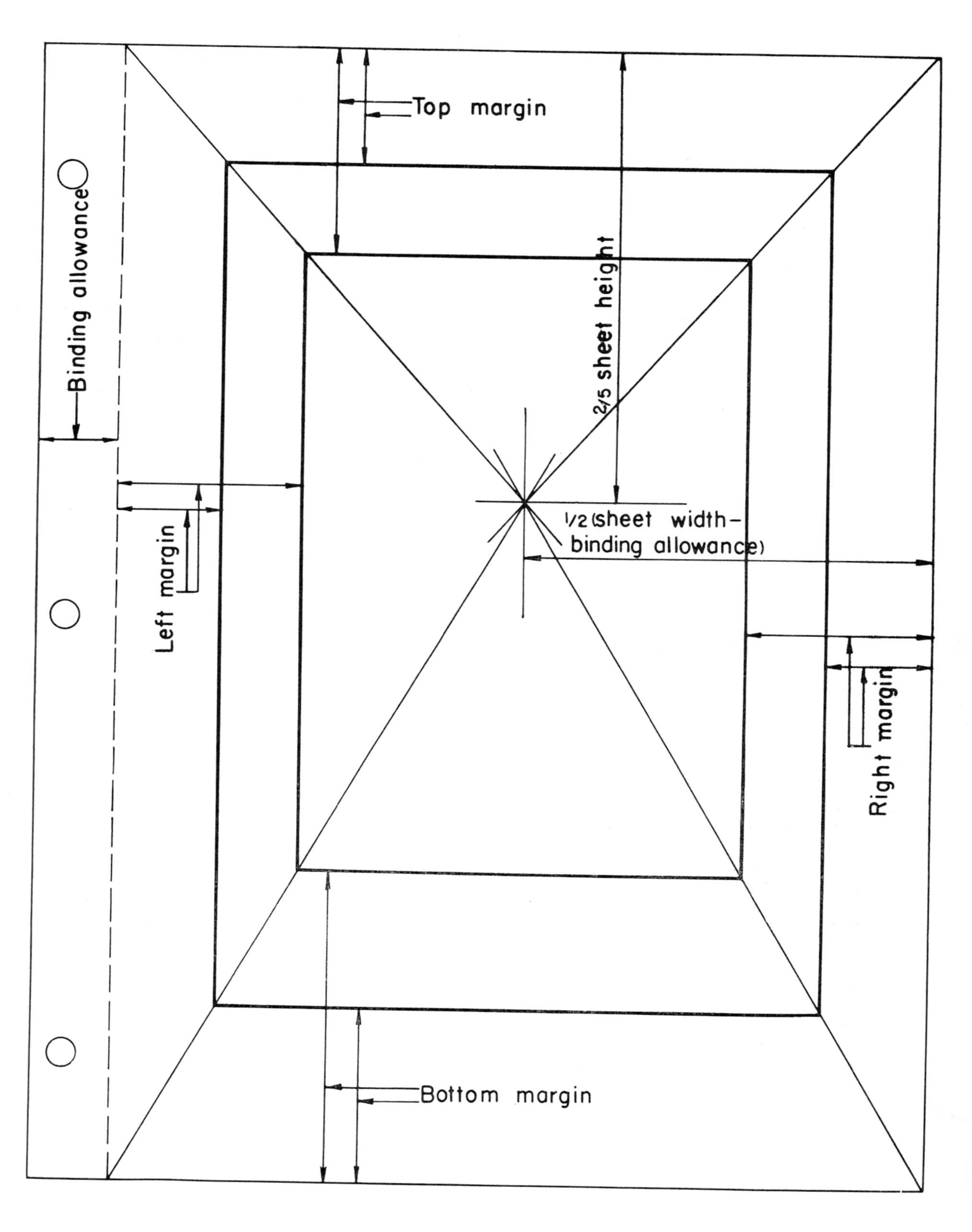
Top margin
Binding allowance
2/5 sheet height
Left margin
1/2 (sheet width-
binding allowance)
Right margin
Bottom margin

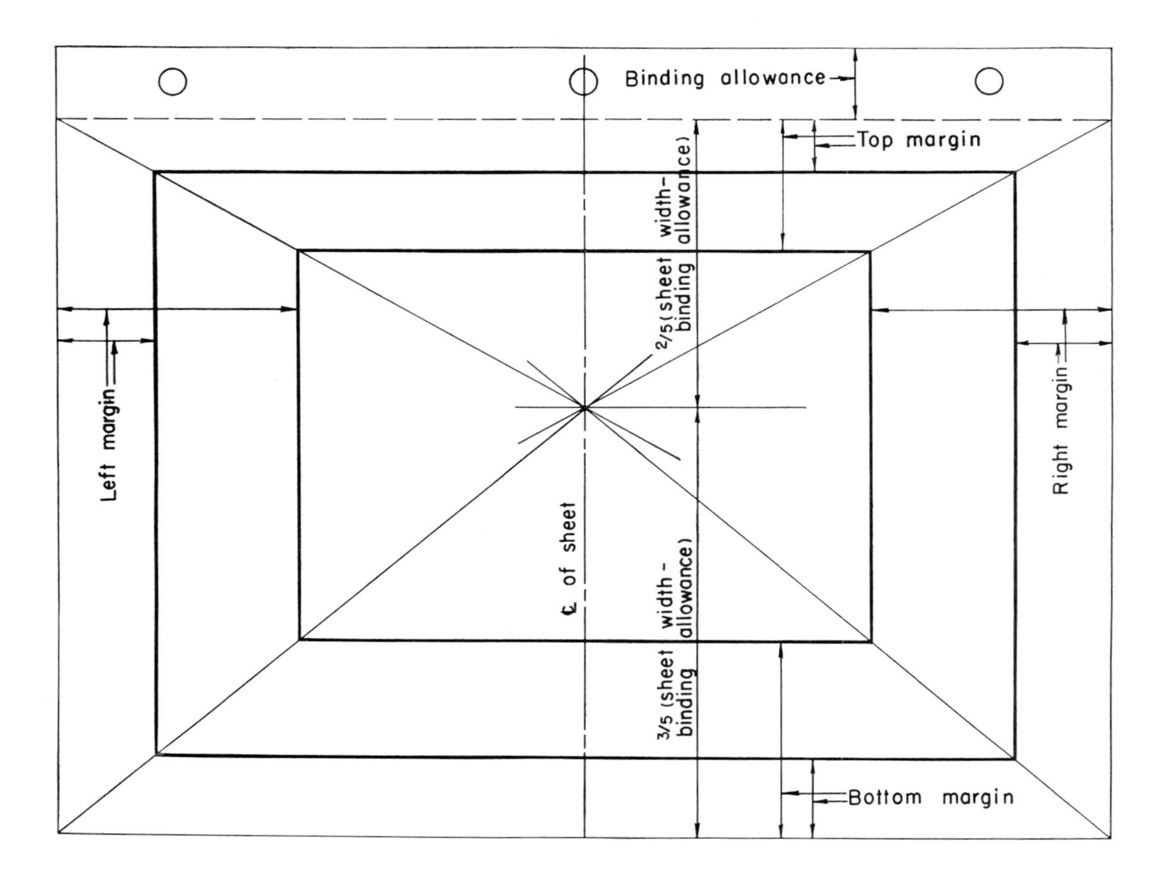

Fig. 5.2. Diagram for laying out pages which are turned 90° clockwise. Illustration is one-half size for an 8½- by 11-in. sheet with a ¾-in. binding allowance.

These pages are bound at the top of the page (at the left of the sheet before it is turned to the reading position). Turned pages are necessary for tables and illustrations which need greater width than can be obtained across the upright page. Dimensions of the larger area illustrated for a ¾-in. binding allowance are:

Right margin	1.00 in.
Left margin	1.00 in.
Top margin without binding	0.55 in.
Top margin with binding	1.30 in.
Bottom margin	0.85 in.
Type page width	9.00 in.
Type page depth	6.35 in.
Ratio, width to depth	0.70
Type area, percentage of effective area	67%

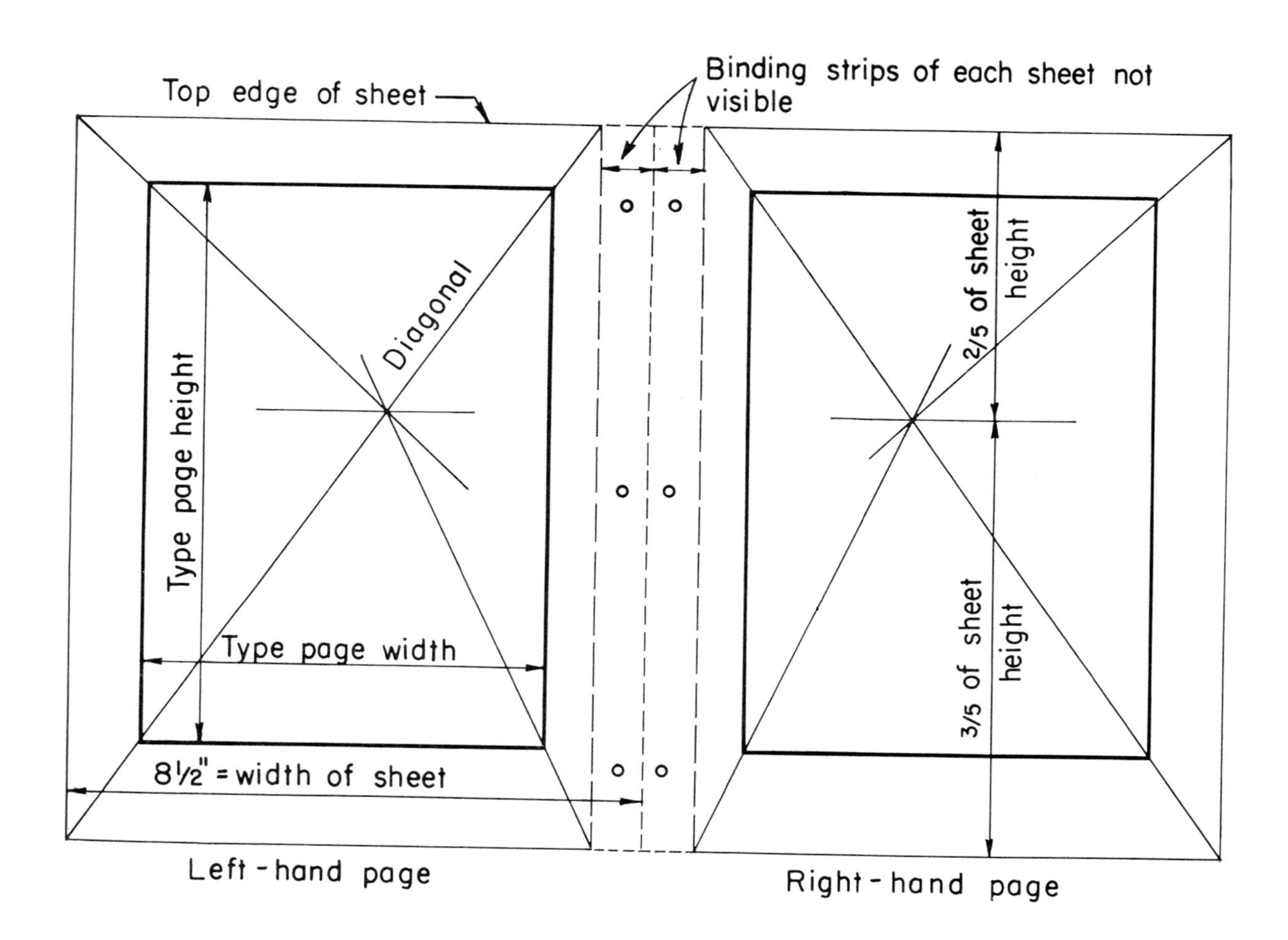

Fig. 5.3. Diagram for determining margins and position of type page for facing pages bound tightly on the side with staples, posts, or clamps.

The illustration is drawn for a ¾-in. binding. The width of strip to allow for binding is dependent upon the number of pages to be bound and the type of binding. The width is increased as the number of pages increases.

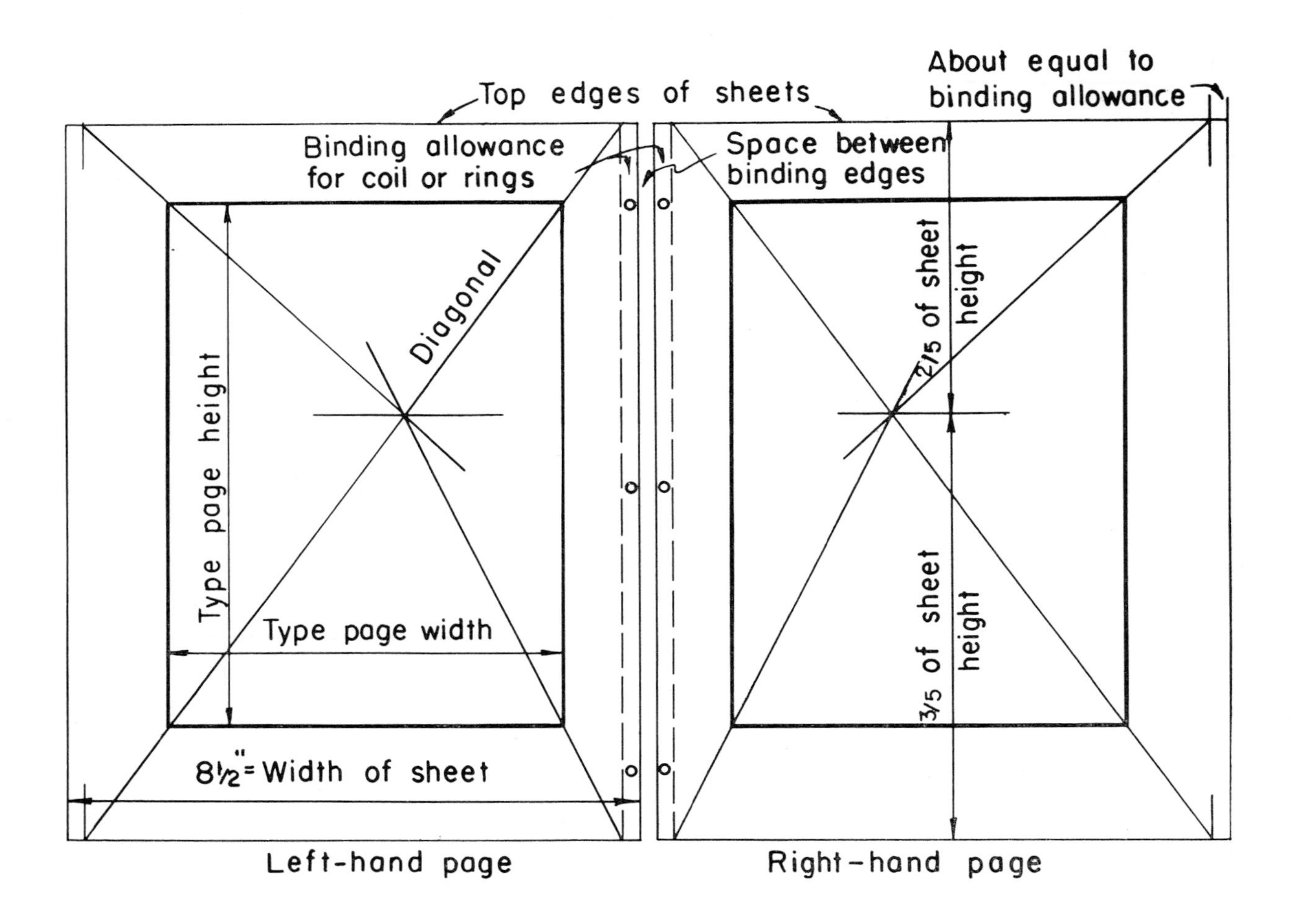

Fig. 5.4. Diagram for determining margins and positions of type page for facing pages having ring, spiral, or sewed bindings which expose the full width of the sheet when the report is open.

Slightly wider outside margins are suggested than are used with any of the side bindings in order to hold down the length of the type line and the ratio of width to length of type page.

CHAPTER 6

Tabular Presentation

Numerical and descriptive data are so common to reports that tabular arrangements have been accepted as a form of technical language associated with reports. The organization of numerical and topical information into an orderly arrangement of lines and columns is frequently difficult. Achieving clarity compactness, and completeness within the mechanical and space limitations of typescript or printer's type is an art as well as a science. The following pages, while not a complete treatise on the preparation of tables, present the main problems encountered by the report writer.

FUNCTION OF TABLES

As a rule, statistical and topical data are presented in tabular form to enable the reader to get quickly a definite understanding of the comparisons, trends, and quantities. The co-ordinate arrangement and arrays possible in tabulations give them a distinct advantage over paragraph arrangement of the same information.

The organization of tabular material calls for clear, concise, and exact use of language, the same as is required elsewhere in the report, but under situations of space limitations. Titles, headings, and notes must be brief, yet complete and understandable. The task of preparing them to achieve clearness of understanding and pleasing arrangement within the space limitations is similar in requirement to the writing of newspaper heads, long regarded as a difficult form of writing.

Flexible standards are allowed in writing tables because tabulation does not lend itself to rigid rules. However, certain principles may be followed to achieve the best results.

A table needs to be complete in itself. Completeness of the material in a table helps to prevent inaccurate interpretations and half-true conclusions. The significance of tables and interpretations may be pointed out in the text, but it should not be necessary to rely upon the text for restrictions of meanings, classifications, or sources of the information given in tabular form. A table should contain all pertinent data as well as useful totals, ratios, classifications, and arrays. To achieve effectiveness of tabular presentation, the material should be written and revised with the same sharp scrutiny that is given to the text material.

TYPES OF TABLES

Tables contain either a tabulation of numerals, of words and descriptions, or of numerals and words combined. Tables may be either closed or open in format, that is, with or without rules to separate the parts of the table. A further classification divides tables into text tables that depend upon the text to disclose their identification and subject and independent or formal tables that are assigned independent titles and numbers.

Open tables (Tables 6.1 and 6.2) are recommended for brief, 1- or 2-column numerical or topical tables, in which there is little likelihood of confusion.

Specimen Table 6.1.
Open table, two columns without heads

TABLE. 6.1. ANALYSIS OF WATER FROM THE CITY SYSTEM

Total hardness, ppm	370	Dissolved oxygen, ppm	4
Magnesium, ppm	46	Chloride, ppm	25
Free CO_2, ppm	29	Residual chloride, ppm	0
Total alkalinity, ppm	273	Iron, ppm	0
		pH determination	7.1

Specimen Table 6.2.
Open table with heads, leaders, and footnote

TABLE 6.2. TYPES OF URBAN MOTOR VEHICLE ACCIDENTS IN 1960*

Type of Accident	Percentage
Two motor vehicles, nonintersection	45.0
Two motor vehicles at intersections	41.0
Vehicle overturned or left roadway	4.4
Collision with other than motor vehicles . . .	4.0
Pedestrian nonintersection accidents	2.4
Pedestrian intersection accidents	1.6
All others	1.6
Total	100.0

*Accident Facts, 1961 Edition. National Safety Council, page 47.

Generally, reports are written with closed or semiclosed tables (Table 6.5) in which the vertical rules are omitted. The closed table (Tables 6.6 and 6.7) has a distinctive appearance which sets it off from text material. The box headings are set off from the entries in the field. Vertical rules are necessary in tables which are crowded either because the number of columns crowds the width of the table or because the box headings tend to become confused (Tables 6.7 and 6.8).

Text tables usually do not exceed three columns with stub, and seldom exceed 10 to 12 lines in the field. Rules are not used and emphasis is achieved by top and bottom spacing combined with short measure on the left or both sides. As an illustration of a text table the following estimate of cost of public address equipment is presented:

Item	Cost
1 Microphone, unidirectional . . .	$ 40.50
6 Speakers, 12 in. p.m., 15-watt . .	242.35
1 Amplifier, 60-watt	157.60
200 Feet of cable	13.50
Total	$453.95

Because text tables are a part of the text, they are not given numbers and titles; therefore, they are referenced by page position. Another example of a text table is given on page 104.

MAIN PARTS OF FORMAL TABLES

Physical parts of the formal, or independent, table are designated in the following outline and are illustrated by Table 6.3:

Identification

Designation number
Main title (table caption)
Subtitle
Headnote

Body

Box head with column headings
Stub, or argument
Field with cells
Line and column designations

Supplementary items

Footnotes and their symbols
Explanatory notes
Evaluation of results, such as by substitution in a formula

The main identification of the table is by the use of a number and title for independent tables. Text tables are identified by the preceding context. Additional identification of the table or of the content of the table is given in subtitles or headnotes when necessary to amplify or restrict the main title or the body of the table (Tables 6.3 and 6.7).

The body of the table, as illustrated by Table 6.3, consists of the central portion and includes all except the titles, headnotes, and supplementary notes. The body is subdivided into four main parts:

1. The box head, in which is given the column headings, is that portion of the body above the field.
2. The stub is the left-hand column, usually of independent character, which serves as the subject index to the lines of the table.
3. The field is that portion beneath the box heading and to the right of the stub. The field is composed of cells which form a checkerboard area, co-ordinate with the columns and lines of the stub, in which the numerical quantities are written.
4. The line and column designating numbers are used in referring to particular material in the field of the body.

Supplementary items consist of footnotes and explanatory notes (See Tables 6.3, 6.5, 6.7, and 6.9). Explanatory notes when placed at the end of the table, follow after any footnotes. Another position for general notes to a table is above the top rule and below the subtitle or title.

Specimen Table 6.3.
Parts of formal tables, their designation and arrangement.

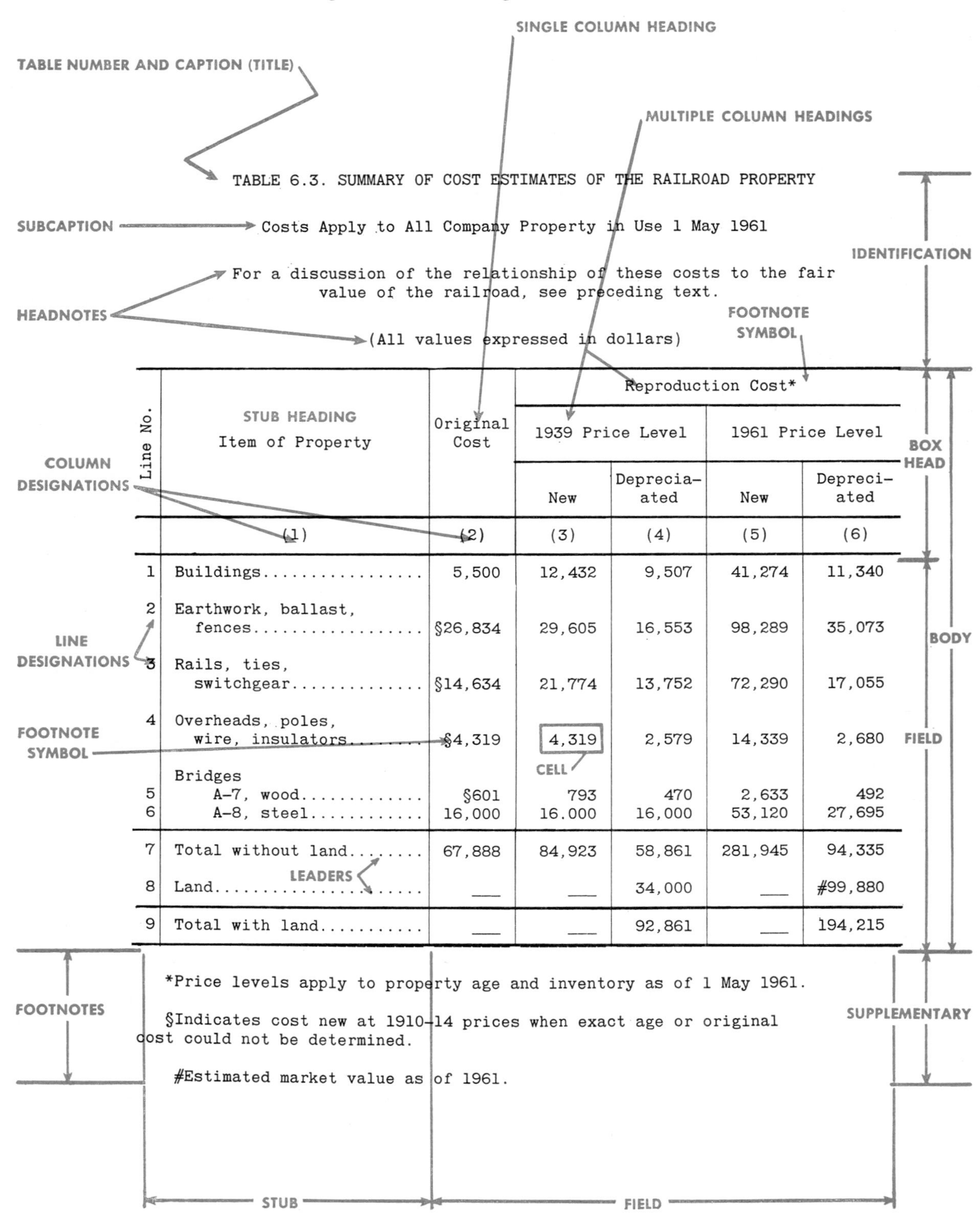

TABLE 6.3. SUMMARY OF COST ESTIMATES OF THE RAILROAD PROPERTY

Costs Apply to All Company Property in Use 1 May 1961

For a discussion of the relationship of these costs to the fair value of the railroad, see preceding text.

(All values expressed in dollars)

Line No.	Item of Property	Original Cost	Reproduction Cost* 1939 Price Level: New		Reproduction Cost* 1961 Price Level: New	
			New	Deprecia-ated	New	Depreci-ated
	(1)	(2)	(3)	(4)	(5)	(6)
1	Buildings................	5,500	12,432	9,507	41,274	11,340
2	Earthwork, ballast, fences.................	§26,834	29,605	16,553	98,289	35,073
3	Rails, ties, switchgear.............	§14,634	21,774	13,752	72,290	17,055
4	Overheads, poles, wire, insulators........	§4,319	4,319	2,579	14,339	2,680
	Bridges					
5	A-7, wood............	§601	793	470	2,633	492
6	A-8, steel...........	16,000	16.000	16,000	53,120	27,695
7	Total without land........	67,888	84,923	58,861	281,945	94,335
8	Land......................	___	___	34,000	___	#99,880
9	Total with land..........	___	___	92,861	___	194,215

*Price levels apply to property age and inventory as of 1 May 1961.

§Indicates cost new at 1910-14 prices when exact age or original cost could not be determined.

#Estimated market value as of 1961.

Specimen Table 6.4.

Closed table showing stub and box head which could be reversed

TABLE 6.4. COUNT OF ALL TRAFFIC ON HIGHWAY 69

Direction	11 to 12 a.m.		5 to 6 p.m.	
	Story Co.	Polk Co.	Story Co.	Polk Co.
Southbound	129	27	210	51
Northbound	75	48	252	120

Specimen Table 6.4A.

Rearrangement of stub and box head of Table 6.4

Hour	Southbound		Northbound	
	Story Co.	Polk Co.	Story Co.	Polk Co.
11 to 12 a.m.	129	27	75	48
5 to 6 p.m.	210	51	252	120

Identification

Good table titles (captions) are those of few words, yet exactly descriptive of the table. Subtitles are often employed as a means of amplifying the main title. Subtitles may be written in lower-case letters and paragraph form in order to conserve space. It is essential in titles of tables to distinguish each table from the others, particularly so when the tables are differentiated only by calendar time or geographical place to which they apply. Key words should appear at the beginning of the title, not at the end.

The unit of the table (where all field columns are in the same unit) may be stated in the title or headnote (Tables 6.3 and 6.8). A satisfactory plan is to state the unit in parentheses on a line immediately above the box heading (Table 6.3).

Subtitles for tables are usually set off from the main title with a line of space. Subtitles may be set in paragraph form and lower-case letters, and if they are more or less a complete statement, they are closed with a period. If the subtitle is in reality a topic title in character, it should be set without a period. Subtitles when short and strictly parenthetical in character should be enclosed in parentheses. Subtitles are used to indicate estimated values, an incomplete or sample study, or other restriction.

Subtitles and headnotes (Tables 6.3, 6.7, 6.8, and 6.9) are for information that applies to the table as a whole, while footnotes apply to particular parts or items within the table (Tables 6.3, 6.5, 6.7, and 6.9). Headnotes describe the tabulated material as a whole, giving the limitations of the information as to completeness, accuracy, recentness, geographical area, source, formulas used in calculations, and limits of application.

Stub or Argument

At the left-hand side of a tabular arrangement is the stub column, sometimes called the argument. This section may be composed of a vertical series of years, loading designations, word descriptions, or other independent variable or control. In the field to the right of these designations, which are often followed by leaders, are entered the dependent quantities, either calculated or observed. Lines in the stub should be arranged chronologically, alphabetically, geographically, quantitatively, operationally, or by other logical sequence which will classify the information in the table. The usual arrangement is to have the first or lowest value of the chosen order on the upper line. For certain types of statistical tables it is advantageous to give the totals on the first line of the stub and field (Tables 6.5 and 6.9). Such arrangement

Specimen Table 6.5.
Semiclosed table with horizontal rules; totals opposite main head in stub to save lines.

TABLE 6.5. DEGREES GRANTED BY COLLEGES AND UNIVERSITIES IN THE UNITED STATES, 1954 to 1957

From U.S. Office of Education, Earned Degrees Conferred by Higher Educational Institutions, 1956-1957, Circular No. 527, April, 1958.

Degree and Sex	School Year			
	1953–54	1954–55	1955–56	1956–57
*Bachelor's, total	292,880	287,401	311,298	340,347
Men	187,500	183,602	199,571	222,738
Women	105,380	103,799	111,727	117,609
Master's, total	56,823	58,204	59,294	61,955
Men	38,147	38,740	39,397	41,332
Women	18,676	19,464	19,897	20,623
Doctor's, total	8,996	8,840	8,903	8,756
Men	8,181	8,104	8.018	7,818
Women	815	826	885	939

*Includes first professional degree.

Specimen Table 6.5A.

Rearrangement of Table 6.5 to reduce width, increase length, and bring totals together; three sections vertically

TABLE 6.5A. DEGREES GRANTED BY COLLEGES AND UNIVERSITIES IN UNITED STATES, 1954 to 1957

From U.S. Office of Education, Earned Degrees Conferred by Higher Educational Institutions, 1956-1957, Circular No. 527, April, 1958.

School Year	Bachelor's Degree*	Master's Degree	Doctor's Degree
	Men		
1953-54	187,500	38,147	8,181
1954-55	183,602	38,740	8,014
1955-56	199,571	39,397	8,018
1956-57	222,738	41,332	7,818
	Women		
1953-54	105,380	18,676	815
1954-55	103,799	19,464	826
1955-56	111,727	19,897	885
1956-57	117,609	20,623	939
	Men and Women		
1953-54	292,880	56,823	8,996
1954-55	287,401	58,204	8,840
1955-56	311,298	59,294	8,903
1956-57	340,347	61,955	8,756

*Includes first professional degree.

saves lines when many subtotals are to be shown, because the totals may be placed opposite main or subheadings in the stub. Ordinarily, however, totals should be given at the bottom.

The stub should be carefully designed because it is the index to the values in the field, and in conjunction with the box head, the stub determines the complete order of presentation of the information of the table.

The ease with which a table may be read is controlled to a large extent by the design of the stub which controls the vertical spacing of the field. When the stub is arranged with good spacing and indentation of subordinate items, the relation of the various entries is easily observed (Tables 6.7 and 6.9).

Leaders (Tables 6.2, 6.3, and 6.7) from the last word or number on each line in the stub to the first column of the field are an aid to the reader in case of wide stubs having some short lines. They are also useful as a guide to typing the tables correctly, line for line. Leaders are recommended where they are of distinct aid to reading, but leaders are unnecessary in stubs of a few lines only, with lines of equal length, or with narrow width stubs. The beginning and end of the line of leaders should be so spaced that the dots do not form unwanted periods.

Box Heading

Across the top of all columns is the box head giving the names and units of the information for each of the columns (Tables 6.3 to 6.9). Some tables would read equally well if the subject items in the stub and box head were reversed in position (Tables 6.4 and 6.5). In general, the arrangement to be preferred is with fewer items (columns) in the box head than there are lines to the field. This plan provides for greater width for column headings and gives the table greater depth. There are other controlling factors, such as arithmetical calculations to be made, logical sequence, number of digits in the numbers, and purpose of the table, all of which must be considered in determining the organization of the table. No generalization as to arrangement should be regarded as controlling.

From left to right the columns should be in logical sequence of time, observation or operation. Order of derivation may be used when one column is calculated from another. Frequently, order of operation results in having the final values in the right-hand column and farthest from the stub where reading is least convenient. In tables which present only basic statistical data, the more important column such as a column of totals may be placed at the left of the field (Table 6.9). This arrangement is better when the column of totals is referred to frequently and the other columns infrequently.

Column headings should be worded carefully, a task frequently difficult because of limited space both horizontally (characters) and vertically (lines). The heading should describe completely the material in the column, qualitatively and quantitatively. Thus, the name of the item and the unit in which it is expressed are given. These two items are separated by a comma provided the unit is not enclosed in parentheses (Table 6.8). The name of the unit may be abbreviated in order to save space.

Heads which span two or more related columns should be used where possible (Tables 6.4, 6.5, 6.7, and 6.9). Such a heading usually saves space, avoids unnecessary repetition, and aids in classification by indicating that the columns have certain characteristics in common.

Although a few publications, particularly those of the U.S. Government Printing Office, place the unit designations for the columns below the box heading and above the first cell of the column, the practice is not frequent. However, for tabulations of dollars the corresponding symbol is frequently used on the first number at the top of the column.

The wording in column heads ordinarily should be parallel to the title of the table. However, in crowded tables having column headings of several words, space may be saved by setting the headings to read from the bottom up, i.e., perpendicular to the table title (Table 6.7).

Specimen Table 6.6.
Three-column table of word descriptions

TABLE 6.6. ADVANTAGES AND DISADVANTAGES OF TYPES OF MICROPHONES

Type	Advantages	Disadvantages
Carbon	Robust Reliable High sensitivity Relatively low cost	Poor stability Background hiss Poor frequency response
Condenser	Good frequency response No background noise	Requires preamplifier Fragile Must be sealed against dust and moisture
Crystal	Good frequency response No background noise Negligible frequency discrimination with nondirectional types	Relatively low output Diaphragm types have frequency discrimination Easily damaged in high temperatures
Moving coil	Good frequency response No background noise Robust and reliable Fairly high sensitivity	Frequency discrimination Diaphragm flutter in wind
Ribbon	Excellent frequency response May be selected to give directional pickup	Relatively low output Very liable to wind flutter

Specimen Table 6.7.
Multiple heads, turned heads, two sections vertically with totals, and column designations

TABLE 6.7. GRADES OF ENGINEERING GRADUATES

All Grades Based Upon the Quarter Term Average

Entering classification and scholastic year	June graduates			Midyear graduates*		
	Number of grades	Quarter grades		Number of grades	Quarter grades	
		Per cent grades 3.0 or more	Median		Per cent grades 3.0 or more	Median
(1)	(2)	(3)	(4)	(5)	(6)	(7)
Freshman matriculants						
Freshman	218	33.9	2.58	169	12.5	2.19
Sophomore	212	29.6	2.52	173	10.5	2.19
Junior	213	28.1	2.54	178	11.8	2.26
Senior	224	40.2	2.83	152	23.0	2.58
All students . .	867	33.1	2.65	672	14.2	2.28
Transfer matriculants						
Freshman	26	19.2	2.68	22	13.6	2.32
Sophomore	93	23.6	2.38	74	4.2	2.04
Junior	150	27.4	2.44	113	9.6	2.07
Senior	159	33.5	2.69	93	21.3	2.47
All students . .	428	28.2	2.56	302	12.2	2.19

*Includes graduates of July, August, December, and March.

Field

The area of the table below the box head and to the right of the stub is the field, containing the numerical entries or other itemizable information. The field is divided into cells, co-ordinate areas opposite the lines of the stub and below each column heading. Arrangement of the field becomes fixed upon design of the stub and order of columns. The number of digits required in the field determines the minimum width of each column. Therefore, in the choice of arrangement of the stub and box head, consideration is given to the required number of digits.

Where the field of the table is made up of two or more parallel sections in vertical arrangement, the subheads for these sections should appear just above their respective sections. See Table 6.5A. It is not correct practice to place the heading for the first subsection above the main box heading.

Cells should not be left blank (Tables 6.3 and 6.8). If the value is zero the cell should so indicate with the numeral zero. If the data are missing or do not apply to that cell, leaders or a dash should be used.

Numbers of four digits or more (Tables 6.3, and 6.9) should be separated into groups of three digits, with commas or spaces pointing off from right to left (10,462). Numerals to the right of the decimal, however, are never pointed off with commas (9.98864). In printer's type composition, thin spaces are sometimes used after each set of three digits to the right of the decimal (9.988 64).

In columns having no integers to the left of the decimal, it is customary to show the "0" to the left of the decimal (0.0096). Where the column has more than 10 lines of such entries, the zero preceding the decimal may be printed on the first and last lines only (Table 7.1). In a column having both decimal forms above and below 1.0, the zero before the decimal is supplied in all cases (8.921, 0.681, 1.420, 0.386). See Table 6.8.

For sake of uniform typographical appearance, it is desirable to record all figures in a column to the same number of digits to the right of the decimal point. This practice is not always proper, however, because the wrong degree of accuracy may be indicated. The preferred form is to record the same number of significant digits in each cell, or to record the values only to the warranted degree of accuracy.

Tables that deal with large numbers, such as populations and federal financing, may be simplified by omitting the last three (or last six) digits. In such case, the subtitle or headnote states that "000 omitted" or "values expressed in thousands" or "all values expressed in thousands of ______" (insert appropriate unit).

Line and Column Designations

For purposes of reference, the columns may be numbered from left to right, on a line below the box heading and above the first line of the field. Also, for reference use, it is desirable to number the lines of the field by using a column on the left of the stub (Table 6.3). For wide tables the line number column may be repeated on the extreme right side of the field. Arabic numbers are used. Line and column numbers are also used for reference purposes on tables that are continued to a second sheet (Table 6.9).

Footnotes

As in text matter, footnotes are used in tabular presentations to provide supplementary information, references, explanations of the cell entries, and to amplify column or stub headings (Tables 6.2, 6.3, 6.5, 6.7, and 6.9). It is preferable to use symbols (signs) or lower-case letters as indices throughout the field of the table. Superior Arabic numerals as used in the text for footnotes may result in confusion when used with base figures. The * (asterisk), † (dagger), ‡ (double dagger), § (section mark), // (parallel), and ¶ (paragraph mark) are the usual symbols used in order given. They may be used in pairs when additional symbols are needed. These symbols are adapted to printer's type but are not usually available on typewriters. In typescript, lower-case letters or the special characters (*, #, @, ¢, ϕ, θ) may be used. The last two special characters are developed on the typewriter by using a lower case "o," back spacing, then striking in a slant mark or a hyphen, respectively. Footnote indices are written one-half line above the word or number to which they refer and immediately following without space. In the footnote the symbol or letter is likewise written one-half line high, but prefixed to the first word of the footnote. In certain usages the index is written on the line, underlined, and followed by the slant or shilling mark (d/). The same form is then used in the footnote with one space before the first word of the footnote.

In tables which have crowded columns so that space between the numbers and the rule to the right is limited, the footnote index symbol is placed to the left of the number in the cell (Table 6.3). Frequently this plan saves space in width because the footnote symbol occurs at numbers of less than maximum number of digits.

The sequence of position for footnote symbols is from top to bottom, line for line, and left to right on the line from the stub to the right-hand column.

Footnotes should be indented paragraphs in single-spaced lines of length equal to the width of the table. They are always placed at the immediate bottom of independent tables, even though there may be lines of text on the page below the table. Footnotes to text tables, on the other hand, are set at the bottom of the page as is illustrated by the following table giving the median school years completed by men 35 to 54 years old for the United States as of March, 1957:[1]

Major occupation group[2]	Per cent	Median school years completed
Professional, technical . .	8.7	16+
Managers, officials, proprietors	14.5	12.4
Clerical, sales	11.0	12.4
Craftsmen, foremen	23.1	10.2
Operatives	21.4	9.1
Farmers and farm managers	7.3	8.6
All other	14.0	8.4
All occupations	100.0	10.8

The form of credit line to use depends somewhat upon the character of the report and upon the extent that credit lines are used. Where credit is to be given for only a part of a table, it is done by the use of a footnote indexed at the proper position within the body of the table. When the entire table is to be credited to another source, and only an occasional table is so credited, a footnote may be used indexed to the end of the table title. For a series of tables, or for several tables in a report, the credit is best indicated in a headnote line. (See Tables 6.5 and 6.9.) Showing the source as a headnote above the table is preferred to a similar arrangement at the end of the table. The source need not be stated in complete reference form where the source is given in full in a list of references or bibliography, but only such material need be given that the reader can easily identify the source in the main listing of references.

GENERAL FORMAT

As with all types of compositions, white space in tabulations improves the readability of the page and aids in comprehension. Where space permits, there should be a blank line or at least a half line of space as follows:

Between main title and subtitle
Between subtitle and headnote
Between last line of headnote and top rule of table
Above and below the first and last lines of column headings
Above the subheadings within the body of the table
Above and below each horizontal rule
Between bottom rule of the table and the first line of the footnotes
Between footnotes to the table when more than one footnote

Tables are easier to read if the horizontal lines are separated by double spacing or by solid grouping of the lines in fours, fives, or sixes with a blank line between groups. In long tables where space precludes the use of the blank lines, readability is increased by using horizontal rules after each fifth line.

---

[1] U.S. Bureau of the Census, Current Population Reports, Population Characteristics, Series P-20, No. 77, December 27, 1957.

[2] Includes only year-round full time workers.

Abbreviations may be used liberally in tables. Even nonstandard abbreviations may be used where necessary to save space, provided the meaning is clear to the reader.

In the interest of simplicity, box headings, stub headings, and subheadings should be set in lower case, with only the initial word capitalized. The alternate form of this is to use capitals and lower case.

The lines of column headings in the box should be centered vertically and each line of words centered horizontally within the box.

At least a character of space should exist to the left and right of each vertical rule. In tables where this spacing is not possible, the vertical rule may be centered in a one-letter space between the columns.

LARGE TABLES

Tables whose width is greater than can be typed across the normal width of the sheet may be turned sidewise (Table 6.9) by rotating the sheet 90 deg. to the right (clockwise). After rotation, the table is prepared in the normal manner, the binding edge being at the top of the table. Page numbers, however, are maintained in their regular position as though the table had not been rotated.

Tabulations that require more width for columns or depth for lines than the standard sheet used for the report will permit, may be handled in one of three ways: (1) The table may be continued to a second sheet; (2) it may be typed on a sheet larger than the standard sheet and then folded to a size ¼ to ½ in. less than the sheet dimension; or (3) it may be typed on a large sheet, reduced in size photographically, and printed on paper with the proper margins on standard size sheets. Table 6.3 has been reduced slightly, and Table 6.9 has been reduced to one-half size. The choice of method of handling the large tables depends upon the character of the report, the time and facilities available, the character of the table, and how much the table is to be used.

For tables that are long in either width or length, it is sometimes possible to type them in sections as illustrated in Tables 6.1, 6.7 and 6.8. These forms are also advisable for tables that are of undesirable proportion, width to length, which can be corrected by doubling in one direction (Table 6.8).

Tables continued to a second or third sheet should be set in the normal manner, with all headings repeated as necessary, but with the line numbers and column numbers continued in sequence (Table 6.9). Tables continued in width to a second page should have the stub repeated under the same column number as given on the first page. Where continuing the table to additional pages does not make it difficult for the reader to follow the material in the table, continued sheets are generally preferable; for tables in which it is desirable to have the full information before the reader at one time, either the folded table or the table reduced by photographic process (Table 6.9) is recommended. For extra large tables a combination of the three methods may be necessary.

PREPARATION OF TABLES

Tabular matter is expensive, time consuming, and difficult to prepare. In preparing a report which will include tabular matter, the author will do well to envision the design and location of his tables at the time he conceives the need for statistical and numerical information.

The preparation of tabular matter begins with collecting the original information. Recopying of data will be less and errors will be fewer when all data forms, summaries, and work sheets used in the early stages of preparing a report are designed in accordance with their ultimate use and location in the final report. Although it takes time to design a table in its final form when the data are being assembled, in the long run time is saved. The writing of longhand tables, the method so frequently used, as copy for the typist should not proceed until the author has given final decision as to how the table is to be formed on the typewriter. This attention requires that he determine the arrangement of the identification material, stub, the box heading, the field, and footnotes. Letter counts and line counts are necessary to insure that the material can be typed within the allotted space on the sheet. Attention should also be directed to the method of duplication, if any, and style and place of binding.

A time-saving method that is practical and economical is to prepare tabular material longhand, giving extra care to achieve a good layout and neat figures. Work copies can then be made by one of the "fast copy" (mechanical-chemical) processes available in most offices. Several such copies can be made for review, editing, and study preparatory to typing the final arrangement.

A second scheme of considerable value in saving time and holding errors to a minimum is to print the final tables by business machines when electronic computing and tabulating machines are used in processing the information. These machines, which print both words and numbers, can be set to reproduce the table in its entirety in suitable form for reproducing final copies for the report. Tabulations from these machines are suitable for printer's photocopy for making plates, either letterpress or offset process. One advantage of printing directly from material prepared by business machines is that proofreading is unnecessary because the table is not transcribed at any stage — the first copy is the one that is reproduced. By photographic process, the machine-made tables can be reduced in size as required for the particular report, or usage. An example of tables prepared for reproduction this way is *A Handbook of Trigonometric Functions — Introducing Doversines* by Leon Kennedy, published by Iowa State University Press.

Specimen Table 6.8.

Four sections arranged horizontally to avoid long table, grouping of lines by sixes, and use of ellipsis

TABLE 6.8.

PER CENT FREQUENCY OF WORD COUNT PER SENTENCE

Composite of samples of 5,016 sentences and 99,918 words taken from engineering reports written by 43 junior and senior engineering students. Median length sentence is 18.02 words, average length is 19.92 words, and the modal frequency is 16 words per sentence.

Words per Sentence	Frequency, %	Words per Sentence	Frequency, %	Words per Sentence	Frequency, %	Words per Sentence	Frequency, %
1	0.02	19	5.06	37	0.70	55	0.04
2	0.06	20	4.84	38	0.60	56	0.02
3	0.08	21	4.42	39	0.42	57	0.04
4	0.26	22	4.03	40	0.44	58	0.04
5	0.46	23	3.73	41	0.40	59	0.00
6	0.84	24	3.37	42	0.30	60	0.06
7	1.20	25	3.09	43	0.30	61	0.04
8	1.81	26	2.75	44	0.20	62	0.02
9	2.51	27	2.45	45	0.16	63	0.00
10	3.21	28	2.07	46	0.10	64	0.04
11	3.65	29	1.81	47	0.10	..	....
12	4.19	30	1.61	48	0.16	70	0.02
13	4.78	31	1.34	49	0.08	71	0.04
14	5.24	32	1.22	50	0.12	..	....
15	5.42	33	1.10	51	0.06	82	0.02
16	5.48	34	0.98	52	0.04	83	0.02
17	5.38	35	0.86	53	0.04	—	----
18	5.30	36	0.74	54	0.02	—	----

Specimen Table 6.9.

Large table continued at the right to second sheet, pica typescript reduced 50 per cent, space instead of commas separating groups of three digits, total column at left of field, total line above component entries, and grouping in lines of four and five

TABLE 6.9.

YEARS OF SCHOOL COMPLETED BY THE CIVILIAN POPULATION 14 YEARS OLD AND OVER FOR THE UNITED STATES, MARCH, 1957*

Source: U.S. Bureau of the Census, Current Population Reports, Population Characteristics, Series P-20, No. 77, December 27, 1957

Age Group	Total	Years of School Completed			
		None	Elementary School		
			1 to 4	5 to 7	8
(1)	(2)	(3)	(4)	(5)	(6)
Total, 14 years and over......	119 333 000	2 377 000	6 739 000	14 842 000	20 567 000
14 to 17 years............	9 877 000	31 000	150 000	1 850 000	2 569 000
18 and 19 years...........	4 083 000	31 000	64 000	207 000	221 000
20 to 24 years............	9 743 000	67 000	212 000	579 000	667 000
25 to 29 years............	11 260 000	93 000	209 000	814 000	1 015 000
30 to 34 years............	12 177 000	82 000	366 000	917 000	1 225 000
35 to 44 years............	23 113 000	231 000	907 000	2 202 900	3 252 000
45 to 54 years............	19 532 000	305 000	1 215 000	2 799 000	4 096 000
55 to 64 years............	14 867 000	509 000	1 417 000	2 660 000	3 755 000
65 years and over.........	14 681 000	1 028 000	2 199 000	2 814 000	3 767 000

TABLE 6.9. (CONTINUED) YEARS OF SCHOOL COMPLETED

Age Group	Years of School Completed				School years not reported	Median school years completed
	High School		College			
	1 to 3	4	1 to 3	4 or more		
(1)	(7)	(8)	(9)	(10)	(11)	(12)
Total, 14 years and over	25 544 000	30 710 000	8 952 000	7 637 000	1 965 000	10.7
14 to 17 years.......	5 122 000	98 000	16 000	...	41 000	9.2
18 and 19 years......	1 424 000	1 740 000	362 000	8 000	26 000	12.0
20 to 24 years.......	2 047 000	4 040 000	1 589 000	457 000	85 000	12.3
25 to 29 years.......	2 304 000	4 412 000	1 150 000	1 157 000	106 000	12.3
30 to 34 years.......	2 661 000	4 515 000	1 125 000	1 194 000	92 000	12.2
35 to 44 years.......	4 782 000	7 831 000	1 761 000	1 894 000	253 000	12.0
45 to 54 years.......	3 602 000	4 210 000	1 487 000	1 466 000	352 000	10.0
55 to 64 years.......	2 089 000	2 299 000	897 000	853 000	388 000	8.7
65 years and over....	1 513 000	1 565 000	565 000	608 000	622 000	8.3

*Estimates based on sample surveys. Members of the armed forces living off post or with their families on post in March, 1957, are included, but all other armed forces are excluded.

CHAPTER 7

Preparation of Illustrations

Many technical reports lend themselves advantageously to illustrative treatment. Photographs, charts, and maps tell stories that are difficult to relate in words.

Pictures speak in a universal language. The early picture language of the Egyptians was the forerunner of their alphabet. Their early designs and drawings can be understood by people today without a knowledge of their language. So it is with current civilization. If illustrations are well drawn, clear and complete in detail, they should survive for all time.

ILLUSTRATIONS DEFINED

Illustrations may include all devices by which information is presented to the reader pictorially rather than by words and tabulations. The following illustrative material is included:

Photographs—pictures produced by optical and mechanical equipment which records images by the action of light on sensitized material. Photographs are used when it is desired to show scenes and objects as they appear to the eye, in black and white or color.

Drawings—pictures and sketches to show designs for equipment, tools, machines, apparatus, buildings, and structures.

Plans—similar to drawings and diagrams.

Charts and graphs—graphical presentation of statistics, operations, organizations, and scientific and technical relationships. There is not a clear cut difference between charts and graphs, though charts may be considered to be those graphical representations which picture related observations on a quantitative basis. Graphs may be considered to be those graphical representations in which a correlation of two or more forces is shown by means of lines or curves.

Other types of charts include the flow chart to show sequence of operations in the handling of materials or production processes; the organizational chart for the purpose of showing the line of authority and responsibility of individuals or departments of an organization; functional charts, similar in purpose to that of the organizational chart, but to show the function or purpose of an organization; and the properties chart to show the interdependence of various properties of a material or action or observation.

Maps and plats (also charts) —a representation of a geographical area, usually for the purpose of showing special features such as roads, topographic relief, land parcels, cultural developments, and economic or sociological conditions.

Reference to illustrative matter is usually by number and title. The individual illustration is variously referred to as *figure, plate, chart, photograph,* or *curve*. The use of *figure* is recommended, regardless of whether it refers to a photograph, chart, map, or other illustration.

Fig. 7.1. Duplicating machines in use for production of multiple copies of office forms.

Small photographs may be mounted on the page with text.

PURPOSE AND SELECTION OF ILLUSTRATIONS

The first and foremost use of illustrations is to show detail that is difficult to describe in words. For instance, the exterior view of an airplane engine, a wrecked truck, or a manufacturing plant defies a word description, but is easily shown by a photograph. Likewise, the correlation of two variables or a comparison of two sets of observations is difficult to describe, but when put in graphical form the reader has a clear picture of the results. Charts should be used in every case where they serve text matter, and definitely aid the reader.

A second important use of illustrative charts is in the analysis of data. In many cases plotting the observations is necessary to correctly analyze the information being examined. In a similar manner graphical presentations are used regularly in design.

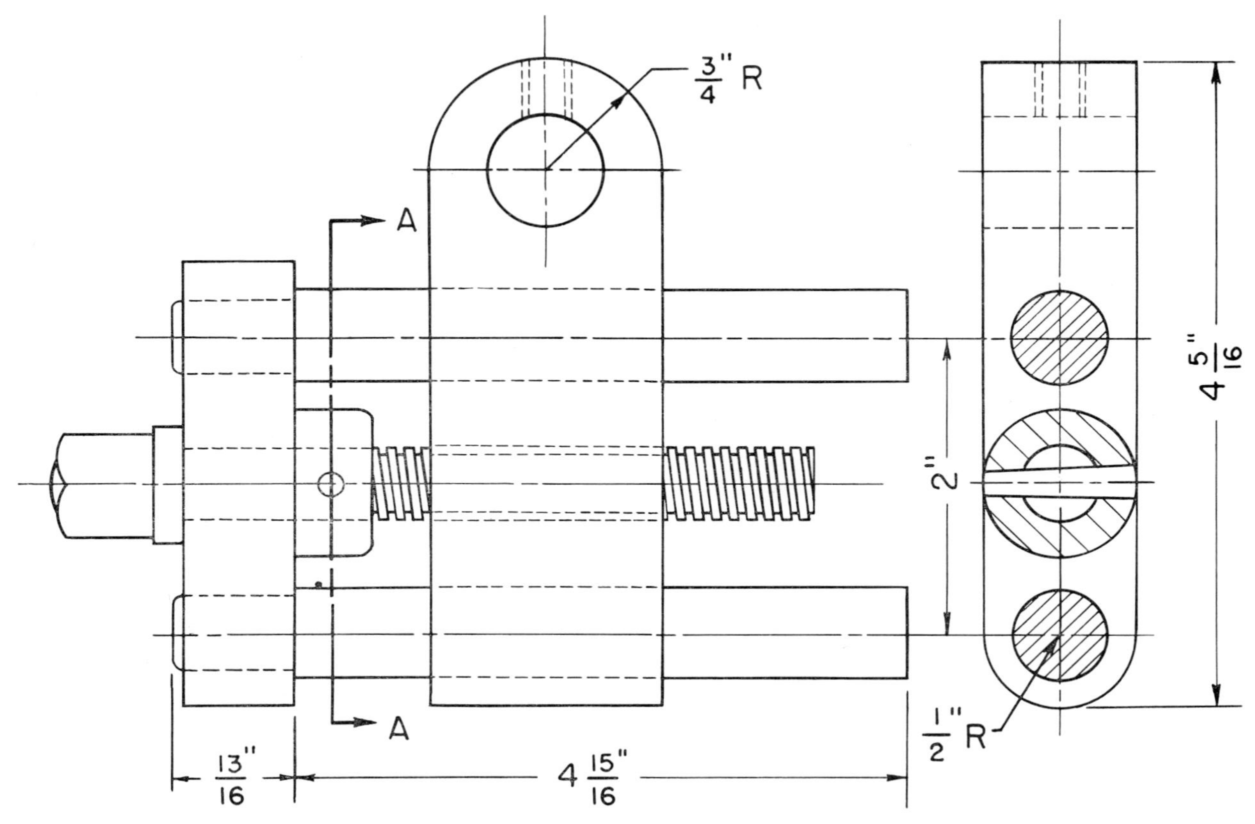

Fig. 7.2. This working drawing (incomplete) shows desirable weights of lines in the finished reproduction.

The third use of illustrative material is to provide added interest. A distinct trend in this direction is noticeable in those reports which are prepared for a large readership such as stockholders of a company. However, because technical reports are usually prepared under conditions not requiring that the report be "sold" to a readership, it is not necessary nor desirable to decorate the report with illustrative or artistic material for the purpose of attracting purchasers or readers. The general rule is to include only those illustrations which are of distinct assistance to the reader. As added interest, however, it is appropriate to include a suitable frontispiece, or an occasional photograph or chart of minor value, simply to break up the monotony of plain text matter. There are promotional types of reports in which illustrations are appropriately used to develop reader attention and interest.

All illustrations must serve the reader. As in the selection of text material, it is better to include doubtful illustrations rather than omit them. The author too often overestimates the reader's understanding of the subject.

In deciding what graphical presentation of data to include, the question arises whether to show the data in tabular form, in chart form, or in both forms. Such a question is difficult to answer except for specific cases. If a graphical presentation of the data will be helpful to the reader and if such was used by the author in making his analysis, then presentation of the data in both table and graph form is desirable. Curves enable the reader to visualize at one glance the interrelationship of the factors presented and to interpolate values more readily than can be done from the tables. Tabulated information taken from other printed sources may be better presented in graph form. However, in some cases it may be desirable to include the table to obtain closer values than can be obtained from the graph. The more important numerical values also may be given on the graph or chart if desirable.

Illustrations should be complete within themselves. The picture or graph, with its legend and any supplementary notes, should tell the story. Occasionally it may be necessary to depend upon the text for some detail that cannot be explained by the illustration or its title. Graphical analysis and pictorial views of data also are of benefit to the author. Hence it is a good procedure to prepare all charts and other illustrative material before the text is written. Tabular and graphical materials help the author understand numerical information and designs readily, and in the same light that the reader is apt to view the material.

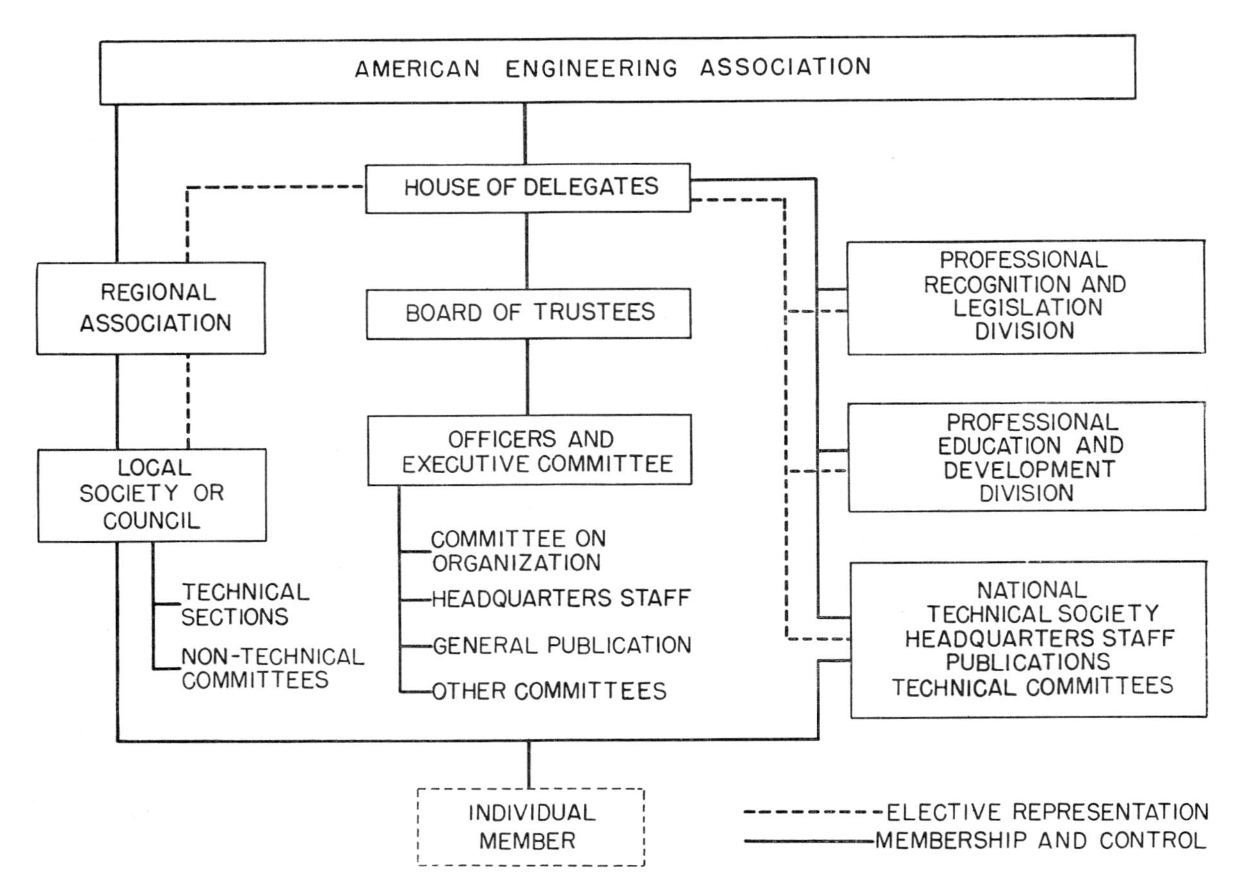

Fig. 7.3. Proposed organization of an American Engineering Association. —*Electrical Engineering*, pp. 496–501, May 1947.

Satisfactory weights of lines and lettering for organization charts.

SELECTION OF FORM OF ILLUSTRATION

Selection of the type of illustration depends upon its use in the report. Factors in this choice are: Whether the illustration will be placed on a page with text or on a separate page; whether originals will be used for all copies; or whether contact prints, reductions, or enlargements will be used. These decisions are of special importance for charts, graphs, or maps in order that the drafting can be completed to standards applicable to the method of presentation.

Size of Sheet

It is desirable to place all illustrations on the standard size of sheet used for the text of the report, usually 8½ by 11 or 8 by 10½ in., regardless of the size of the original photographs, charts, or drawings. Oversize material can be reduced photographically to the standard page size (Fig. 7.19) or folded to slightly less than standard size (Fig. 7.18). The size of the larger sheets is preplanned to accommodate the final folded arrangement.

Photographs and other small illustrations are glued or cemented to the standard sheet in such manner that they will not come loose or be separated from the sheet. When an aqueous glue is used, care should be taken not to wrinkle the sheet or the illustration. Glues and cements are now available which do not wrinkle the paper. Cements which evaporate and lose their adhesiveness are to be avoided. When care is taken, it is sufficient to make only the corners and edges secure. The black, triangular, glued corner mountings are not recommended because they are unattractive and do not prevent the illustration from being removed.

Charts, sketches, and diagrams may be made up on sheets of the size adopted for the report; this eliminates the need for mounting (Figs. 7.7 and 7.9). This plan is generally preferred, even for those illustrations to be enlarged or reduced photographically to correct sheet size.

Illustrations which cannot be reduced to satisfactory size and proportion for a single page of standard size may be made larger in one dimension. It is better to extend to the right by enlarging the 8½-in. dimension as much as is necessary, and then fold in as may be required (Fig. 7.18). Folding from both the right and the top is to be avoided whenever another means of obtaining an acceptable size is available. Original drawings which will not stand reduction, such as extensive maps and detailed plans, usually must be folded.

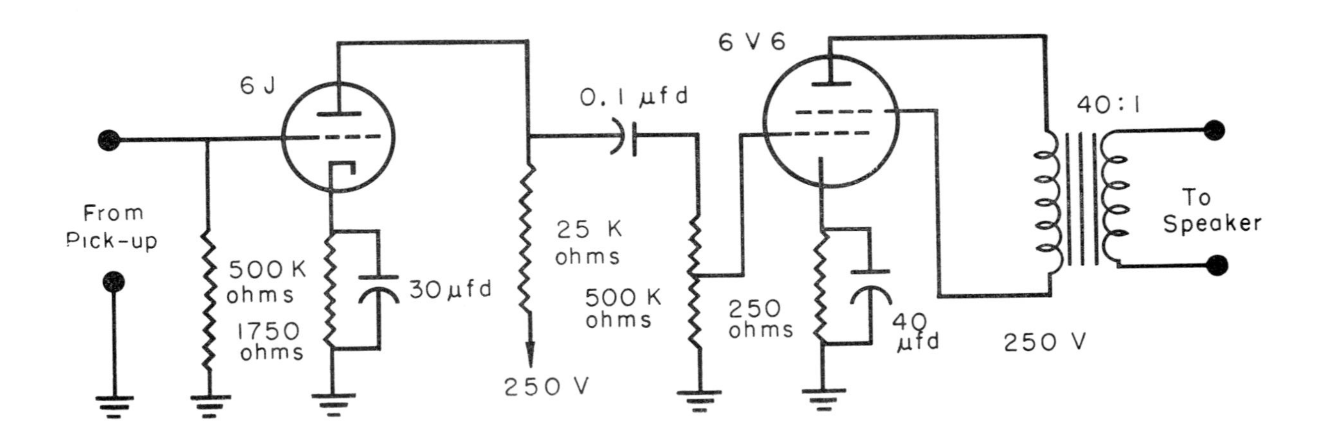

Fig. 7.4. Simple drawings, such as this amplifier circuit, may be drawn directly on pages of the report when only a few copies are wanted.

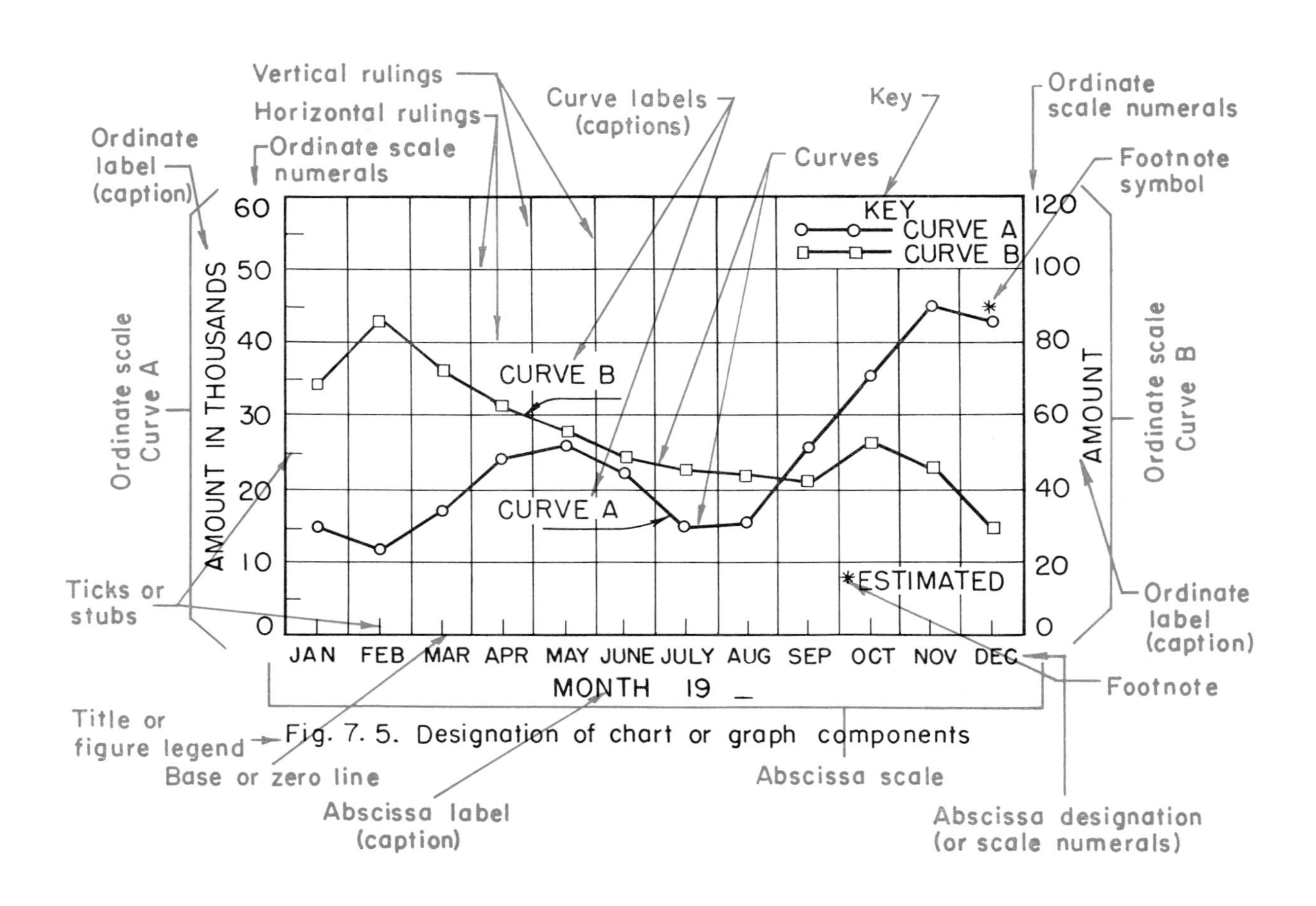

Fig. 7. 5. Designation of chart or graph components

Photographic Copies

Photographic processes, with or without reduction in size, are recommended for charts and graphs (1) when more than four copies of the report are to be prepared, and (2) when the illustration is such that the expense of drawing a number of original copies is greater than the cost of photographic reproduction. The reduction technique is also of advantage in handling of charts and drawings, because it is usually more convenient to draw them to a larger size than that which can be accommodated on the standard size of report paper (Figs. 7.3, 7.13, 7.14, 7.15, and 7.19).

An alternate process is to first draw the chart on standard graph paper (Figs. 7.6 and 7.7) and then so trace it that the required margins and layout may be provided on the contact prints made from the tracing (Figs. 7.8, 7.9, 7.10, and 7.18). Tracing the graph offers a low cost method of duplication and results in an improved product because the minor subdivisions of the grid, which do not print well from original graph paper, may be left off the tracing.

STANDARDS OF FORMAT

Layout of illustrations follows the same principles of design that apply to type pages (see page 81). Margins on pages bearing illustrations are the same as the margins on pages of type. The same principle applies to other format problems. Clearness to the reader is of first consideration, but if good standards of format and drafting are used, the illustration will be easily understood, provided that the wording and treatment of the technical subject are also handled clearly.

Page Layout

The desirable position for an illustration, whether alone or with text material, is slightly

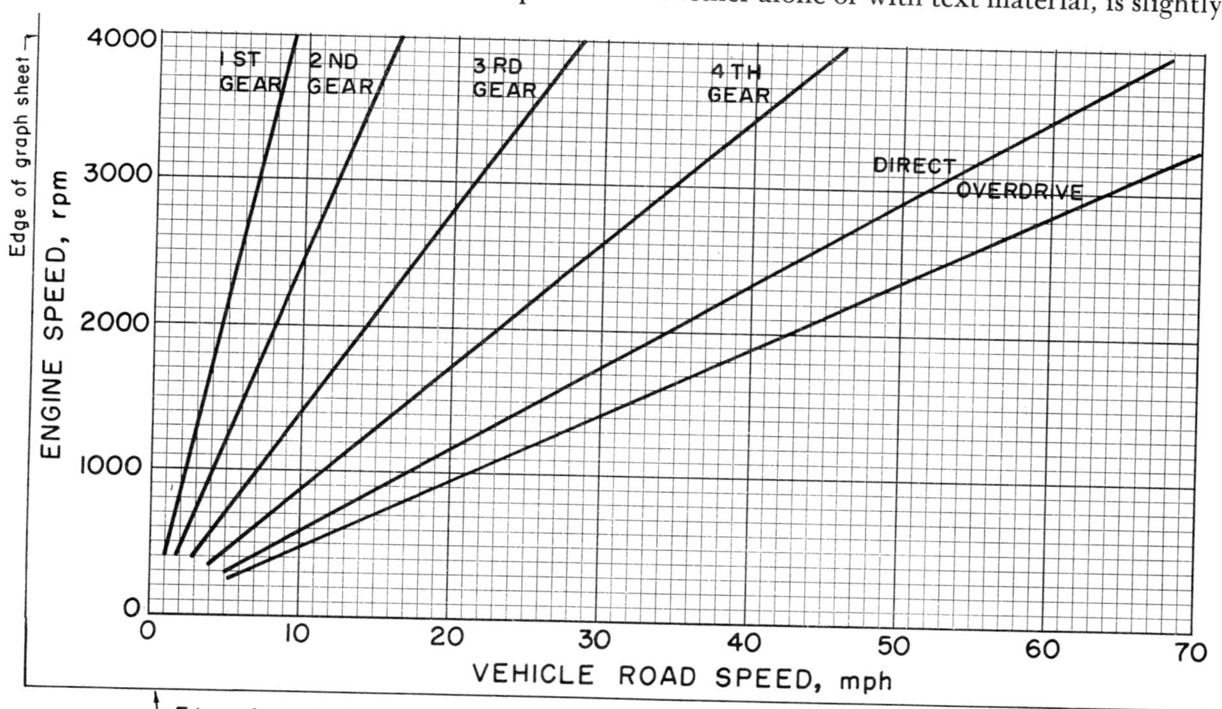

Fig. 7.6. Engine speed and road speed of an automobile engine. Undesirable crowding of left and bottom margins on commercial graph paper. Redraw as illustrated in Figs. 7.8 and 7.9.

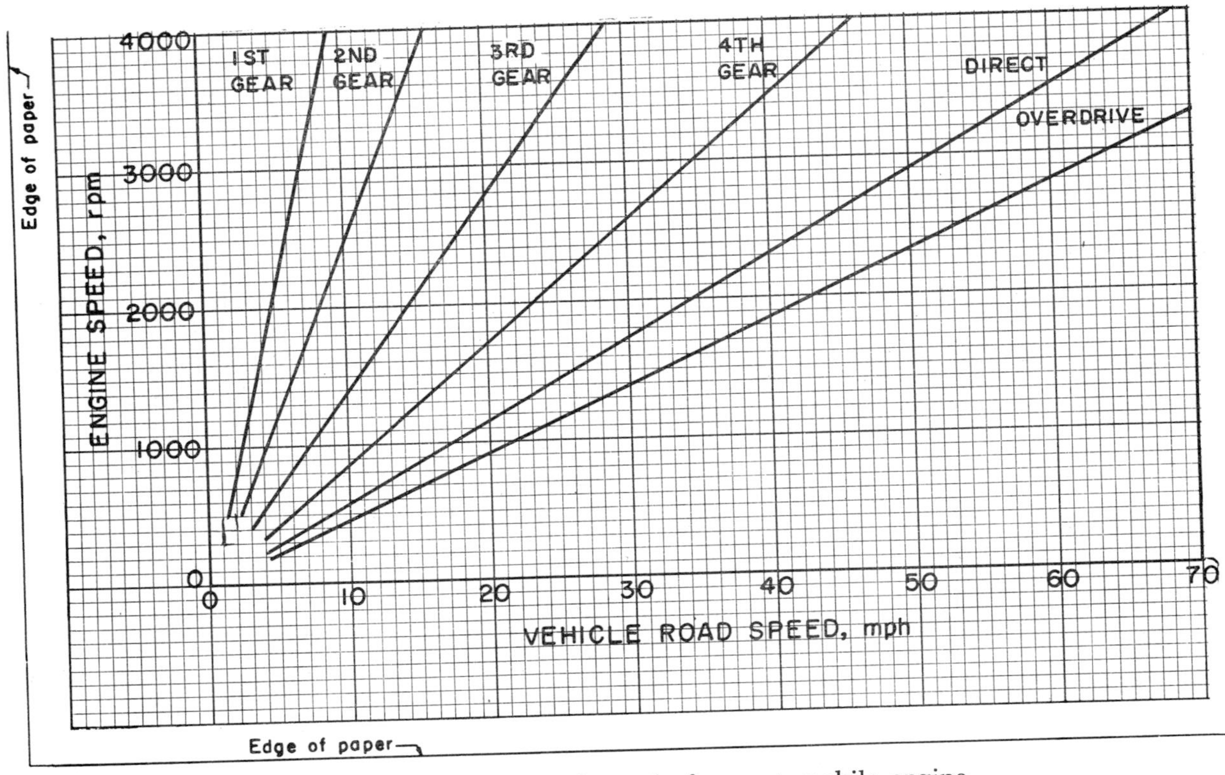

Fig. 7.7. Engine speed and road speed of an automobile engine.

Base lines are set in to gain proper left and bottom margins. This practice may be used when commercial graph paper has insufficient margins, though the preferred practice is to place the scales, labels, and legend outside the grid. Commercial graph paper frequently compels a choice between narrow margins or placing the scales within the grid. The least objectionable should be chosen, or the graph can be traced and printed as shown by Figs. 7.8 and 7.9.

above the center of the page. This would have the apparent center of mass fall about 2/5 the height of the sheet from the top edge, or such that the bottom margin is about 50 per cent greater than the top margin. Likewise, the photograph or chart should have a ratio of width to height of 0.71 or at least be between 0.67 and 0.77. This position and proportion hold whether the illustration is turned 90 deg. to the right (Fig. 7.19), or is upright on the page. Desirable proportions and positions are illustrated in Figs. 5.1 to 5.4 which show methods of designing the type page.

Left, top, side, and bottom margins should be the same on full page illustrations as they are on pages of text. Because most commercial graph papers have margins too narrow for labels and legends (Figs. 7.6 and 7.8), it is usually advisable to redraw or trace the charts to provide the proper margins (Figs. 7.8 and 7.9). Should the original graph paper be used in the final report, it is acceptable, although not the best practice, to set the base lines in from the edge of the grid area so that there is sufficient marginal space for the labels of the abscissa and ordinate and for the legend (Fig. 7.7).

All parts of a graph require proper labels or descriptions (Fig. 7.5). On charts and graphs the ordinate and abscissa labels contain both the name of the item shown and the unit in which the item is expressed (Figs. 7.7 and 7.9). These labels should be outside of the grid in clear margins. Within the boundary lines, each curve is given a label as necessary. The key and other necessary explanation is given in an appropriate space (Figs. 7.13, 7.14, 7.15, and 7.18). Each illustration should be complete so that the reader will understand it without referring to the text for explanations.

Footnotes are seldom needed with illustrations, but when used they may be placed within the illustration (Figs. 7.5 and 7.11), in the margins just above the title, or in the legend, whichever seems the most appropriate.

The title (legend) of the illustration should be placed below the illustration, following the pattern set by many book publishers. One reason for this practice is that the chart will not need to be redrawn if the report is to be issued in a printed edition. Also, this bottom position may be retained uniformly for all illustrations, whereas such uniform position is not possible within the area of the illustration itself, particularly for photographs and bar and column charts. The legend, consisting of the figure number and a title descriptive of the illustration, is placed about one blank line below the lowest portion of the illustration, and written in ordinary paragraph form, either with typewriter or with engineering lettering.

Drafting Standards

Excellence in drafting and graphic expression comes through the exercise of certain artistic principles — balance, harmony, unity, climax, and rhythm. Line widths and letter heights, width of rulings and outlines, shadings, and over-all proportions are important items that when skillfully combined produce a pleasing result. Large lettering and heavy lines direct the reader's eye away from the text or other parts of the illustration. Good illustrations blend with the text.

In the preparation of charts, graphs, maps and similar illustrations for reports, the desirable standard of workmanship is that of high-grade engineering drawing. Drafted parts of a report constitute a graphic language and,

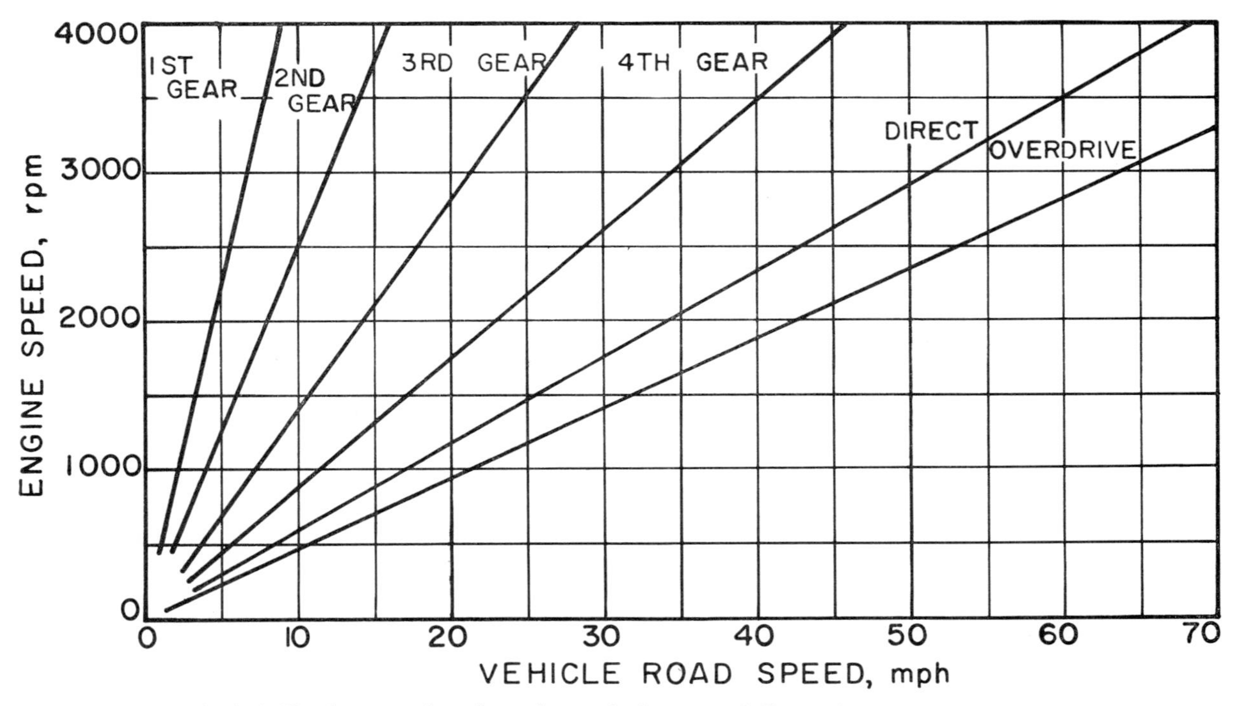

Fig. 7.8. Engine speed and road speed of automobile engine.

Plotting on commercial graph paper was traced, scales, labels, and legend placed outside grid area, ample margins provided.

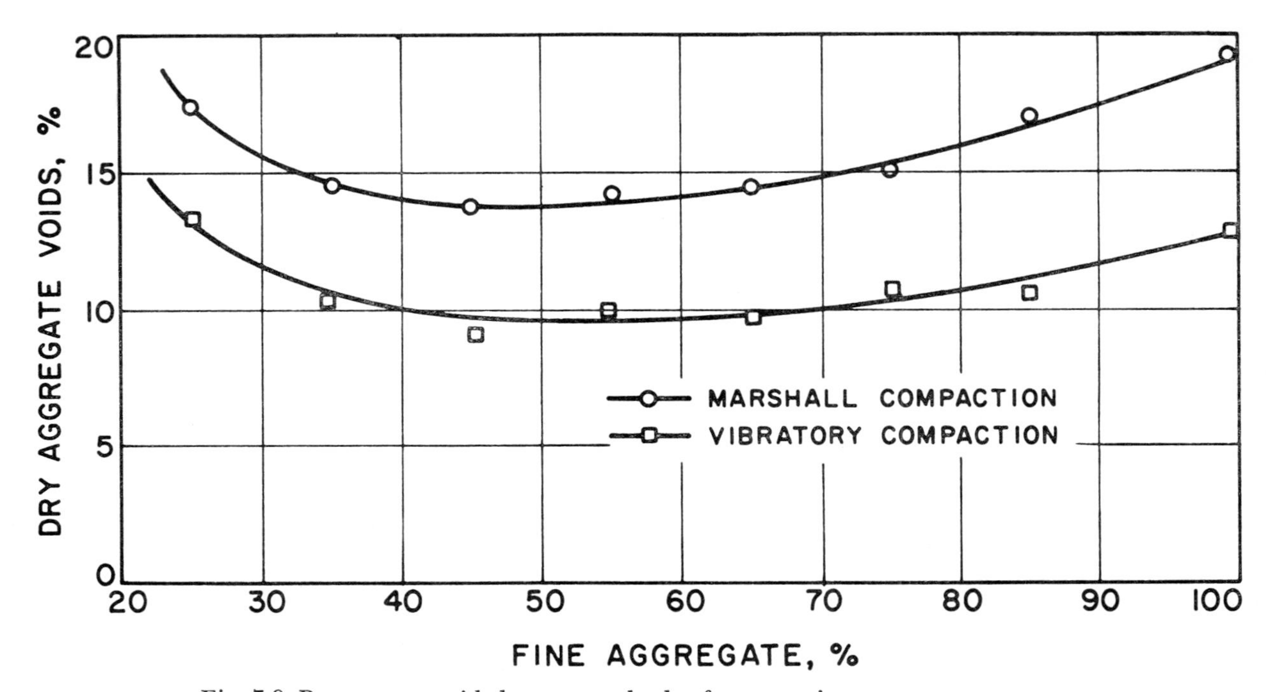

Fig. 7.9. Percentage voids by two methods of compacting aggregates.

Good margins, open grid, and broken grid at labels. Note curves drawn to but not through plotted points.

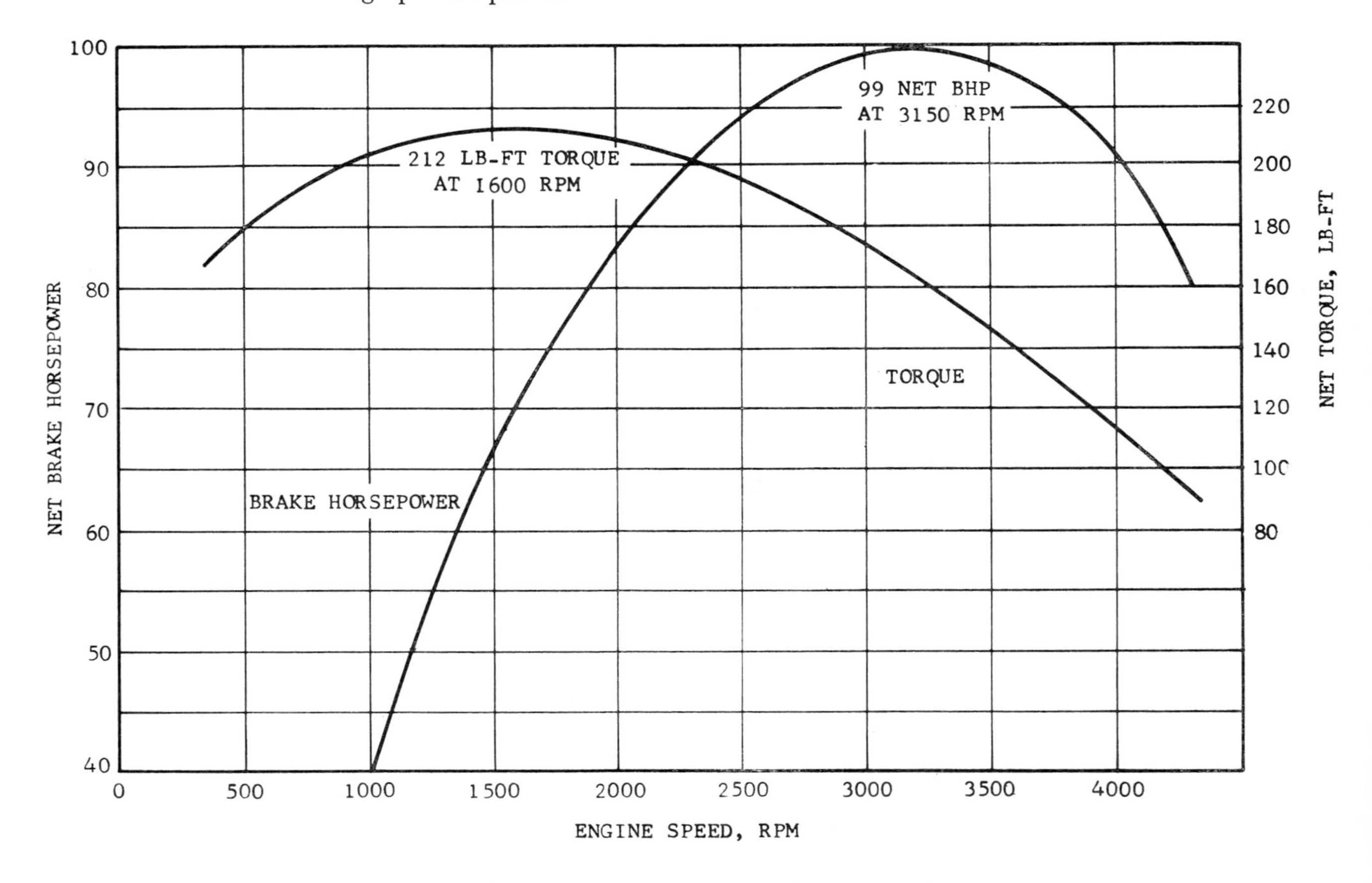

Fig. 7.10. Horsepower and torque of automobile engine.

Where appropriate and when desirable to save time in preparation, wording on charts may be typescript.

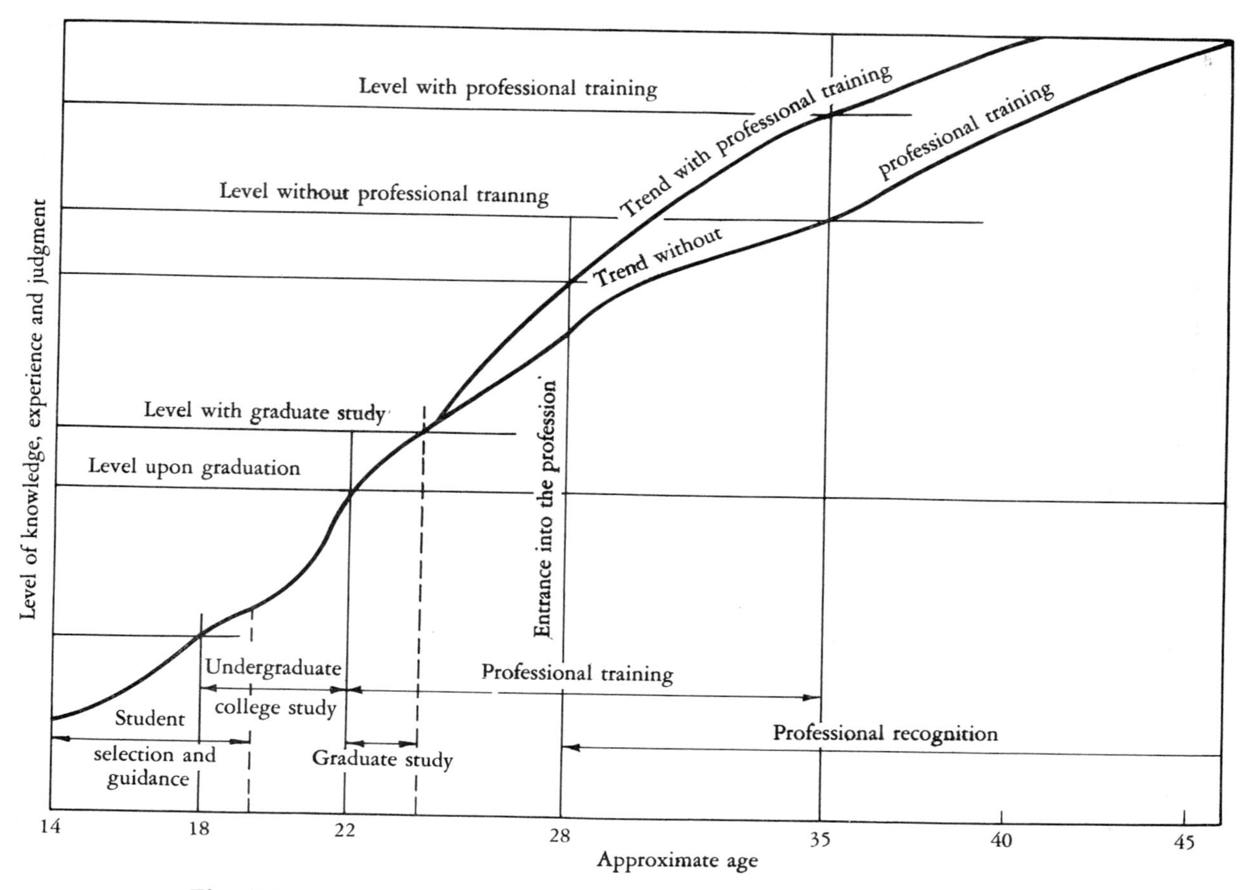

Fig. 7.11. Professional growth of the engineer. —Adapted from Fifteenth Anniversary Booklet, Engineers Council for Professional Development, June 1947.

For magazine and book work and for reports when the facilities are available, the wording for a chart may be set in printer's type and pasted on the original before it is photographed for reproduction.

as such, need to have definite powers of exact expression.

Although not all reports are ultimately reproduced in print, it is advisable to prepare illustrations on the basis that they may be used in a printing process. One reason for following this practice is that the standards for printing require original copy suitable for the typewritten report, either directly or through photographic reproduction. Good illustrations harmonize with the printed page; harmony is achieved through the grayness of tone to match that of the type and from lines and lettering of a size and weight about equal to that of the printer's type used. Likewise, illustrations in typewritten reports can be of such design that they harmonize with the general format of typescript.

If illustrations are to be duplicated they should be drawn with the limitations of the duplicating process in mind.

Dimensions, scales, layout, and lettering should be chosen to present the information to the best advantage. If photographic reduction is to be used, it is essential to draw all parts of the original sufficiently large so that after reduction each item is easily read.

Pleasing results with all forms of graphs,

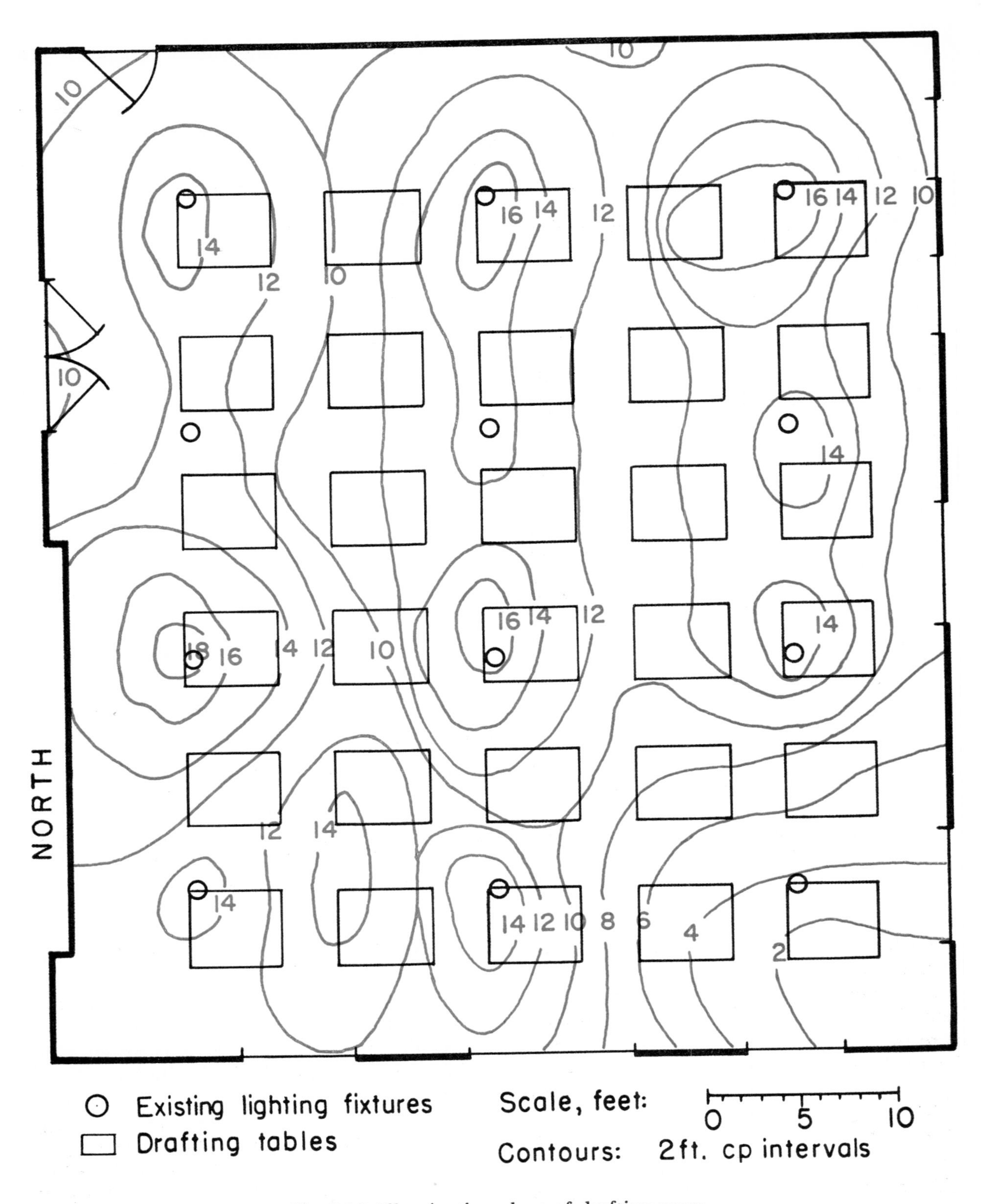

Fig. 7.12. Illumination chart of drafting room.

Contours and other superimposed lines are effective when drawn in color to contrast with the base drawings.

charts, and drawings are to be had from contrasting weights of lines according to their importance. Table 7.1 shows desirable widths of lines and heights of letters for ordinary graphical presentations for reports. Accuracy is sacrificed and spottiness is produced by heavy lines. Lightness of tone is to be desired in preference to heaviness of lines and lettering.

When drawing curve, bar or column charts, the scales should be chosen on the basis of three principles. First, the vertical and horizontal scales should be such that the slope of the curve is about 45 deg. Curves that are either steep or flat do not have the pleasing appearance of a 45-deg. slope. Second, the scales need to be chosen so they can be read to the accuracy demanded by the nature and use of the chart. In a population graph, for instance, there is ordinarily no need to use a scale that will permit reading the population to the nearest 100. Third, the chart should be kept to a manageable size in each dimension consistent with the data presented. Folded sheets may be used to avoid reductions of such smallness that reading of the chart becomes difficult. On the other hand, desirable scales permit satisfactory use of the chart without undue distortion, either condensed or extended. Judgment is the guide in this respect. No general rule can be stated.

The choice of scales is controlled to some extent by proportions of width to height of chart. Aesthetic proportions are those of about 5 to 7, or the root-two proportion of 1:1.41. Tall and narrow, wide and low, or square proportioned figures are not pleasing to the eye.

For the grids of curve charts, the ordinate and abscissa lines should form rectangles. Grid lines on the final copy should be not closer than about 3/16 in. Each second, fifth, tenth, or other suitable interval line should be slightly heavier than the other grid lines to facilitate reading. Where smooth curves are to be drawn through observed points, it is customary to show the plotted observations.

Good lettering is a wise combination of letter height and width as well as spacing. The ratio of width to height and the spacing of letters generally used is that followed in the printing trade and in standards of display drafting. The width of the stems of lettering should be about 1/10 to 1/15 of the letter height. All lettering should be nonserif, and well-rounded with firm, sharp beginning strokes. Hair lines and tapered stems are undesirable. The openings in letters such as A, B, e, and s, should be large and the spacing between letters tend to the open rather than to the tight. Uniformity in height, slope, weight, and style is the essential requirement for good lettering.

Lettering on illustrations may be either freehand or mechanical. Freehand, when done by a skilled draftsman, is more versatile because any size, weight, and spacing can be used.

In some printed works, the graphs are prepared for printing by setting all labels and titles in type, then pasting prints of them at the proper positions on the line work (Fig. 7.11). This process is used extensively in map production.

Where space permits, the labels and descriptive wording on a chart or graph should be placed in horizontal position (Fig. 7.9). This facilitates reading and produces an orderly appearance of the completed drawing.

Cross hatching is the standard method of indicating sectional views in working drawings (Fig. 7.2). Surface, column, and bar charts and diagrams use both cross hatching and shading in black or color to distinguish parts or areas of the illustration (Figs. 7.16, 7.17, 7.39, 7.43, 7.44, 7.47, and 7.48).

For ordinary black and white work, excellent results are obtained by cross hatching in accordance with engineering drawing practice. Various degrees of shading are accomplished by varying the spacing and weights of the lines of cross hatching (Figs. 7.16, 7.42, 7.43, and 7.47), or by the use of various densities of dots (Fig. 7.44). Transparent material available in a variety of designs and densities,

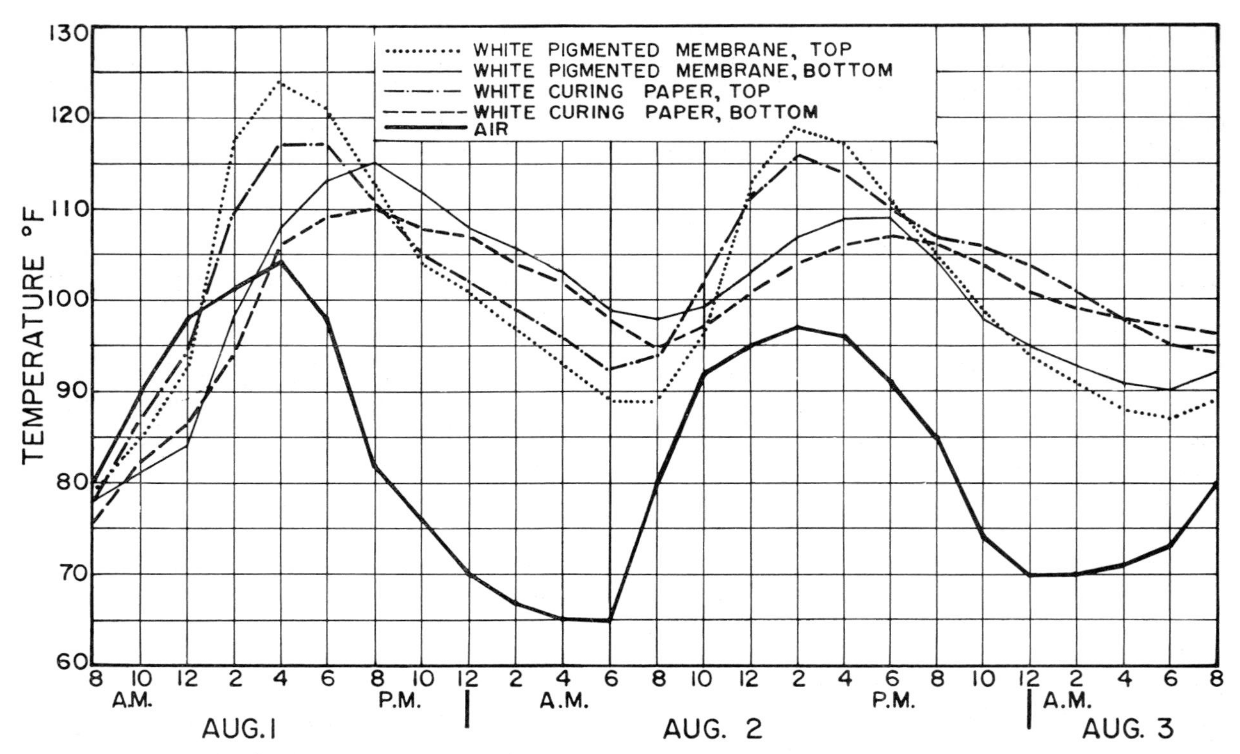

Fig. 7.13. Comparison of temperatures and two methods of curing concrete pavement.

Use of broken lines to distinguish the curves of a group.

may be cut to desired shape and pasted to the chart (Figs. 7.16, 7.39, 7.40, and 7.44). Color effects are produced by hand tinting or by line work (Figs. 7.12, 7.15, and 7.17).

DRAWING FOR PHOTOGRAPHIC REDUCTION AND REPRODUCTION

Most printed charts and drawings are reduced to 20 to 80 per cent of the size of the original. Thus care must be taken to draw the originals so they will be legible when reduced to the printed size. Too frequently one sees reproductions which are far from satisfactory because they are out of harmony with the printed page, spotty from heavy lines and large lettering, or illegible because of minute lettering. These objectionable features are avoided by predetermining first the final printed dimensions and second, the size of lettering and width of lines suited to these dimensions. Each feature of the original chart is then drawn correspondingly larger in accordance with the planned reduction ratio.

Many excellent working drawings and maps are practically worthless when reduced to half the original size because the lettering becomes too small to read and certain details run together or blot out. All drawings to be reduced in size need to be drawn with more openness, more roundedness, and more clearness than is required in ordinary engineering drawing. The same principles of balance, harmony, contrast, emphasis, and clearness should prevail.

Reading material, provided it is of a clean Gothic type of letter, is legible when the ratio of the height of letter to the distance from the reading page to the eye is about 1:250. With good vision, good lighting, and excellent type of letter a ratio of 1:350 is acceptable, but with ordinary freehand lettering a ratio of 1:200 is preferred.

The normal reading distance is about 15 to 18 in. Using a ratio of 1:250, the minimum height of capital letter which should be used for ordinary reading of charts is 15/250 or 0.06 in. This is smaller than elite typewriter type and the 10- or 11-point type commonly used in text books. In order to harmonize with the printed page, 0.06-in. high lettering is about correct, with 0.05 in. a minimum and 0.08 in. a maximum.

Various combinations of height of letter and width of stem are shown in Figs. 7.20 to 7.31. A study of these figures will show the favorable and unfavorable sizes of lettering for different reductions.

The single stroke letter used in engineering drawing is a letter of good legibility (Figs. 7.26 to 7.31). The sans-serif block type of letter used in the Leroy and Wrico lettering sets is also good (Figs. 7.20 to 7.25). Proper width of letter to use is that generally used in engineering drawing and in printing. The condensed letter is to be avoided. Rather than expanded letters, slightly more space may be used between letters.

Lettering which is ¼ to ½ in. high is legible when the thickness of the stem of the letter is as great as one-eighth of the height

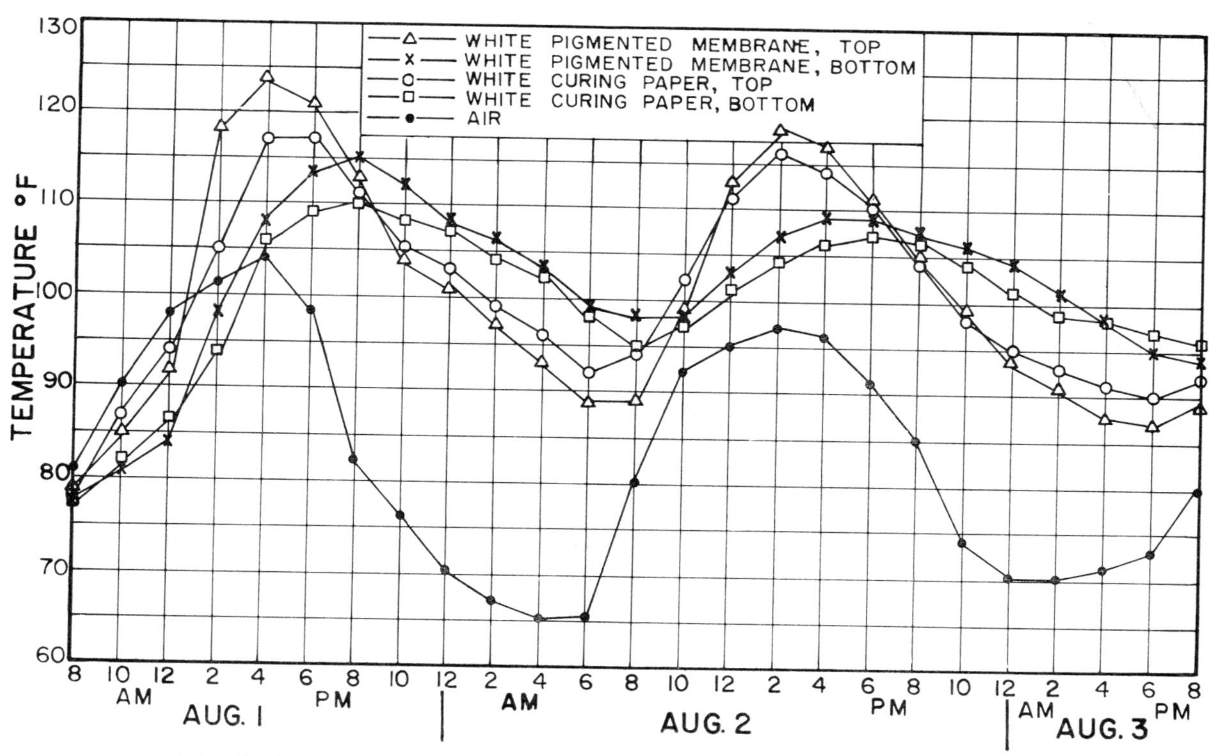

Fig. 7.14. Comparison of temperatures and two methods of curing concrete pavement.

Use of symbols to distinguish curves of a group.

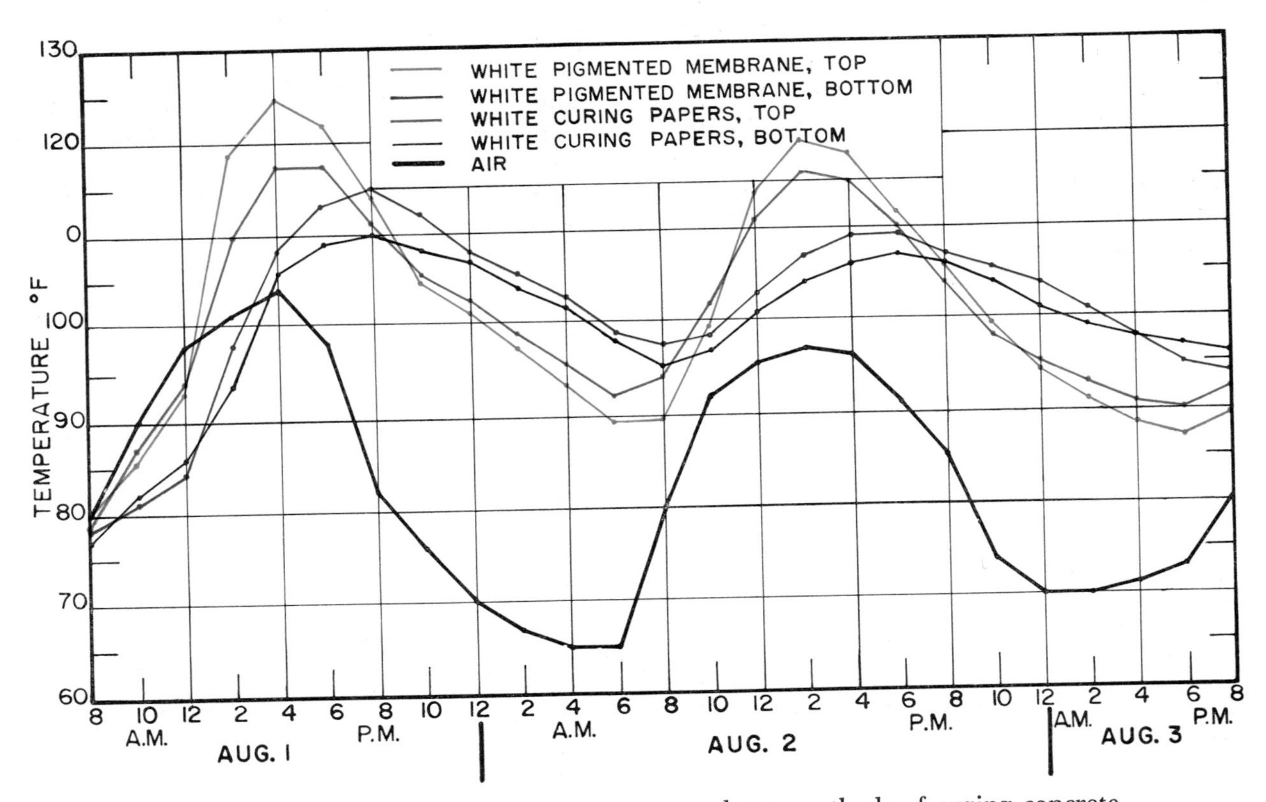

Fig. 7.15. Comparison of temperatures and two methods of curing concrete pavement.

Use of color to distinguish the curves of a group.

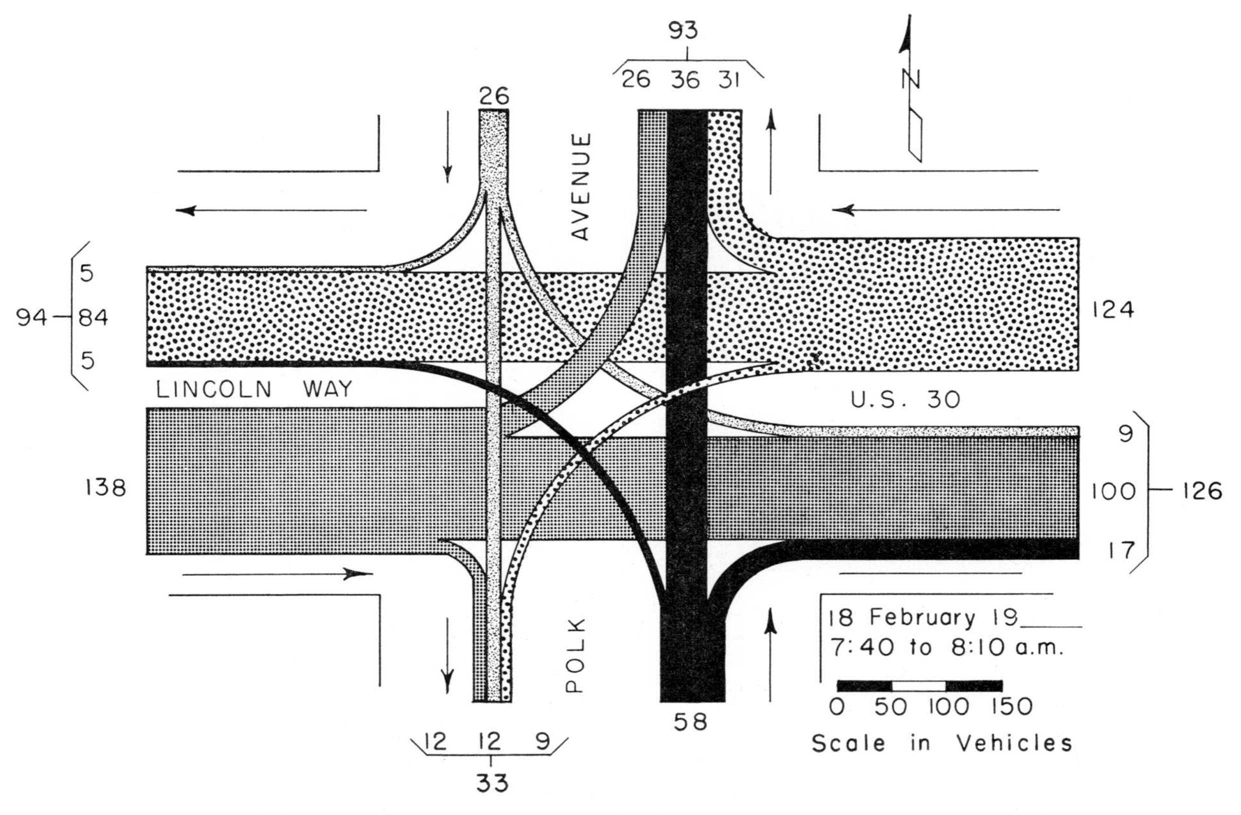

Fig. 7.16. Morning rush hour traffic flow at intersection of Lincoln Way and Polk Avenue.

Various shadings or cross hatchings may be used to distinguish areas or bands when color is not available.

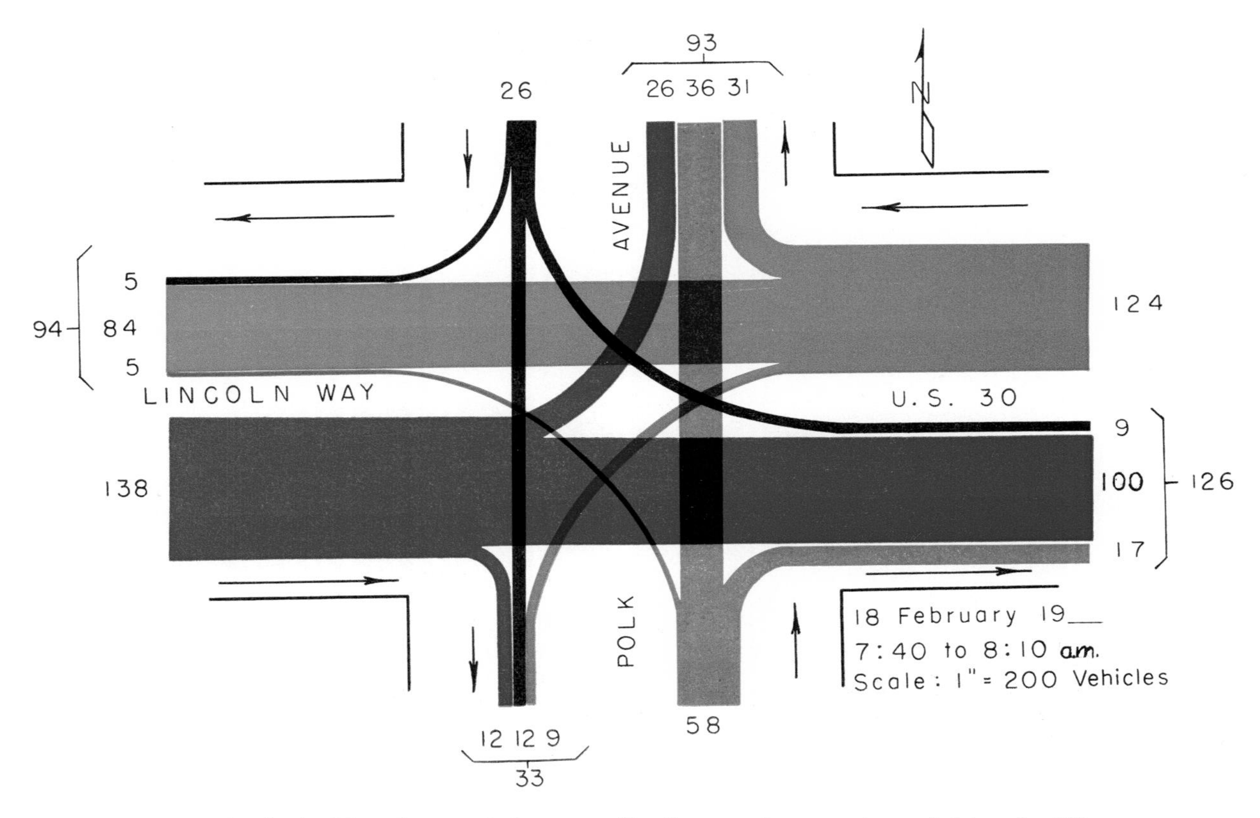

Fig. 7.17. Morning rush hour traffic flow at intersection of Lincoln Way and Polk Avenue.

Colored areas are an appropriate device by which to show traffic flows and similar diagrams.

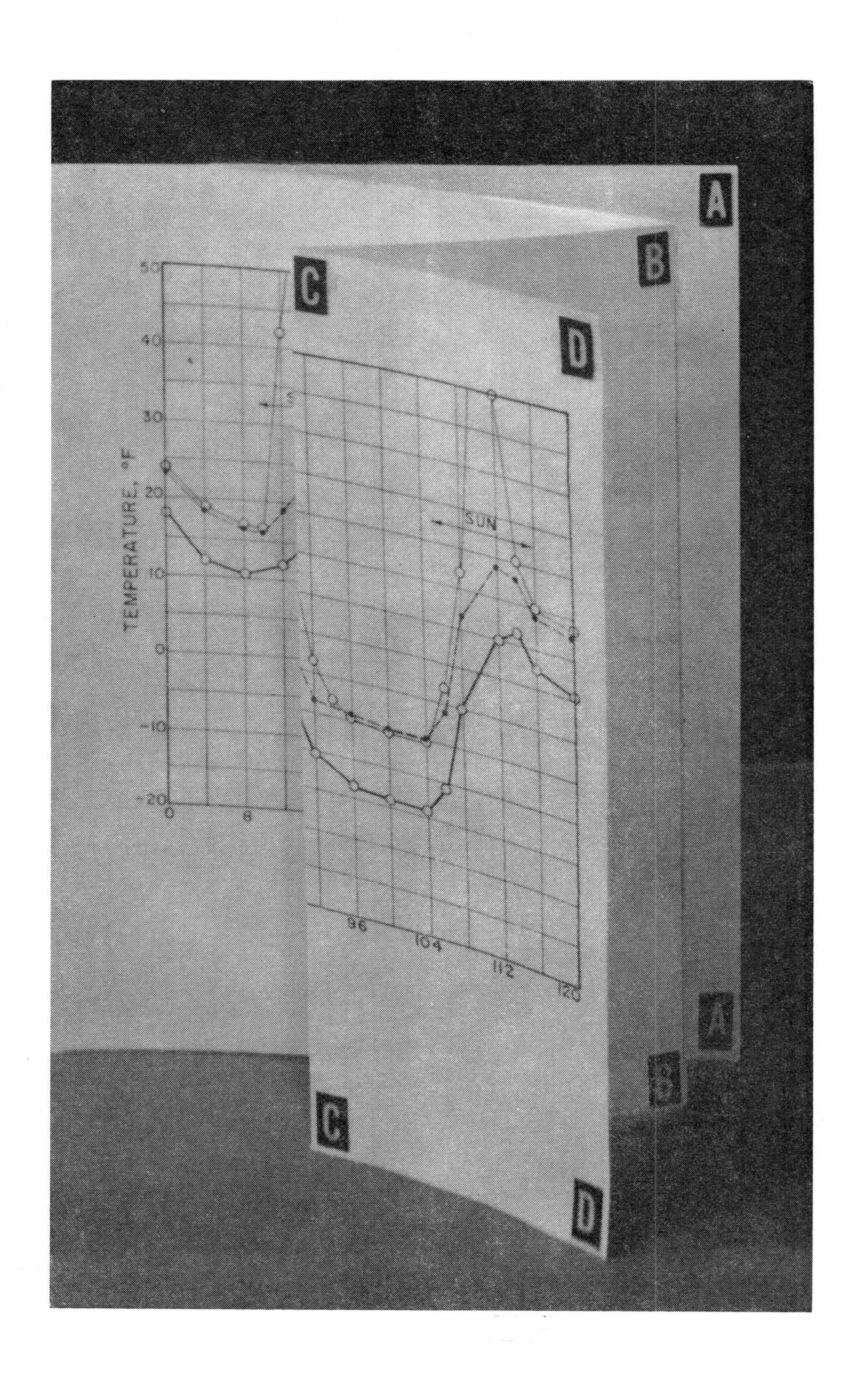
A
B
C
D
TEMPERATURE, °F
SUN
50
40
30
20
10
0
-10
-20
0
8
96
104
112
120
A
B
C
D

Fig. 7.18. Tables and figures larger than page size, when it is not feasible to photographically reduce them in dimension (see Fig. 7.19), may be folded. First fold *BB* is about ¼ inch inside the edge *AA* of sheets not folded, to allow for trim and to prevent wear of the folded edge. Second fold *CC* is short of the margin so that the binding will not hold down the folded edge, *CC*. Edge *DD* is held ½ inch to left of fold *BB* so that fingers can grasp edge *DD* easily to unfold sheet outward to right.

←

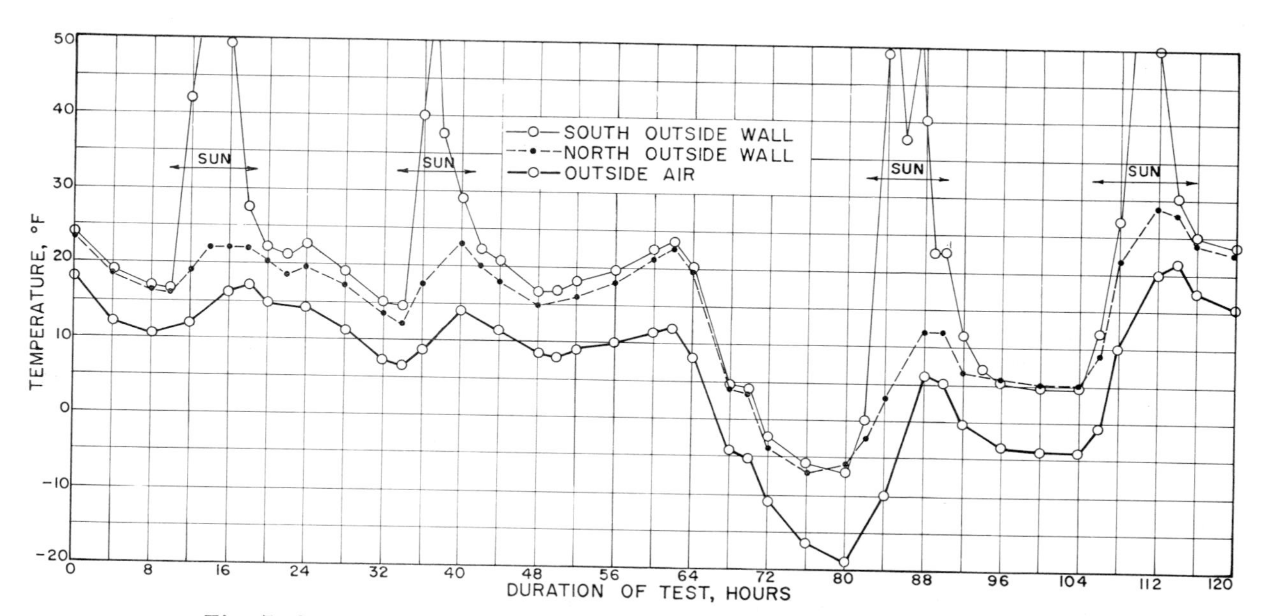

Fig. 7.19. Temperatures on outside walls of residence compared to air temperature.

Tables and figures larger than page size may be reduced in dimensions by some photographic process. When a process of reduction is available, reducing in size is preferable to folding. The reduction in this figure is to 40 per cent of original dimensions. See Fig. 7.18 for method of folding.

TABLE 7.1. SIZE OF LINES, RULES, CURVES, AND LETTERING ON CHARTS AND DRAWINGS PREPARED FOR REPRODUCTION

(One point is 0.013837 or approximately 1/72 in.)

Component of chart or drawing	Desirable size when printed		Size of original for the reductions indicated					
			One-third		One-half		Two-thirds	
	Points	Inches	Points	Inches	Points	Inches	Points	Inches
Principal or single curve	1 1/8	0.016	1 11/16	0.023	2 1/4	0.031	3 3/8	0.047
Major curves of group	7/8	.012	1 5/16	.018	1 3/4	.024	2 5/8	036
Minor curves of group	3/4	.010	1 1/8	.016	1 1/2	.021	2 1/4	031
Reference or base lines	1/2	.007	3/4	.010	1	.014	1 1/2	.021
Major rulings of grid	3/8	.005	9/16	.008	3/4	.010	1 1/8	.016
Minor rulings of grid	1/4	.004	3/8	.005	1/2	.007	3/4	.010
Ticks	1/4	.004	3/8	.005	1/2	.007	3/4	.010
Box enclosures within grid	3/8	.005	9/16	.008	3/4	.010	1 1/8	.016
Indicators, pointers, leaders	1/4	.004	3/8	.005	1/2	.007	3/4	.010
Outline of columns and bars	3/4	.010	1 1/8	.016	1 1/2	.021	2 1/4	.031
Plotted points, line width	1/4	.004	3/8	.005	1/2	.007	3/4	.010
Circle, diameter	---	.050	---	.075	---	.100	---	.150
Solid dot, diameter	---	.045	---	.068	---	.090	---	.135
Square, side	---	.045	---	.068	---	.090	---	.135
Triangle, side	---	.060	---	.090	---	.120	---	.180
Working drawings								
Outlines	1	.014	1 1/2	.021	2 1/2	.035	3 3/4	.052
Hidden lines	3/4	.010	1 1/8	.016	1 1/2	.021	2 1/4	.031
Cross hatching	3/8	.005	9/16	.008	3/4	.010	1 1/8	.016
Center and dimension lines	1/4	.004	3/8	.005	1/2	.007	3/4	.010
Turned section arrow lines	1 1/2	.021	2 1/4	.031	3	.042	4 1/2	.062
Capital letter height for labels of scales and curves	---	.060	---	.090	---	.120	---	.175
Capital letter height, main heads with subheads	---	.080	---	.120	---	.160	---	.240
Stem width of letters, 1/12 to 1/14 of height	3/8	0.005	9/16	0.008	3/4	0.009	1 1/8	0.013

(Fig. 7.20). As the lettering is reduced in height this ratio should be likewise reduced if the same legibility is to be retained. For lettering only 0.06 in. high the ratio of stem thickness to height of capitals should be about 1:14 if good legibility is to be had (Figs. 7.20 to 7.31). Lettering about ⅛ to ¼ in. high is more convenient to do than larger or smaller sizes, so corresponding reductions of one-third to two-thirds will usually produce over-all satisfactory illustrations when reduced.

Curves, grids, outlines, and other rulings on drawings or charts are made to perform their function not by making the main lines heavy but by proper contrast in thickness of the lines performing different functions. A light over-all tone of a drawing is far more effective than is a heavy tone. The light lines permit greater accuracy in reading the drawing and the drawing as a whole blends well with the printed page. Table 7.1 gives the recommended sizes of lines for drafted illustrations for reductions of one-third, one-half, and two-thirds; specimens of these lines are given in Fig. 7.26.

THIS IS A .013 PEN with a 120 guide AZ
THIS IS A .017 PEN with a 120 guide Y

THIS IS A .013 PEN with a 140 guide
THIS IS A .017 PEN with a 140 guide
THIS IS A .021 PEN with a 140 guide ABCDEFG

THIS IS A .013 PEN WITH AN 80 GUIDE
THIS IS A .017 PEN WITH AN 80 GUIDE
THIS IS A .013 PEN WITH A 100 GUIDE
THIS IS A .017 PEN WITH A 100 GUIDE

THIS IS A .013 PEN WITH A 175 GUIDE QR
THIS IS A .017 PEN WITH A 175 GUIDE XY
THIS IS A .021 PEN WITH A 175 GUIDE CK

THIS IS A .013 PEN with a 200 guide O
THIS IS A .017 PEN with a 200 guide
THIS IS A .021 PEN with a 200 guide
THIS IS A .026 PEN with a 200 guide

LEROY PEN	SIZE IN.
00	0.013
0	.017
1	.021
2	.026
3	.035
4	.043
5	.055
6	.067

THIS IS A .017 PEN with a 240 guide rst
THIS IS A .026 PEN with a 240 guide
THIS IS A .035 PEN with a 240 guide

THIS IS A .017 PEN with a 290 guide
THIS IS A .021 PEN with a 290 guide
THIS IS A .026 PEN with a 290 guide
THIS IS A .035 PEN with a 290 guide

.021 PEN WITH A 350 guide %
.026 PEN WITH A 350 guide
.035 PEN WITH A 350 guide
.043 PEN WITH A 350 guide

Fig. 7.20. Actual size reproduction of original lettering with lettering pens and guides. Sizes given are in thousandths of an inch. Compare this reproduction with its reductions in Figs. 7.21 to 7.25.

THIS IS A .013 PEN with a 120 guide AZ
THIS IS A .017 PEN with a 120 guide Y
THIS IS A .013 PEN with a 140 guide
THIS IS A .017 PEN with a 140 guide
THIS IS A .021 PEN with a 140 guide ABCDEFG

THIS IS A .013 PEN WITH AN 80 GUIDE
THIS IS A .017 PEN WITH AN 80 GUIDE
THIS IS A .013 PEN WITH A 100 GUIDE
THIS IS A .017 PEN WITH A 100 GUIDE

THIS IS A .013 PEN WITH A 175 GUIDE QR
THIS IS A .017 PEN WITH A 175 GUIDE XY
THIS IS A .021 PEN WITH A 175 GUIDE CK
THIS IS A .013 PEN with a 200 guide O
THIS IS A .017 PEN with a 200 guide
THIS IS A .021 PEN with a 200 guide
THIS IS A .026 PEN with a 200 guide

LEROY PEN	SIZE IN.
00	0.013
0	.017
1	.021
2	.026
3	.035
4	.043
5	.055
6	.067

THIS IS A .017 PEN with a 240 guide rst
THIS IS A .026 PEN with a 240 guide
THIS IS A .035 PEN with a 240 guide

THIS IS A .017 PEN with a 290 guide
THIS IS A .021 PEN with a 290 guide
THIS IS A .026 PEN with a 290 guide
THIS IS A .035 PEN with a 290 guide

.021 PEN WITH A 350 guide %
.026 PEN WITH A 350 guide
.035 PEN WITH A 350 guide
.043 PEN WITH A 350 guide

Fig. 7.21. Reduced one-fourth.

THIS IS A .013 PEN with a 120 guide AZ
THIS IS A .017 PEN with a 120 guide Y
THIS IS A .013 PEN with a 140 guide
THIS IS A .017 PEN with a 140 guide
THIS IS A .021 PEN with a 140 guide ABCDEFG

THIS IS A .013 PEN WITH AN 80 GUIDE
THIS IS A .017 PEN WITH AN 80 GUIDE
THIS IS A .013 PEN WITH A 100 GUIDE
THIS IS A .017 PEN WITH A 100 GUIDE

THIS IS A .013 PEN WITH A 175 GUIDE QR
THIS IS A .017 PEN WITH A 175 GUIDE XY
THIS IS A .021 PEN WITH A 175 GUIDE CK

THIS IS A .013 PEN with a 200 guide O
THIS IS A .017 PEN with a 200 guide
THIS IS A .021 PEN with a 200 guide
THIS IS A .026 PEN with a 200 guide

LEROY PEN	SIZE IN.
00	0.013
0	.017
1	.021
2	.026
3	.035
4	.043
5	.055
6	.067

THIS IS A .017 PEN with a 240 guide rst
THIS IS A .026 PEN with a 240 guide
THIS IS A .035 PEN with a 240 guide

THIS IS A .017 PEN with a 290 guide
THIS IS A .021 PEN with a 290 guide
THIS IS A .026 PEN with a 290 guide
THIS IS A .035 PEN with a 290 guide

.021 PEN WITH A 350 guide %
.026 PEN WITH A 350 guide
.035 PEN WITH A 350 guide
.043 PEN WITH A 350 guide

Fig. 7.22. Reduced one-third.

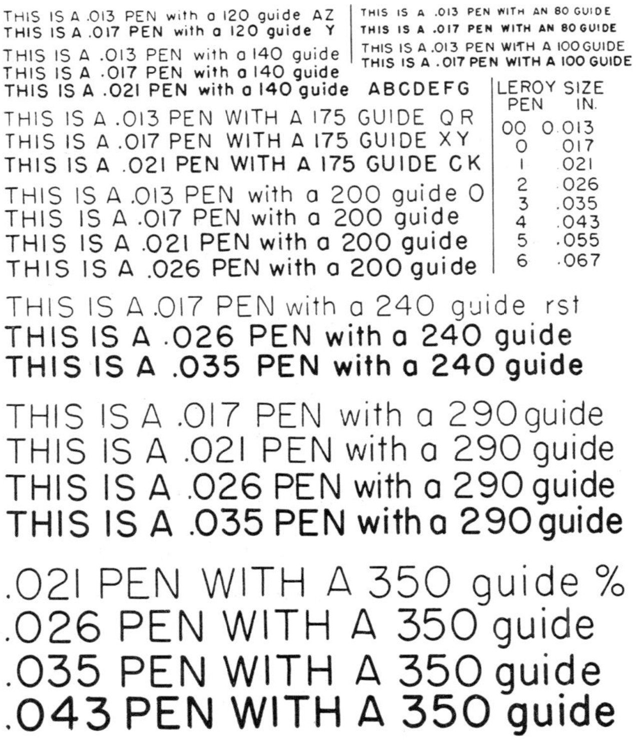

THIS IS A .013 PEN with a 120 guide AZ
THIS IS A .017 PEN with a 120 guide Y
THIS IS A .013 PEN with a 140 guide
THIS IS A .017 PEN with a 140 guide
THIS IS A .021 PEN with a 140 guide ABCDEFG

THIS IS A .013 PEN WITH AN 80 GUIDE
THIS IS A .017 PEN WITH AN 80 GUIDE
THIS IS A .013 PEN WITH A 100 GUIDE
THIS IS A .017 PEN WITH A 100 GUIDE

THIS IS A .013 PEN WITH A 175 GUIDE QR
THIS IS A .017 PEN WITH A 175 GUIDE XY
THIS IS A .021 PEN WITH A 175 GUIDE CK
THIS IS A .013 PEN with a 200 guide O
THIS IS A .017 PEN with a 200 guide
THIS IS A .021 PEN with a 200 guide
THIS IS A .026 PEN with a 200 guide

LEROY PEN	SIZE IN.
00	0.013
0	.017
1	.021
2	.026
3	.035
4	.043
5	.055
6	.067

THIS IS A .017 PEN with a 240 guide rst
THIS IS A .026 PEN with a 240 guide
THIS IS A .035 PEN with a 240 guide

THIS IS A .017 PEN with a 290 guide
THIS IS A .021 PEN with a 290 guide
THIS IS A .026 PEN with a 290 guide
THIS IS A .035 PEN with a 290 guide

.021 PEN WITH A 350 guide %
.026 PEN WITH A 350 guide
.035 PEN WITH A 350 guide
.043 PEN WITH A 350 guide

Fig. 7.23. Reduced one-half.

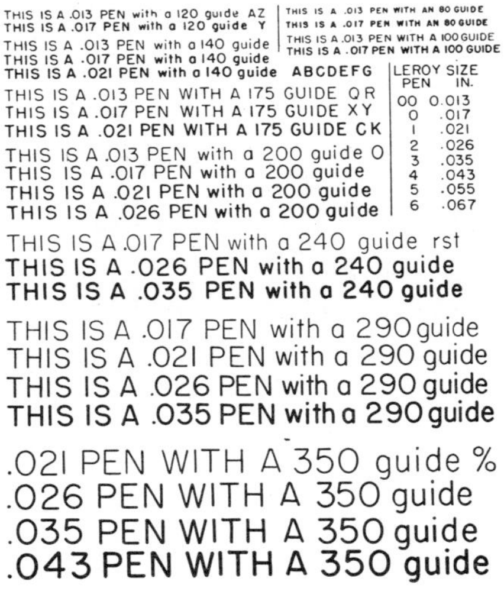

THIS IS A .013 PEN with a 120 guide AZ
THIS IS A .017 PEN with a 120 guide Y
THIS IS A .013 PEN with a 140 guide
THIS IS A .017 PEN with a 140 guide
THIS IS A .021 PEN with a 140 guide ABCDEFG
THIS IS A .013 PEN WITH AN 80 GUIDE
THIS IS A .017 PEN WITH AN 80 GUIDE
THIS IS A .013 PEN WITH A 100 GUIDE
THIS IS A .017 PEN WITH A 100 GUIDE
THIS IS A .013 PEN WITH A 175 GUIDE QR
THIS IS A .017 PEN WITH A 175 GUIDE XY
THIS IS A .021 PEN WITH A 175 GUIDE CK
THIS IS A .013 PEN with a 200 guide O
THIS IS A .017 PEN with a 200 guide
THIS IS A .021 PEN with a 200 guide
THIS IS A .026 PEN with a 200 guide
LEROY SIZE PEN IN. 00 0.013 0 .017 1 .021 2 .026 3 .035 4 .043 5 .055 6 .067
THIS IS A .017 PEN with a 240 guide rst
THIS IS A .026 PEN with a 240 guide
THIS IS A .035 PEN with a 240 guide
THIS IS A .017 PEN with a 290 guide
THIS IS A .021 PEN with a 290 guide
THIS IS A .026 PEN with a 290 guide
THIS IS A .035 PEN with a 290 guide
.021 PEN WITH A 350 guide %
.026 PEN WITH A 350 guide
.035 PEN WITH A 350 guide
.043 PEN WITH A 350 guide

Fig. 7.24. Reduced two-thirds.

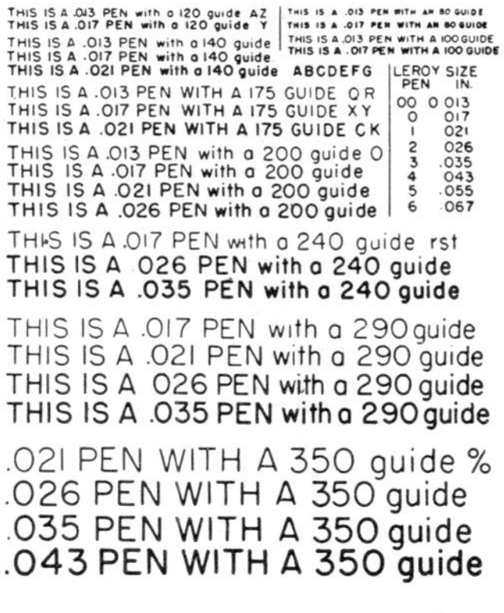

THIS IS A .013 PEN with a 120 guide AZ
THIS IS A .017 PEN with a 120 guide Y
THIS IS A .013 PEN with a 140 guide
THIS IS A .017 PEN with a 140 guide
THIS IS A .021 PEN with a 140 guide ABCDEFG
THIS IS A .013 PEN WITH AN 80 GUIDE
THIS IS A .017 PEN WITH AN 80 GUIDE
THIS IS A .013 PEN WITH A 100 GUIDE
THIS IS A .017 PEN WITH A 100 GUIDE
THIS IS A .013 PEN WITH A 175 GUIDE QR
THIS IS A .017 PEN WITH A 175 GUIDE XY
THIS IS A .021 PEN WITH A 175 GUIDE CK
THIS IS A .013 PEN with a 200 guide O
THIS IS A .017 PEN with a 200 guide
THIS IS A .021 PEN with a 200 guide
THIS IS A .026 PEN with a 200 guide
LEROY SIZE PEN IN. 00 0.013 0 .017 1 .021 2 .026 3 .035 4 .043 5 .055 6 .067
THIS IS A .017 PEN with a 240 guide rst
THIS IS A .026 PEN with a 240 guide
THIS IS A .035 PEN with a 240 guide
THIS IS A .017 PEN with a 290 guide
THIS IS A .021 PEN with a 290 guide
THIS IS A .026 PEN with a 290 guide
THIS IS A .035 PEN with a 290 guide
.021 PEN WITH A 350 guide %
.026 PEN WITH A 350 guide
.035 PEN WITH A 350 guide
.043 PEN WITH A 350 guide

Fig. 7.25. Reduced three-fourths.

SPECIMEN LINE OR RULE	LINE WIDTH POINTS*	INCHES
	1/4	0.0035
	3/8	.0052
	1/2	.0069
	3/4	.0104
	1	.0138
	1 1/4	.0173
	1 1/2	.0208
	1 3/4	.0242
	2	.0277
	2 1/2	.0346
	3	.0415
	3 1/2	.0484
	4	.0553
	5	.0692
	6	0.0830

FREEHAND VERTICAL

3/32-in high CAPITALS made with a 170 GILLOTT pen point.
4/32-in high CAPITALS made with a 356 ESTERBROOK.
6/32-in CAPITALS made with a 357 pen.
8/32 CAPITALS 358

FREEHAND SLANT

3/32-in high CAPITALS made with a 170 GILLOTT pen point.
4/32-in high CAPITALS made with a 356 ESTERBROOK.
6/32-in. CAPITALS made with a 357 pen.
8/32 CAPITALS 358

PICA TYPEWRITER

PICA TYPEWRITER TYPE HAS 10 characters to the inch of line and 6 lines to the inch. Exact size and design of face vary slightly with the manufacturer.

ELITE TYPEWRITER

ELITE TYPEWRITER TYPE HAS 12 characters to the inch of line and 6 lines to the inch. Exact size and design of face vary slightly with the manufacturer.

*The printer's measure of type size. One point is 0.013837 or approximately 1/72 of an inch. A pica is 12 points.

Fig. 7.26. Standard lines, freehand lettering, and typescript unreduced in size.

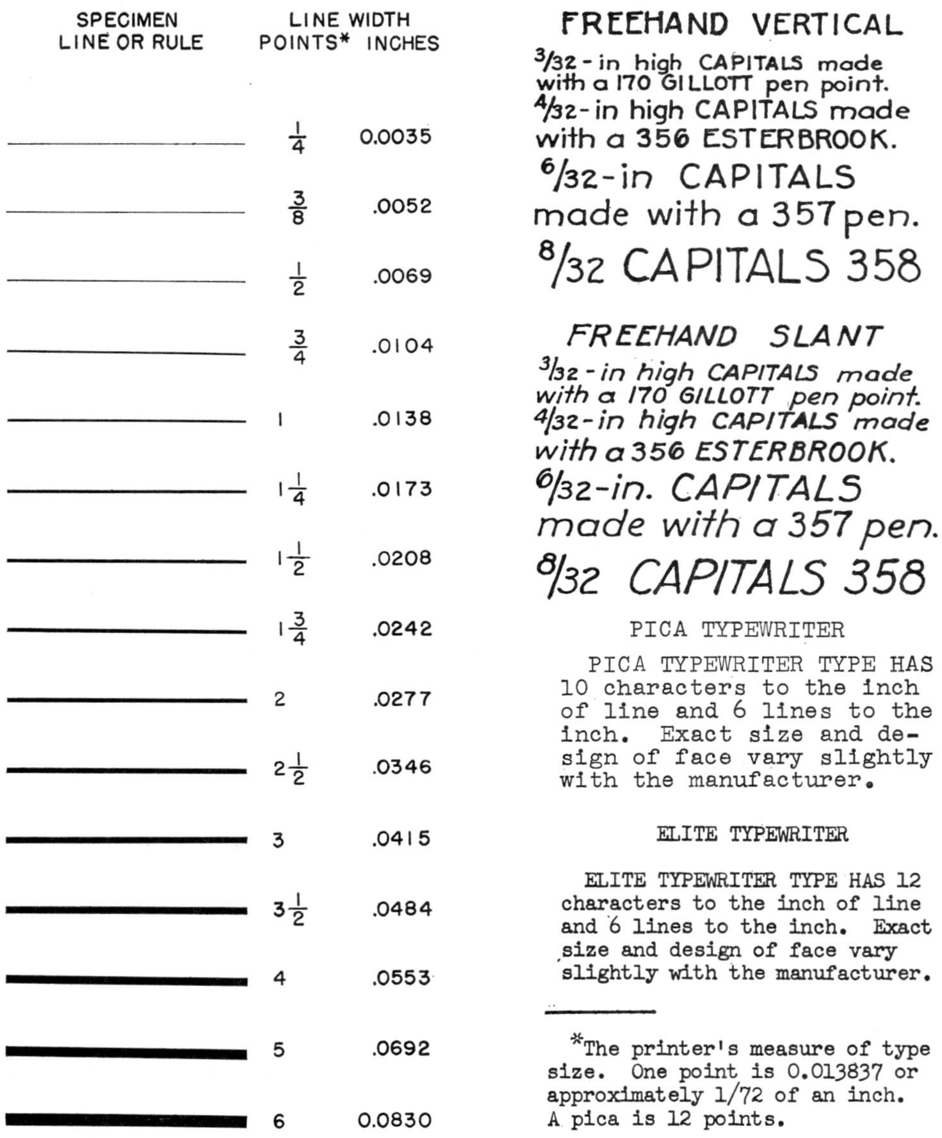

SPECIMEN LINE OR RULE	LINE WIDTH POINTS*	INCHES
	$\frac{1}{4}$	0.0035
	$\frac{3}{8}$	.0052
	$\frac{1}{2}$	.0069
	$\frac{3}{4}$	.0104
	1	.0138
	$1\frac{1}{4}$	.0173
	$1\frac{1}{2}$	.0208
	$1\frac{3}{4}$	.0242
	2	.0277
	$2\frac{1}{2}$	.0346
	3	.0415
	$3\frac{1}{2}$	.0484
	4	.0553
	5	.0692
	6	0.0830

FREEHAND VERTICAL

3/32-in high CAPITALS made with a 170 GILLOTT pen point.
4/32-in high CAPITALS made with a 356 ESTERBROOK.
6/32-in CAPITALS made with a 357 pen.
8/32 CAPITALS 358

FREEHAND SLANT

3/32-in high CAPITALS made with a 170 GILLOTT pen point.
4/32-in high CAPITALS made with a 356 ESTERBROOK.
6/32-in. CAPITALS made with a 357 pen.
8/32 CAPITALS 358

PICA TYPEWRITER

PICA TYPEWRITER TYPE HAS 10 characters to the inch of line and 6 lines to the inch. Exact size and design of face vary slightly with the manufacturer.

ELITE TYPEWRITER

ELITE TYPEWRITER TYPE HAS 12 characters to the inch of line and 6 lines to the inch. Exact size and design of face vary slightly with the manufacturer.

---

*The printer's measure of type size. One point is 0.013837 or approximately 1/72 of an inch. A pica is 12 points.

Fig. 7.27. Reduced one-fourth.

SPECIMEN LINE OR RULE	LINE WIDTH POINTS*	INCHES
——	1/4	0.0035
——	3/8	.0052
——	1/2	.0069
——	3/4	.0104
——	1	.0138
——	1 1/4	.0173
——	1 1/2	.0208
——	1 3/4	.0242
——	2	.0277
——	2 1/2	.0346
——	3	.0415
——	3 1/2	.0484
——	4	.0553
——	5	.0692
——	6	0.0830

FREEHAND VERTICAL

3/32-in high CAPITALS made with a 170 GILLOTT pen point.
4/32-in high CAPITALS made with a 356 ESTERBROOK.
6/32-in CAPITALS made with a 357 pen.
8/32 CAPITALS 358

FREEHAND SLANT

3/32-in high CAPITALS made with a 170 GILLOTT pen point.
4/32-in high CAPITALS made with a 356 ESTERBROOK.
6/32-in. CAPITALS made with a 357 pen.
8/32 CAPITALS 358

PICA TYPEWRITER

PICA TYPEWRITER TYPE HAS 10 characters to the inch of line and 6 lines to the inch. Exact size and design of face vary slightly with the manufacturer.

ELITE TYPEWRITER

ELITE TYPEWRITER TYPE HAS 12 characters to the inch of line and 6 lines to the inch. Exact size and design of face vary slightly with the manufacturer.

---

*The printer's measure of type size. One point is 0.013837 or approximately 1/72 of an inch. A pica is 12 points.

Fig. 7.28. Reduced one-third.

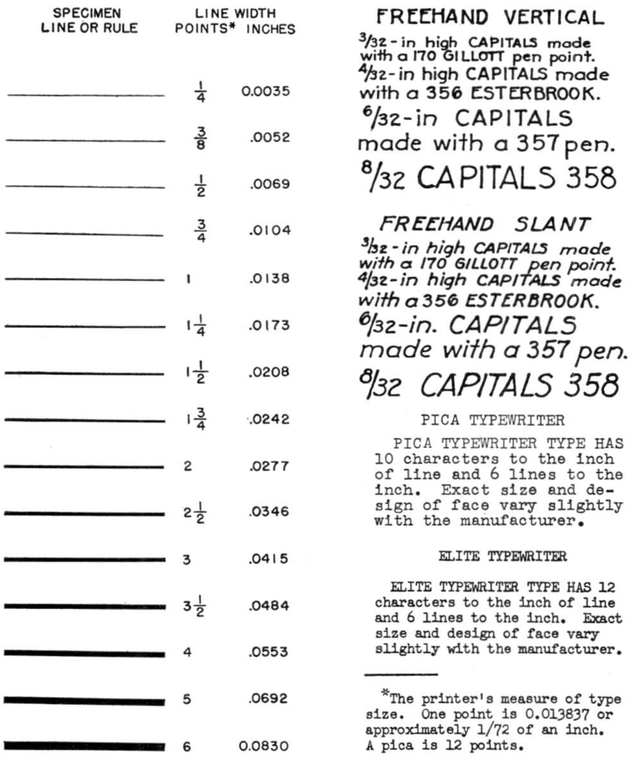

SPECIMEN LINE OR RULE	LINE WIDTH POINTS*	INCHES
	$\frac{1}{4}$	0.0035
	$\frac{3}{8}$	.0052
	$\frac{1}{2}$	.0069
	$\frac{3}{4}$	.0104
	1	.0138
	$1\frac{1}{4}$	.0173
	$1\frac{1}{2}$	.0208
	$1\frac{3}{4}$	.0242
	2	.0277
	$2\frac{1}{2}$	.0346
	3	.0415
	$3\frac{1}{2}$	.0484
	4	.0553
	5	.0692
	6	0.0830

FREEHAND VERTICAL

3/32-in high CAPITALS made with a 170 GILLOTT pen point.
4/32-in high CAPITALS made with a 356 ESTERBROOK.
6/32-in CAPITALS made with a 357 pen.
8/32 CAPITALS 358

FREEHAND SLANT

3/32-in high CAPITALS made with a 170 GILLOTT pen point.
4/32-in high CAPITALS made with a 356 ESTERBROOK.
6/32-in. CAPITALS made with a 357 pen.
8/32 CAPITALS 358

PICA TYPEWRITER

PICA TYPEWRITER TYPE HAS 10 characters to the inch of line and 6 lines to the inch. Exact size and design of face vary slightly with the manufacturer.

ELITE TYPEWRITER

ELITE TYPEWRITER TYPE HAS 12 characters to the inch of line and 6 lines to the inch. Exact size and design of face vary slightly with the manufacturer.

*The printer's measure of type size. One point is 0.013837 or approximately 1/72 of an inch. A pica is 12 points.

Fig. 7.29. Reduced one-half.

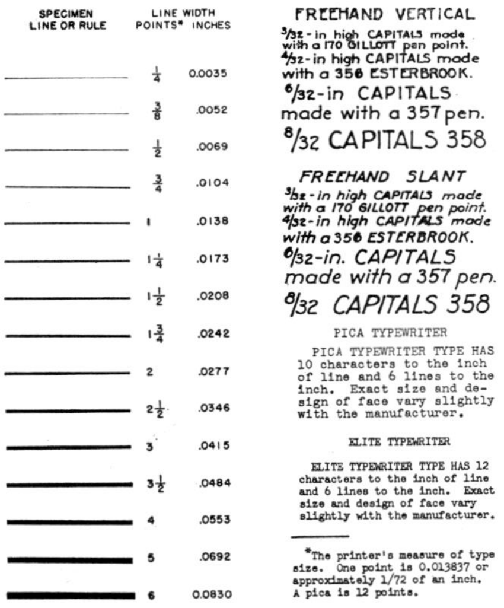

SPECIMEN LINE OR RULE — LINE WIDTH POINTS* INCHES
1/4 0.0035; 3/8 .0052; 1/2 .0069; 3/4 .0104; 1 .0138; 1 1/4 .0173; 1 1/2 .0208; 1 3/4 .0242; 2 .0277; 2 1/2 .0346; 3 .0415; 3 1/2 .0484; 4 .0553; 5 .0692; 6 0.0830
FREEHAND VERTICAL
3/32-in high CAPITALS made with a 170 GILLOTT pen point.
4/32-in high CAPITALS made with a 356 ESTERBROOK.
6/32-in CAPITALS made with a 357 pen.
8/32 CAPITALS 358
FREEHAND SLANT
3/32-in high CAPITALS made with a 170 GILLOTT pen point.
4/32-in high CAPITALS made with a 356 ESTERBROOK.
6/32-in. CAPITALS made with a 357 pen.
8/32 CAPITALS 358
PICA TYPEWRITER
PICA TYPEWRITER TYPE HAS 10 characters to the inch of line and 6 lines to the inch. Exact size and design of face vary slightly with the manufacturer.
ELITE TYPEWRITER
ELITE TYPEWRITER TYPE HAS 12 characters to the inch of line and 6 lines to the inch. Exact size and design of face vary slightly with the manufacturer.
*The printer's measure of type size. One point is 0.013837 or approximately 1/72 of an inch. A pica is 12 points.

Fig. 7.30. Reduced two-thirds.

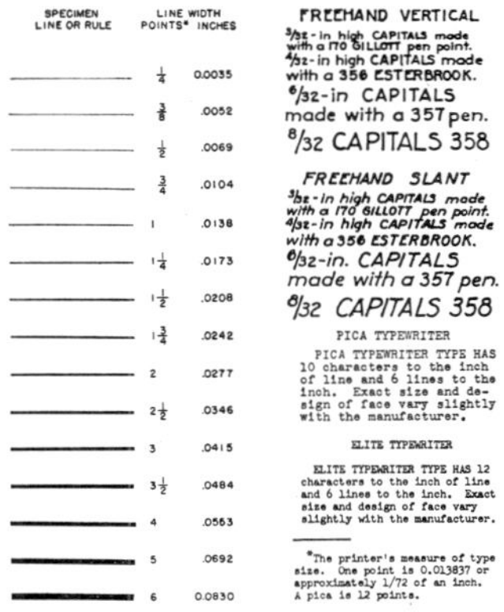

SPECIMEN LINE OR RULE — LINE WIDTH POINTS* INCHES
1/4 0.0035; 3/8 .0052; 1/2 .0069; 3/4 .0104; 1 .0138; 1 1/4 .0173; 1 1/2 .0208; 1 3/4 .0242; 2 .0277; 2 1/2 .0346; 3 .0415; 3 1/2 .0484; 4 .0553; 5 .0692; 6 0.0830
FREEHAND VERTICAL
3/32-in high CAPITALS made with a 170 GILLOTT pen point.
4/32-in high CAPITALS made with a 356 ESTERBROOK.
6/32-in CAPITALS made with a 357 pen.
8/32 CAPITALS 358
FREEHAND SLANT
3/32-in high CAPITALS made with a 170 GILLOTT pen point.
4/32-in high CAPITALS made with a 356 ESTERBROOK.
6/32-in. CAPITALS made with a 357 pen.
8/32 CAPITALS 358
PICA TYPEWRITER
PICA TYPEWRITER TYPE HAS 10 characters to the inch of line and 6 lines to the inch. Exact size and design of face vary slightly with the manufacturer.
ELITE TYPEWRITER
ELITE TYPEWRITER TYPE HAS 12 characters to the inch of line and 6 lines to the inch. Exact size and design of face vary slightly with the manufacturer.
*The printer's measure of type size. One point is 0.013837 or approximately 1/72 of an inch. A pica is 12 points.

Fig. 7.31. Reduced three-fourths.

Lantern Slides

Illustrative charts, curves, diagrams, and tables are frequently made both for reproduction in a written report and as copy for lantern slides.[1] Usually the same technique in drafting will hold for both uses. Lantern slide copy, however, needs to be prepared with special reference to the distance from the screen to the spectator farthest from the screen.

Tests and experience show that the ratio of the height of letter on the screen to the farthest spectator should never be less than 1/350 and need not exceed 1/250, or about a 1-in. capital letter height for each 25 ft. of distance. Using average conditions of a 12-in. focal length of projection lantern with the most distant spectator the same distance from the screen as the lantern, the height of the letter on the slide is a minimum of 0.04 in. For general use, particularly if lower-case letters are used, the height of capital letters on the slide should be at least 0.045 in.

Allowing for a reduction of two-thirds in size, the lettering on the original copy should have a capital letter height of at least 0.135 in. for the standard lantern slide 3¼ x 4 in. The clear field on the slide is about 2¾ x 3 in., so the original drawings for a two-thirds reduction should not exceed a height of 8¼ in. and a width of 9 in. Copy to be reduced only one-half should be drawn to a field size of 5½ x 6 in. with a letter height of at least 0.09 in. At least a two-thirds reduction is recommended when mechanical lettering guides are used because the width of the stroke of the smallest pen is too heavy for the 0.09-in. height of letter. Reductions greater than two-thirds may be used provided the lettering is increased proportionally from that recommended above.

The standards of line width, ratio of width of letter stroke to height of letter, and layout for lantern slides are generally the same as for drawings to be reproduced through the printing process. A ratio of 1:10, stroke width to height, can be used for lantern slides; but 1:14 is preferred for the engraving process in printing. Table 7.1 serves as a guide for either lantern slides or engraver's copy.

Typescript tables may be used for lantern slide copy, but unless they are typed with a carbon ribbon or a thoroughly black fine-textured cloth ribbon the screen reproduction will be grayish and lacking in sharpness. Pica type (10 characters to the inch) may be used up to about a reduction of 60 per cent. The size of pica typescript copy should not exceed 6¾ x 7½ in. Elite type (12 characters per inch) should not be reduced more than 50 per cent.

The 2 x 2-in. lantern slide has a clear field of only 1 x 1½ in. Allowing for a two-thirds reduction, original copy should be not greater than 3 x 4½ in. which is too small for satisfactory drafting of copy. The reduction should be greater than two-thirds with correspondingly higher lettering. Typescript copy for the 2 x 2-in. lantern slide should be not larger than 2½ x 3⅞ in., also too small to be of practical application.

The 2 x 2-in. slide made from standard 35 mm. motion picture film is a popular development. The negative, black and white or color, is mounted in a cardboard frame and used directly in projection. Special projectors are used, or an adapter slide carrier is used in the standard projector for 3 x 4½-in. slides. This small slide is suitable for gatherings up to 50 people and for larger groups when a suitable projection lantern is available. The 35 mm. film is especially desirable for colored slides.

Satisfactory standard lantern slides are illustrated in Figs. 7.32 and 7.33 in exact size.

Colored lantern slides are effective. They may be made by direct color photography or the color may be applied by hand to the slide. While most slides are made in the positive, the negative slide with dark background and light lines is easier on the eyes and costs less than the positive slide.

---

[1] This section is based on recommended practice of the American Standards Association. See Z 15.1–1932, Engineering and Scientific Charts for Lantern Slides, November 1932, and Y 15.1—1959, Illustrations for Publication and Projection.

TYPES OF CHARTS

Data to be presented graphically may be displayed in one of a number of ways. On the following pages are illustrated curve charts, surface charts, column charts, and bar charts. Each of these types has specific applications. The best results are obtained when the selection is made with due consideration of the data and the purpose for which the chart is presented.

Curve Charts

Many applications of science and technology include observations which follow a mathematical law that can be expressed to advantage by a continuous curve. Frequently, observations are plotted as a means of analysis of the data. Curve charts are the results of these plottings. The independent variable, such as time, is always plotted as the abscissa. Scales should be chosen to express relationships in a pleasing proportion and such that the scale values can be read as closely as is desired. Usually, a condensing of the plotted points or a compressing of the curve vertically is to be preferred to a scale that scatters the observations or that causes the curve to have extreme vertical movement as compared to the horizontal.

Surface Charts

Charts in which the area beneath the curve or broken lines is shaded or colored may be classed as surface charts. Shading has the advantage of giving emphasis to the magnitude of the quantity and contrast between components of the total, if more than one quantity is shown. Where the chart is a 100 per cent total chart, the surface chart emphasizes the magnitude above the curve as well as below the curve. Surface charts are not desirable when the ordinate changes abruptly in successive abscissa intervals. Surface charts are not area charts, because they are not read on a two-dimensional basis. The ordinate must start at zero in order to preserve the correct impression of the changes.

Column Charts

In column charts the height of the vertical bar or column represents the numerical value or percentage of the quantity measured. Time is usually the horizontal interval. Column charts are effective in showing noncontinuous data, such as yields or productions for a series of years. The item shown should be the same qualitatively in a given chart, except, of course, where multicolumn charts are used.

Fig. 7.32. Reproduction of a lantern slide, 3¼ by 4 in. made from original copy reduced two-thirds. The lettering in the original drafting was done with a Leroy pen No. 0 which has a stroke of 0.017 in. The ordinate and abscissa scales and labels were made with a No. 140 guide; the curve labels and legend were made with a No. 175 guide; and the credit line was made with a No. 120 guide.

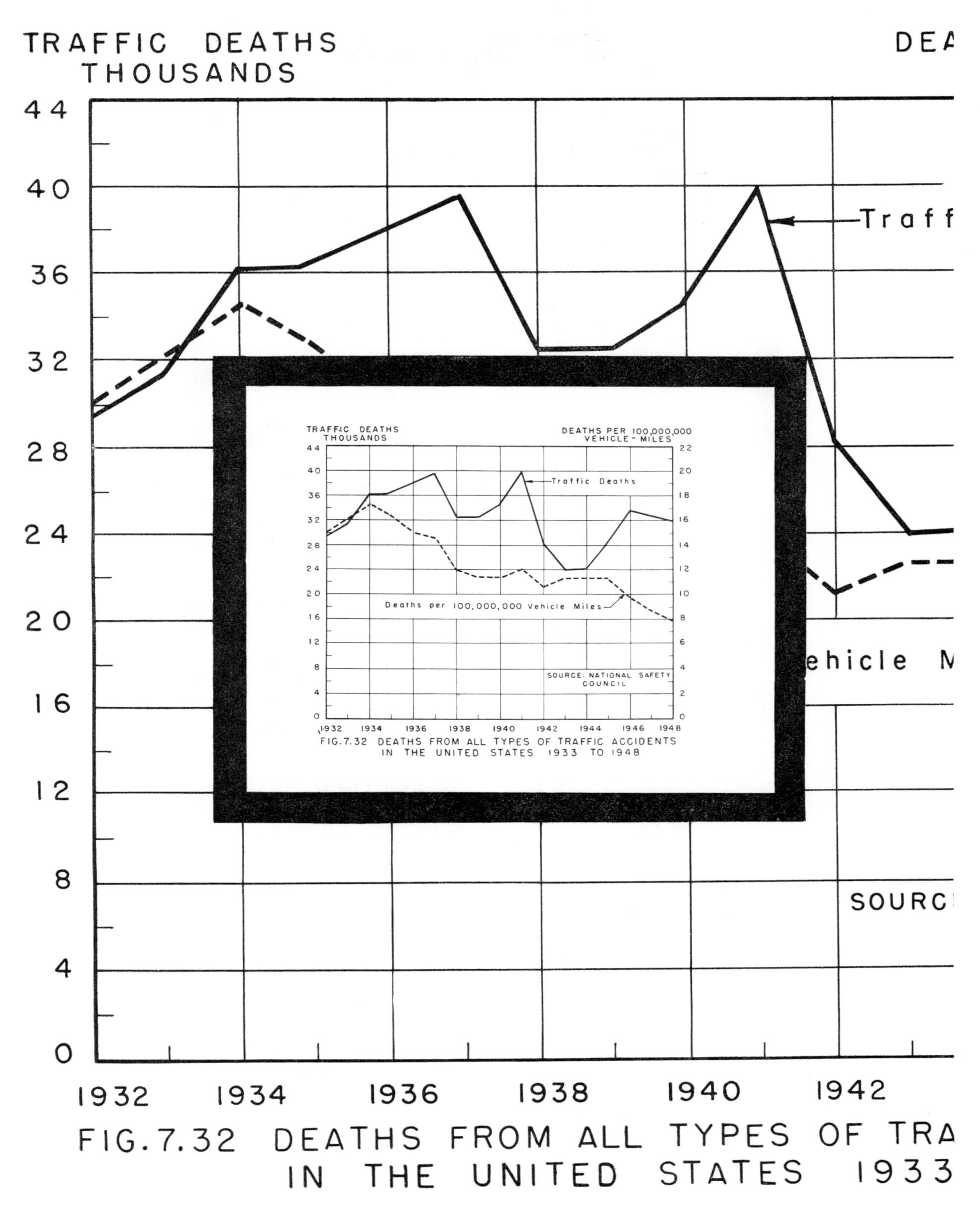

FIG. 7.32 DEATHS FROM ALL TYPES OF TRAFFIC ACCIDENTS IN THE UNITED STATES 1933 TO 1948

TABLE 6.7. GRADES OF ENGINEERING GRADUATES

All Grades Based Upon the Quarter Term Average

Entering classification and scholastic year	June graduates			Midyear graduates*		
	Number of grades	Quarter grades: Per cent grades 3.0 or more	Quarter grades: Median	Number of grades	Quarter grades: Per cent grades 3.0 or more	Quarter grades: Median
(1)	(2)	(3)	(4)	(5)	(6)	(7)
Freshman matriculants						
Freshman	218	33.9	2.58	169	12.5	2.19
Sophomore	212	29.6	2.52	173	10.5	2.19
Junior	213	28.1	2.54	178	11.8	2.26
Senior	224	40.2	2.83	152	23.0	2.58
All students . .	867	33.1	2.65	672	14.2	2.28
Transfer matriculants						
Freshman	26	19.2	2.68	22	13.6	2.32
Sophomore	93	23.6	2.38	74	4.2	2.04
Junior	150	27.4	2.44	113	9.6	2.07
Senior	159	33.5	2.69	93	21.3	2.47
All students . .	428	28.2	2.56	302	12.2	2.19

*Includes graduates of July, August, December, and March.

Fig. 7.33. Reproduction of a lantern slide made from Table 6.7, page 102. Table 6.7 is typed in elite type (12 characters per inch). The table width of 6.375 in. was reduced to 3.08 in., a reduction of about 50 per cent. Elite type should not be reduced more than 50 per cent.

Bar Charts

Where it is desired to show the comparison of several items for the same period or under the same conditions, the bar, or horizontal, chart should be used. The horizontal bar chart measures magnitudes horizontally from a vertical zero line at the left. There is no vertical scale used in bar charts, but each bar in the vertical arrangement represents a separate item to be compared for the same conditions or time interval. Arrangement of the bars should be in some advantageous sequence, the choice of which depends upon the nature of the data shown. Alphabetical, logical, geographical, quantitative, qualitative, or progressive arrangements may be used. All bars should begin at the vertical zero line.

Area and Volume Charts

Area charts should be restricted in use; usually the simple bar, column, or curve chart presents the data more effectively than does the pie or box chart. The eye measures linear distances (one dimension) in comparisons with greater accuracy and ease than it does areas or volumes. While the pie chart has a certain popular appeal, technical readers will usually be served to better advantage by the bar or column chart.

Symbolic Charts

Instead of using the simple curve, column, or bar charts, many popular presentations use symbolic presentations in the design of humans, animals, stacks of dollars, machinery, and the like. Where creation of reader interest is a factor and where exactness of scale and impression are not required, such presentations may have value. In technical reports it is better to adhere to the standard designs that use curves, columns, bars, and shadings for all graphical illustrations. Also symbolic charts are difficult to use when the magnitude of the amount is desired. When each symbol represents 1,000 or other number of units, the reader is compelled to count the units.

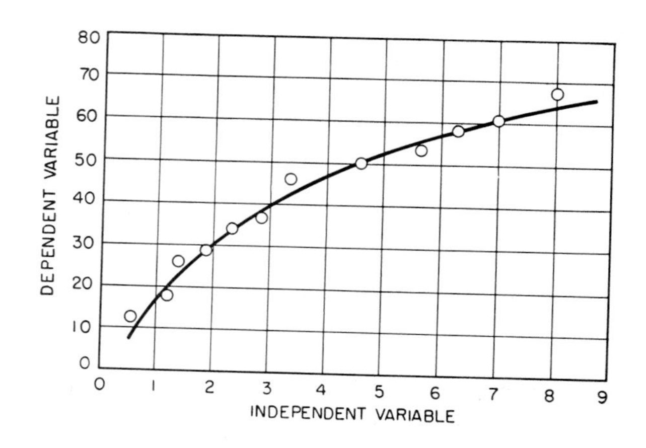

Fig. 7.34.

SIMPLE CURVE CHARTS show by curve the relation of a dependent variable (ordinate) with change in the independent variable (abscissa). Time is a frequently used abscissa.

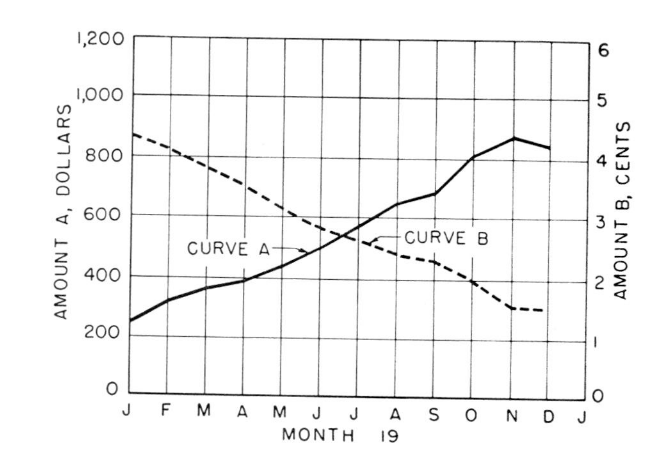

Fig. 7.35.

MULTIPLE CURVE CHARTS consist of two or more curves of related character plotted on the same grid. Two or more ordinate scales may be used. Unless the curves are uniformly spaced, confusion may result if more than four curves are placed on the same chart.

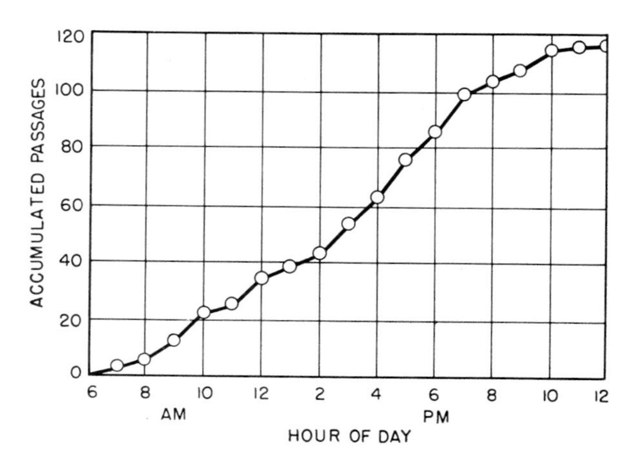

Fig. 7.36.

CUMULATIVE CURVE CHARTS show the accumulation of the dependent variable for consecutive periods of time or other independent variable. Cumulative curves are frequently desirable in plotting frequency observations which vary widely from a smooth distribution.

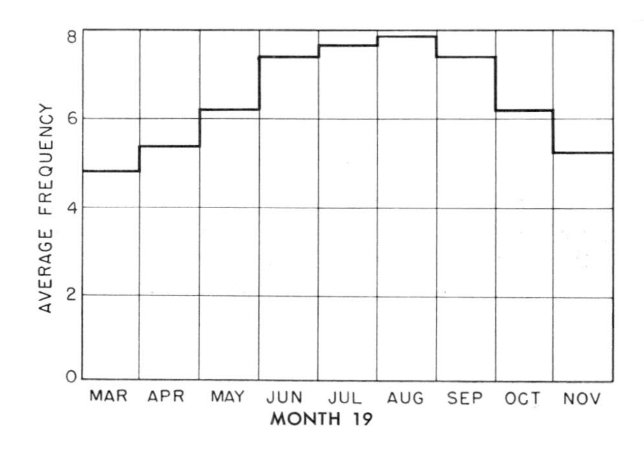

Fig. 7.37.

STAIRCASE CURVE CHARTS are desirable when average or total amounts for periods, equal or unequal, are to be plotted.

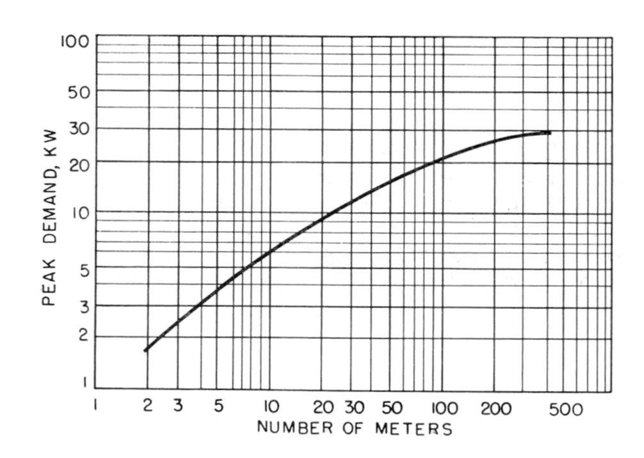

Fig. 7.38.

LOGARITHMIC SCALE CHARTS are desirable when the rate of change is an important observation. Arithmetic scales show only the amount of change. Logarithmic scales are also useful to reduce the height or width of chart which is caused by large values at the upper ranges of the variables.

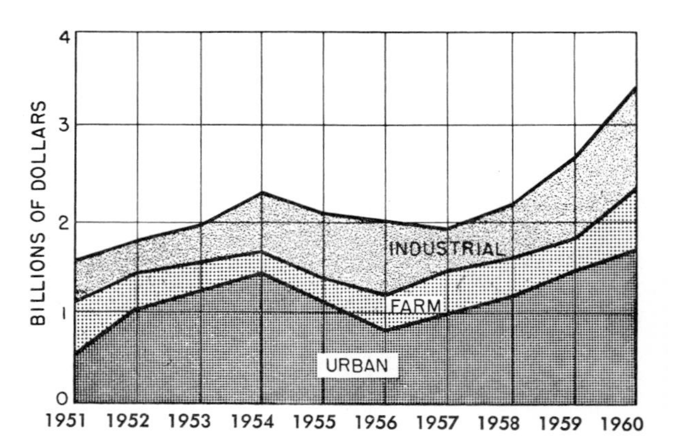

Fig. 7.39.

SUBDIVIDED SURFACE CHARTS show the values of component series by the height of surface layers. Surface charts emphasize the magnitudes of the total rather than the changes or differences.

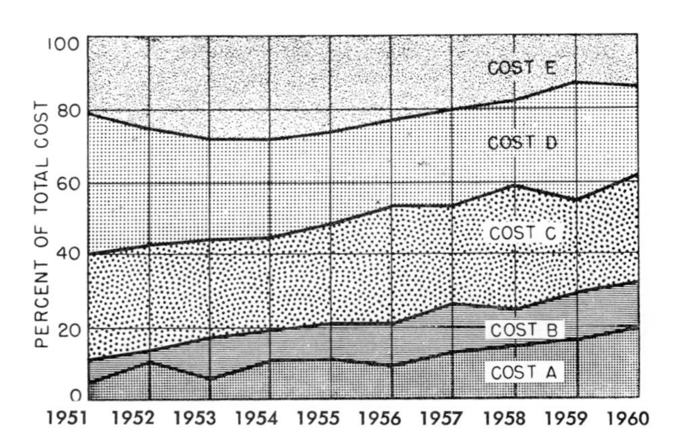

Fig. 7.40.

MULTIPLE SURFACE CHARTS OF 100-PER CENT ORDINATE show the relative change of each component in the total.

Fig. 7.41.

FREQUENCY AND OTHER CONTINUOUS CURVES are used to show distributions of observations by class intervals, cumulative observations and other types of continuous functions.

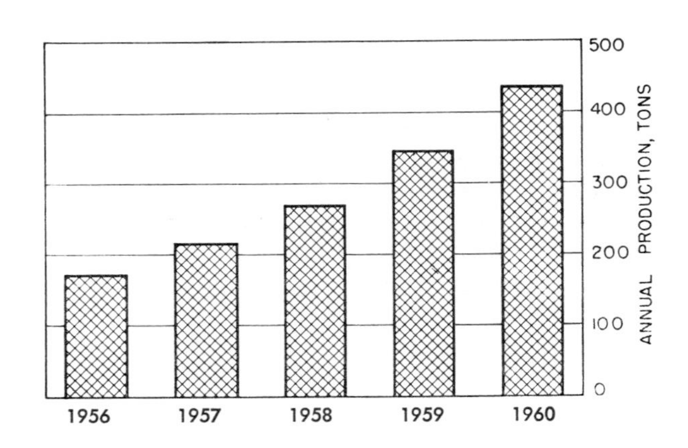

Fig. 7.42.

SIMPLE COLUMN CHARTS are often more effective in showing growth and changes for intervals of time than is the ordinary curve chart. The upper ends of the columns indicate in pronounced manner the relative differences in values, and the height of column produces the effect of area.

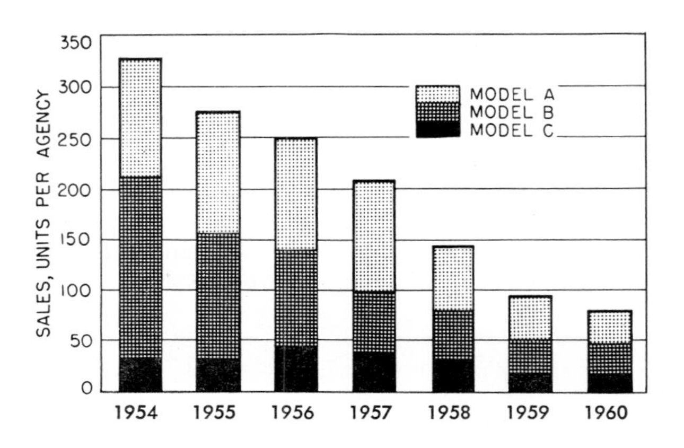

Fig. 7.43.

SUBDIVIDED COLUMN CHARTS present within the same column, two to five variables. By this means it is possible to present a comparison of the subitems as well as of the total amounts observed as shown by the height of total column.

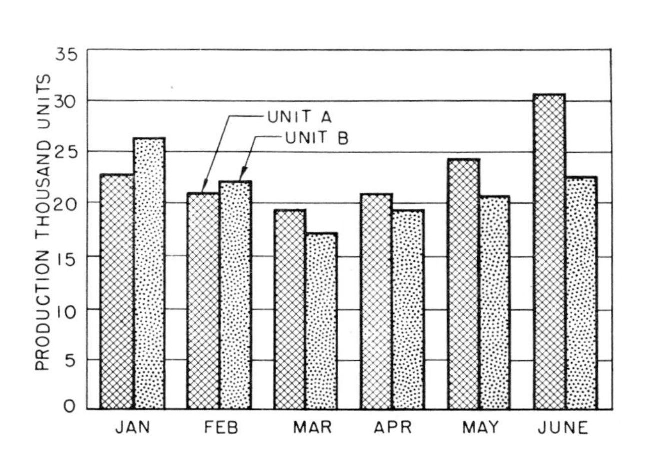

Fig. 7.44.

GROUPED COLUMN CHARTS are a convenient device for comparing two to three variable quantities for the same time intervals or other condition of observation.

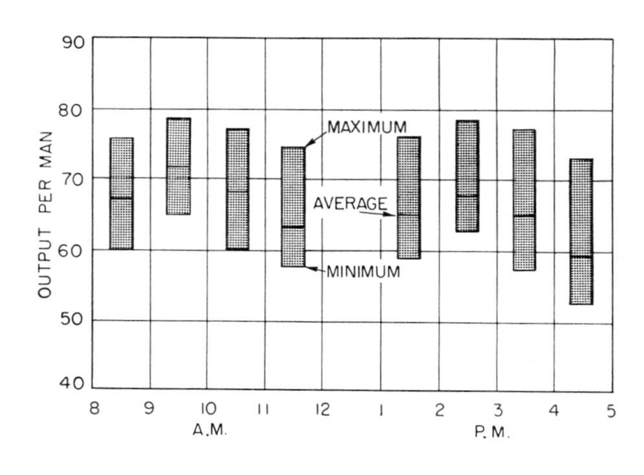

Fig. 7.45.

RANGE CHARTS are useful in showing the minimum, maximum, and average values as well as the variations over the time interval shown.

Fig. 7.46. (right)

SIMPLE BAR CHARTS measure the comparative values of a series of items from a vertical base line to the left. Each horizontal bar represents a different item observed under comparable conditions.

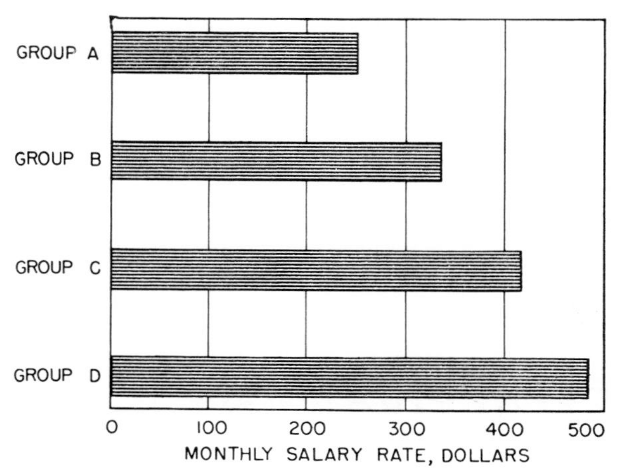

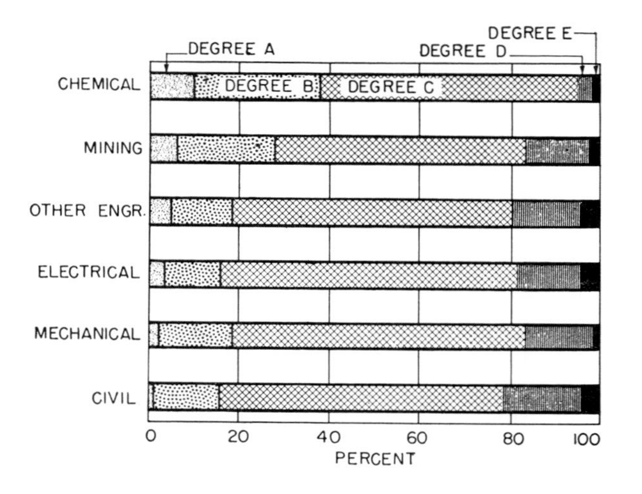

(left) Fig. 7.47.

SUBDIVIDED BAR CHARTS are those in which the bars are subdivided by appropriate shadings into horizontal segments. The most important or the largest subitem should be placed to the left at the zero line. Subdivided bar charts may or may not total 100 per cent in their length.

Fig. 7.48. (right)

The simple bar chart may be developed into a GROUPED BAR CHART by presenting two or three related subitems as a group of horizontal bars. The bars are shaded in a contrasting manner. Vertical white space between the groups should be slightly less than the vertical width of a single bar.

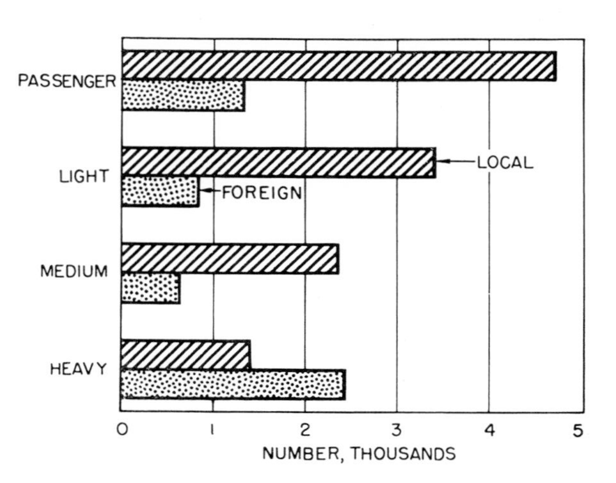

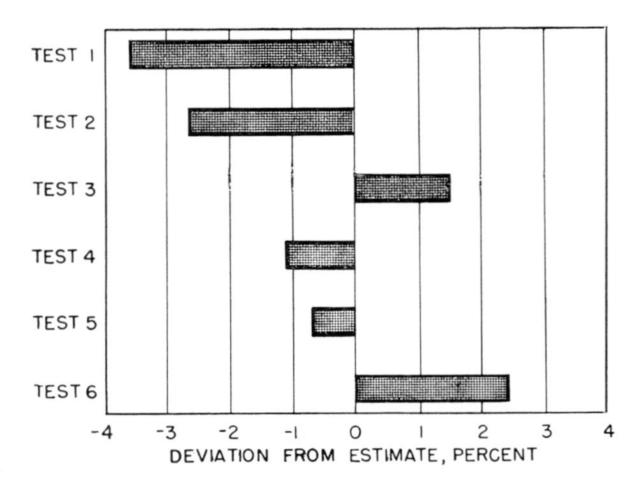

(left) Fig. 7.49.

DEVIATION BAR CHARTS are made to extend to the left and right of a base line and are useful in showing plus and minus deviations, such as excesses and deficiencies or the departure of observed values from theoretical or estimated values.

CHAPTER 8

Effective Writing

The technically trained person has at his service many ways of presenting his thoughts. But this chapter is devoted to only one of those methods of thought presentation—writing. Effective writing is achieved when thoughts are efficiently and accurately recorded and when they are easily and correctly understood by the reader.

THE EXPRESSION OF THOUGHT

The product of the mind is thought. The raw material of thought is the succession of impressions made on the mind. Impressions are carried to the mind through the senses, of which hearing and seeing are the most useful in communicating ideas. The mind gathers, classifies, stores, and recombines these impressions. Upon receiving an outside stimulus, the mind gives evidence of thought through speech and action.

One system by which the character of man's thought may be classified is based on these skills:

Manipulation
Knowledge
Reasoning
Judgment
Creativeness

The order of these skills is not intended to indicate their relative importance. Unusual proficiency in each brings unstinted reward. The ability to perform a delicate surgical operation, to complete a difficult construction or manufacturing job, or to assemble by hand a high precision instrument are examples of *manipulative* skill at its best. On the other hand, certain simple jobs in mass production require skill in only one operation, repeated hundreds of times each hour or day.

The *knowledge* required to plan a complete power plant is broader than that required to design a steam turbine or a single element of the turbine. Yet, a turbine design specialist probably possesses the same quality of knowledge as the designer of the complete power plant. Knowledge and manipulative skills are essential if one is to reason, judge, or create.

Reasoning is the skill by which knowledge and manipulation are combined to arrive at a solution to any problem or a management decision.

Judgment, the technical term for horse sense or common sense, is the skill one needs to make a spontaneous choice or to provide an unmeditated answer. Judgment is that quality of the mind which enables it to go directly from the question to the answer. Judgment must be based on experience and knowledge and the alertness to relate these to the answer.

Creativeness is that skill which enables the mind to focus its efforts upon the explanation of unknown phenomena or the development of new methods and mechanisms. Creativeness is built upon manipulation, knowledge, reasoning, and judgment.

Since the above skills are the classifications of thought, the legitimate question is: By what methods can one person transmit the content of his thought to another? Sound and symbol are the basic vehicles. Each person possesses a transmitter, the vocal chords, and a receiver, the ear. Through these mechanisms the vocal expression of thought is associated with common relationships by persons conversing. But the voice has two limitations; it does not carry far and is not permanently recorded. Therefore, man invented and developed a scheme by which his ideas could be preserved and sent to distant places. This scheme is the art of making symbols. Letters, words, numbers, diagrams, pictures, and models are forms of symbols. The mind associates symbols with objects, ideas, and experiences. Thoughts are given expression by systems of symbols.

The rigorous training of scientists and engineers places at their disposal several systems by which to express thoughts effectively. These systems are speech, writing, mathematics, drawing, and modeling. The basic system of symbols in preserving speech is writing as represented by the alphabet; in mathematics, the alphabet plus the numerals; and in drawing, orthographic projection plus the alphabet plus the numerals. The elements in the foregoing systems of symbols may be likened to the fundamental materials, sand, stone, cement, wood, metals, and others, which can be combined to create homes, factories, radios, machines, automobiles, and an indefinite number of other items. But to convert fundamental materials into useful commodities requires the application of thought in terms of the properties of the materials and the principles that govern their behavior.

The systems of symbols developed for recording thought can be readily learned and understood. To learn to use them effectively is the problem of learning how to communicate through writing. Learning to communicate through speech is acquired with much less effort than learning to communicate through the written language. In oral communication the speaker can be effective because he has a variety of tools at his command. In written communication the reader must depend upon words and symbols only.

Fig. 8.1 is an illustration of two-way oral communication with its several aids as contrasted with one-way written communication and its limited aids. The spoken word can be given that particular degree of emphasis, warmth, sincerity, and attention the speaker desires by use of his voice and body. In the printed form the same word can have only that meaning the reader puts into the word. In addition, oral communication can be achieved through a two-way exchange of ideas until perfect understanding is reached; in written communication there is no certainty of perfect understanding and thus no certainty of communication.

Communication through writing is an art difficult to master. But it can be mastered through labor, patience, study, and practice. Learning to communicate through writing really has to start with gaining an understanding of words and their function. In brief, effective writing results from putting the appropriate words in that sequence which will express to the reader just the same attitude, picture, and understanding the author himself has.

WORDS—THEIR CHARACTER, PERSONALITY

The foregoing discussion emphasizes the place of sound and symbol in the communication of thought. The word is to thought what the atom is to matter. The word is one of a huge number of combinations of the 26 letters of the alphabet. Therefore, the word can be and is used to represent an infinite number of images, experiences, concepts, theories, hypotheses, principles, facts, and laws. In a similar manner atoms are the combination of electrons and neutrons in a specific manner. Each atom possesses its own characteristics which may or may not combine to form innumerable substances. Words are not the product of a scientific develop-

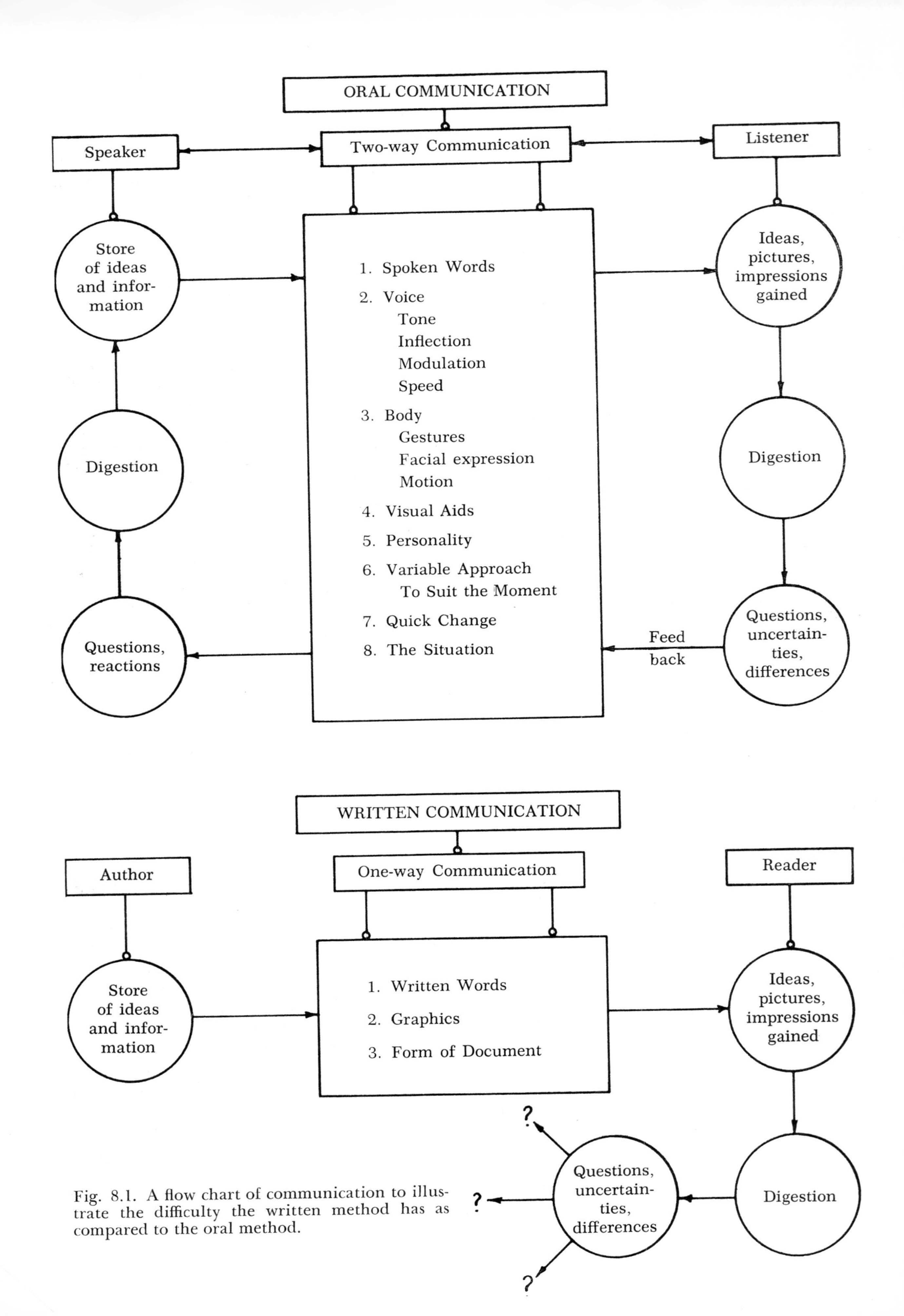

Fig. 8.1. A flow chart of communication to illustrate the difficulty the written method has as compared to the oral method.

ment based on principles; otherwise, it would not be possible to have as many words for an object as there are languages. A horse is called *un cheval* by the French, *ein pferd* by the Germans, and *egy lo* by the Magyars. But call it what you will a horse is a horse in any language. On the other hand mathematical symbols and processes and graphical constructions by orthographic projection are international in their acceptance. One may, therefore, reasonably conclude that language, spoken and written, is perhaps the first and oldest form of communicating thought.

In recent years the important relationship between thought and words has been definitely established. The better the vocabulary of a person the more intelligent he is considered to be. Intelligence is the efficient and effective use of knowledge. The educated person in any field of human endeavor realizes the value in improving and extending his vocabulary to serve him at all times and on all occasions. In all of the following situations people do more effective work when they possess a mastery of the vocabulary that is common to their daily needs:

1. The workman and his employer exchange instructions and experiences.
2. The scientist performs experiments which must be recorded by him and explained to others.
3. The engineer develops plans that need to be drawn to convey space and form requirements, as well as specifications to define materials and methods of construction.
4. The administrative officer issues programs and receives reports to control the management and progress of his organization.

Tests are available to substantiate the conclusion that persons who are successful in the professions or in business consistently rate high in selecting words to convey their intent forcefully and accurately.

It is never too late to broaden and clarify one's vocabulary. The process may be pleasant, yet useful. The following suggestions are from a booklet published by the Merriam Company:

1. One of the best methods of building up your vocabulary is through reading, especially through reading the works of authors who are recognized masters of style. You should train yourself to notice unfamiliar words, to look them up in the dictionary to make sure that you know their meaning, and to practice using the words that you learn until their use becomes natural to you.
2. To build up a large and accurate vocabulary, you should make a practice of using the exact word to express your thought in writing or speaking. The treatment of synonyms in Merriam-Webster dictionaries, with illustrations to clarify the fine distinctions in meaning, enables you to choose accurate words.
3. In writing, one often finds that he has repeated the same word several times in a sentence or paragraph. By consulting the dictionary, he can discover, in the definitions or among the synonyms given, a word to use to avoid this repetition, and frequently the substituted word will be more exact and forceful than that originally used.
4. There are certain words, similar in form or related in meaning, which are frequently misused. Acquiring a sure knowledge of the correct use of such words will help you to build a precise vocabulary. The dictionary is an unfailing guide and should be consulted whenever you are in doubt as to the proper use of a word. [1]

SENTENCES—WORDS IN ACTION

The mind performs two distinct types of functions: First, it receives, classifies, and stores impressions conveyed to it; and, second, it sorts, recombines and arranges, and issues the previously acquired impressions to solve new problems or to create new explanations and inventions. The means of communicating thought are the senses, and the commonly used materials of communicating thought are sound and symbol. But thought units alone merely create isolated images or impressions. The usual college dictionary contains about 150,000 words representing as many isolated images and impressions. These 150,000 word symbols may be transformed into innumerable related images, impressions, ideas, concepts, hypotheses, theories, principles, laws, and statements of facts through the vehicle of the sentence.

The sentence is a combination of two distinct classes of words; namely, words which

[1] G. & C. Merriam Co. *Vocabulary Building, Bibliography, and Word Study*, pp. 3–5. 1937.

name substances, ideas, and impressions and words which imply action, predication, or assertiveness. Words which name things are called "nouns"; substitutes for nouns are called "pronouns." Words which assert or predicate are called "verbs."

In its simplest form, then, a sentence consists of a noun plus a verb. The noun is the substance of the sentence; the verb is the life of the sentence. The noun is the material element of thought; the verb is the dynamic element of thought. The noun names a thing; the verb gives significance to the thing. The combination of a noun with an appropriate verb completely satisfies the thought processes of the writer and reader. Thus, one may conclude that a sentence is that combination of words which completely expresses the thought.

The writer needs to practice the design of sentences for the correct, complete, concise, clear, and convincing expression of his thoughts. To meet these specifications the writer needs to become acquainted with the principal parts of speech. The parts of speech are the basic elements that make up the structure of a sentence. To write well or to improve one's skill in writing requires careful analysis of sentences. Then, gradually, the mind becomes relieved of the rules; and, good writing, that is, the fluent and correct expression of thought, comes more spontaneously.

The minimum basic sentence contains a "subject" and a "predicate."

The explorer arrived.

In this sentence the subject is *explorer,* and the verb is *arrived. The* is the modifier of *explorer.*

The basic sentence may be extended to give more information by the addition of an "object" to the predicate.

The explorer calmed the natives.

In this sentence the subject is *explorer* and the predicate is *calmed the natives.* The object of the verb, calmed, is *natives.* The sentence could have been written,

He calmed them.

In this case *he* and *them* are pronouns used in place of *explorer* and *natives.*

The *experienced* explorer *quickly and completely* calmed the *marooned and excited* natives.

In this sentence a more vivid impression of the explorer and the natives is gained as well as of the manner of calming the natives. Nouns are modified by words, "adjectives," to describe the noun; thus, *experienced, marooned* and *excited* are adjectives. Verbs are modified by words, "adverbs," to describe the verb; thus, *quickly* and *completely* describe the rate and thoroughness with which the explorer calmed the natives.

The experienced explorer *from the distant mainland* quickly and completely calmed, *with the aid of his helpers,* the marooned and excited natives.

The parts of speech thus far mentioned are words used as nouns, verbs, pronouns, adjectives, and adverbs. Phrases are parts of sentences used as modifiers. In the expanded sentence, *from the distant mainland* is an adjective phrase because it modifies a noun; *with the aid of his helpers* is an adverb phrase because it modifies a verb; *of his helpers* is an adjective phrase modifying aid. The relationship between words and phrases is accomplished with "prepositions" such as *from, with, of, to, on, upon,* and others. Words of equal or contrasted values are joined by "connectives" such as *and, but,* and *or.*

The experienced explorer from the distant mainland, *which was settled by Europeans,* quickly and completely calmed, with the aid of his helpers, the marooned and excited natives *who had been without food for many days.*

The original elementary sentence with three words has been expanded to one with 35 words and the final sentence which follows has 38 words:

When he arrived, the experienced explorer from the distant mainland, which was settled by Europeans, quickly and completely calmed, with the aid of his helpers, the marooned and excited natives who had been without food for many days.

This sentence contains additional modifiers called "adjective clauses." These clauses, which modify the nouns *mainland* and *native,* are: *which was settled by Europeans* and *who had been without food for many days.* "Adverb clauses" are used to modify verbs or adjectives; the expression, *when he arrived* is an adverb clause modifying the verb *calmed.*

In general, it is desirable to keep sentences short. This statement should be interpreted not in terms of the number of words, but rather in terms of the principle of streamlining. Many short elementary sentences to express ideas may accumulate to more total words than one or two smoothly expressed longer sentences. Variation in the length of sentences and in the order of their principal parts creates writing that is dynamic, readable, interesting, and mature — writing that keeps the reader alert.

Choppy, short, monotonous, immature:

The explorer calmed the natives.

The explorer was experienced.

The natives were marooned and excited.

The explorer calmed them quickly and completely.

The explorer came from the distant mainland.

The distant mainland was settled by Europeans.

The natives were calmed with the aid of the explorer's helpers.

The natives were without food for many days.

Fifty-five words are required to do the work of the 38. How can 38 words do the work of 55 words? How can 40 watts of electricity provide as much illumination by fluorescent lighting as was formerly provided by about 300 watts with carbon-filament lighting? In both cases, efficiency, development, and improvement are introduced by the application of fundamental rules and principles. In the sentence, the structure represented by the principal parts and the thoughts represented by the words may be conceived to resemble an electric circuit. The principal parts of an electric circuit are the prime mover, the generator, the transmission line, the circuit breaker, the induction coil, and the load. Principles of grammar are to the sentence what principles of nature are to the electric circuit and to all scientific and technical knowledge.

The usual sequence is subject, predicate, object, with each group of modifiers as close as possible to the principal parts. This sequence may be varied to good advantage by interchanging the principal parts of the sentence.

1. A phrase:

As a nation of great industry we are proud of the achievements of our scientists and engineers.

2. An adverb:

Quickly and *completely* the natives were calmed by the explorer.

3. A verb:

Hoist sail, and Santa Cruz will soon be in sight.

4. A clause:

Once leadership has been achieved, the task of maintaining it often becomes difficult.

In order that a better appreciation of some of the underlying influences may be gained, these notes have been prepared.

5. An interjection:

Alas, he cannot do it.

Sentences may be classified on the basis of the manner in which they are articulated.

1. A simple sentence may contain the subject, predicate, and object:

The airplane carried thirty passengers.

The principal passenger carriers are airplanes, automobiles, and railway passenger cars.

The man mixed and placed the concrete into the forms.

2. Double, or compound, sentences are formed by the use of conjunctions such as *and, but,* and *or.* Each sentence has a subject and predicate:

The top soil was first removed; then, the excavation for the foundation was commenced.

They were not interested in the improvement of corn production, but they were interested in the mechanism of heredity and in the effect of close inbreeding.

3. The complex sentence contains two clauses, one an "independent" clause and the other a "dependent" clause (in italics):

The waste product of the green-leaf laboratories is oxygen *which is turned back into the atmosphere.*

When the mixture is heated by a direct-current arc, the carrier material and impurities are volatilized into the arc.

PARAGRAPHS—SENTENCES IN ACTION

Thus far the expression of thought has been discussed in terms of the word and the sentence. The accumulation of words to build up the writer's vocabulary and the selection and assembly of words to express a single thought by a sentence draw mainly upon the "manipulation" and "knowledge" skills in thinking.

These words and sentences can be put to work, as one gains knowledge and experience, to develop ideas, topics, or concepts. Extension in the expression of thought draws upon the writer's skill in reasoning, exercise of judgment, and initiative in creativeness. An assembly of sentences selected and arranged to develop a single idea, topic, or point is called a paragraph.

Each sentence in a paragraph is designed to contribute an essential thought. The content of each sentence depends upon the knowledge at the disposal of the writer. The selection of the pertinent thoughts results from the judgment of the writer. The sequence and arrangement of the sentences follow the principles and requirements of reasoning. The over-all quality of the paragraph reflects the writer's skill in applying certain rules and regulations of rhetoric.

Although a paragraph is normally the development of only one idea, or unity of thought, a paragraph is also defined as a distinct subdivision of a discourse. In order to develop a composition that has pleasing typography and an arrangement conducive to ease of reading, paragraphs are made at suitable logical intervals, regardless of whether the discussion of a topic has been completed. In single-spaced typescript at least two paragraph indentations should be made per page, and at least one on a double-spaced typed page.

Rigid adherence to keeping the complete development of an idea within a paragraph would result in a paragraph many pages in length. Good appearance and the requirements of readability dictate that paragraphs be from 1 to 10 sentences in length.

A paragraph indentation may be thought of as a mark of punctuation. In this sense the paragraph ending becomes a stop of greater weight than the stop indicated by the period. In fact, in early writings the symbol ¶ was used without our present day indentation to indicate a change in subject.

The Topic Sentence

The key to good writing is to establish ideas clearly, accurately, forcefully, and pleasantly. To achieve this specification the writer has, among other resources to be considered, the "topic sentence." The distinguishing characteristic of this type of sentence is that it contains in a nutshell the principal topic of a paragraph, chapter, report, bulletin, or even a book. Skill in creating topic sentences can be developed by planned practice. The formulation of topic sentences builds up one's ability to present good introductions, to write effective paragraphs and to prepare useful outlines. All the foregoing achievements are ingredients of good writing—good reports, both written and oral.

Topic Sentences for Paragraphs. It has already been stated that the paragraph is a sentence-by-sentence development of one idea. This requirement of the paragraph calls for some device that will focus the reader's attention upon the central idea. Once the attention of the reader is fixed upon the principal topic his thoughts will be directed towards its logical development. General usage places the topic sentence at the beginning of the paragraph. For variety and emphasis, the topic sentence is sometimes placed at the end. In such instances the topic sentence also serves to summarize the idea or to clinch the argument. Infrequently, the topic sentence follows an introductory transition sentence. Topic sentences are illustrated in the next section.

Topic Sentences and Transitions. Besides serving the reader as introductions to the separate subjects as they come up for discussion, topic sentences can be combined with transitional phrases and sentences. These transition indicators serve as guides to keep the reader oriented; he is then aware of where he has been and where he is going next. The following passage on automatic controls for motor vehicles on the highways will illustrate both topic sentences and transition devices:

[1] Turning now to interurban travel we find that high speed is a paramount factor because of the great distances involved. [2] But compared to travel in the urban area interurban travel is more technical and less political, and there are now interesting developments under discussion.

[3] With the high speed desired for interurban travel we normally have to expect low vehicular volumes. [4] With some way to control the individual vehicles, however, this desired high speed might be maintained together with high volume of travel. [5] In principle this control can be achieved by putting the vehicles on a moving belt, hitching them to a moving cable, or combining them into a train.

[6] Recently suggested have been several systems which are simply versions of the moving belt or moving cable idea. The vehicle to be controlled is brought into an automatically controlled electronic radiation field. This field is then moved along the highway at a chosen rate of speed. [7] The controls can be placed in the pavement or overhead. Another system carries the wheels suspended on a monorail. The power is furnished by an individual electronic device for each vehicle. These systems are technically feasible and they have been developed in model form. [8] Full scale adoption of them is far in the future, however, because of high cost and unreliability.

[9] Paralleling development of the belt or cable plan of transporting the motor vehicle is the attention being given to new types of vehicles, such as the aircar, a vehicle that travels on an air bearing rather than on wheels.

Sentence [1] uses the phrase, "turning now to interurban travel," to indicate a change in subject. The transition is continued into sentence [2], which also is a topic sentence. In a way all three sentences starting with [3] can be considerd as introducing the next subject. Note how logically sentence [4] follows from [3] and [5] follows from [4].

Sentence [6] is a topic sentence for its paragraph. The other sentences in the paragraph develop the idea introduced by this sentence. Sentence [8] is a concluding or summary sentence. It contains, also, a hint that the author has finished with the moving belt systems.

The final sentence [9] combines the functions of transition with introducing a new topic — aircars. Presumably this composition would then continue with a discussion of the development of the aircar type of vehicle.

Skillful use of transitionary words, phrases, sentences, and paragraphs and of topic sentences assures an author that his reader will not get lost. The reader's retention will also be improved, because he can visualize the organization of the subject.

Development of Good Paragraphs

The topic sentence is important because it indicates the essential idea to be developed in order to produce the understanding necessary for a complete comprehension of the final report. The good topic sentence also serves as the medium by which the mind selects, develops, and offers pertinent and related ideas according to the law of association.

Unity is an essential characteristic of the paragraph. To achieve unity the writer uses only those thoughts that bear directly upon the single idea to be developed. He is careful to omit irrelevant matter or not to repeat the same thoughts when no advantage is gained in clarity and emphasis. The thoughts relating to one idea should not be scattered through several chapters in which other single ideas are being developed. An orderly sequence of thoughts arranged to build up the final climax of the paragraph requires the exercise of good judgment in evaluating the relative contribution of each sentence. The sentences when well arranged give the impression of steady progress in a definite direction. Each sentence "belongs" just as the component parts of a generator, diesel engine, or bridge fit into their proper places and perform their expected functions. Each sentence completes the thought in the preceding one and anticipates the thought in the next.

Connectives, directives, and transitional phrases may be used to join preceding sentences with new sentences. Their function is similar to that of the baton passed from one runner to the next in a relay race. Connectives provide an element of sequence and motion. They keep the reader posted with regard to the progress of thought. Grammars and books on English composition provide lists of connectives, directives, and transitional phrases; one example of each is shown here to indicate their use.

Addition — *Besides,* the samples arrived late.

Abatement — The evidence, *so to speak,* was conclusive.

Comparison — The shelter was bad, the food was *worse.*

Concession — *After all,* the data were carefully selected.

Continuation — *Moreover,* the entire experiment demonstrated the anticipated results.

Contrast — *On the other hand,* several of the tractors had to be abandoned.

Culmination — *To be brief,* the results warranted the effort.

Doubt — *Perhaps* some of the equipment may be saved.

Example — *For instance,* the airplane industry is typical.

Inference — *Certainly,* the witnesses should be questioned.

Progress in sequence — *First,* soundings were taken, *then* the alignment was established, and *finally* the type of structure was selected.

Progress in space — *Opposite* the generator there were several instrument panels.

Progress in time — *After seven days,* the specimens were tested in tension.

Purpose — *For this purpose,* the chief engineer allocated ten thousand dollars.

Result — *Thus,* all of the tests were useful in arriving at the conclusions.

Specification — *Namely,* the choice between weight and size had to be made.

Techniques of Paragraph Development

The paragraph has greater significance than the mere structural assembly of words into sentences and sentences into paragraphs. The full value of a word is developed by its function and position in a sentence rather than only by its definition in a dictionary. Likewise, sentences contribute mostly to the central idea in a paragraph when they follow some recognized system of development. Several well-established techniques for the development of paragraphs are discussed in the following pages.

Definition. The term "definition" usually brings to mind the dictionary type of definition. Actually, the criteria that are present in the well-written definition may be extended to an entire paragraph. Definition is the assignment of some specific meaning to a term; it can also be the development, by a paragraph or two, of a fuller meaning and interpretation of the concise definition stated as a topic sentence. The primary purpose of a definition is to establish a common and universal concept of an object, process, or idea. The definition of a word establishes its meaning within certain clearly defined limits; the extension of the single sentence definition into a paragraph enables the writer to develop his topic thoroughly and broadly. Some of the criteria in development by definition are as follows:

1. Statements are generally applicable to every item in the class defined.
2. Essential and primary characteristics of the concept are included.
3. Characteristics are peculiar to the concept and are distinguished from other concepts in the same class.
4. Definition is expressed in other concepts than those involving the term to be defined.
5. Language employed is clear and direct in contrast with obscure and figurative.
6. Positive statements are used for effectiveness.

Illustrations or Examples. Specific examples of ideas and statements implied in the topic sentence assist in the clarification of concepts. Illustrations and examples are of particular value in exposition and argumentation. They indicate possible application of the general idea, thereby creating full and accurate understanding.

From the Whole to the Part. The mind lends itself to an over-all exposure followed by detailed references to the component parts. Although this method is applied to all forms of writing, it is commonly used in description. The general proportions and dimensions of a power plant are first presented. Then the major units are described. Finally, the special devices and mechanisms are introduced. In discussing the organization of a company, its place, significance, and relation to the industry can be followed by a description of the major operating divisions. Then the relations of departments to each other and to the division are explained. Finally, the specific organization of each department is developed in detail. Classification and outlining serve as useful means of development from the whole to the part. Classification involves the arrangement of knowledge according to some rational system of comparison. Beams may be considered as a class of structural elements. They may be classified (a) according to the functions they perform in a structure as joists, purlins, lintels, girts, beams, girders, stringers, and floorbeams; (b) according to the materials of construction employed as timber, steel, aluminum, reinforced concrete, and reinforced clay tile; and (c) according to the nature of the supporting elements as cantilever, simple, continuous, restrained, and fixed. Once an orderly listing is made of the parts, the writer can usually supply the detailed descriptions, explanations, and relations.

Reasoning. The ability of the mind to select and evaluate that information and experience which has a bearing upon a certain problem is usually called reasoning. The mind has the faculty of marshaling facts, knowledge, and experience in order to arrive at a conclusive solution. Although these solutions are subject to error, nevertheless, they can be checked and corrected. One phase of reasoning involves the analysis of conditions. A problem is recognized and the whole situation is analyzed, or taken apart, into its component and contributing parts. Then each part or element is tested to determine whether it adds to the eventual solution. The process of selecting and reassembling only those parts which have a direct bearing on the solution is called synthesis, or putting together. Another method for developing a paragraph by reasoning is to study and relate causes with effects. In writing, one may state the effect first to arouse interest, and then present the various causes.

Division. Frequently a topic sentence presents an outline of the major features of a paragraph. This method makes the development clear and logical. The writer's outline or pattern needs only to be amplified, and the reader is conscious of the progress of the development at all stages. A chapter or paragraph may be oriented by the topic sentence:

> An examination of past predictions in the fields of airplanes, radios, television, and warfare should indicate the value of this procedure for forecasting the effects of invention.

With this topic sentence, the writer can either develop the idea in one concise paragraph or, as the subject implies, in four paragraphs preceded and followed by introductory and concluding paragraphs. The method of division is effective in oral presentation because the speaker as well as the listener can tally the major divisions as they are introduced and completed.

Time Sequence. The explanation — exposition — of processes lends itself to the method of time sequence. The writer arranges each step in construction, fabrication, and production in the order of the work. Sometimes, in complicated processes, two or more parts or elements are started simultaneously. Then, at various stages of production they are brought together and continue until completion or until another element joins them in the production line. In these complex instances the writer can resort to the "from the whole to the part" technique to sketch the over-all major phases of the production process; then, he can present in sequence and in detail the production of each part. Having completed the explanation of the production of each process, he can bring the parts together in a summary sentence or paragraph.

Space Sequence. In describing an object, machine, or structure the relative place or position of parts can be used as the method of developing the paragraph. Explanations of how machinery operates can utilize the space sequence idea by calling attention to the relative positions of major and auxiliary parts. The reader is brought to the position of the writer. Then, the writer guides the reader from point to point. The route or sequence should preferably be continuous, starting with the large and important and ending with the small and dependent objects or ideas.

Comparison and Contrast. Another method of development is to emphasize likenesses and differences in order to create a new image in terms of established images. The writer has a number of choices at his command. He may treat the comparisons as a separate group, the contrasts as a separate group, or he may intermingle comparisons with contrasts.

Forms of Paragraph Development

Although sentences may be developed into paragraphs by any of the foregoing techniques they, nevertheless, possess one other quality usually called "form." The form of a paragraph may be likened to its personality or distinguishing characteristic. Narration, description, exposition, and argumentation are the four forms of prose writing. On the basis of importance and frequency of use in reports, exposition ranks first; description, second; argumentation, third; and narration, fourth. Actually, a complete report utilizes all of these forms to the extent demanded by the content and ultimate purpose.

Exposition. Two types of material are found in exposition: The explanation of a process and of an idea. The function of both types of exposition is to provide clear understanding by giving instruction and by providing information. The characteristics of exposition are exactness of knowledge, orderly outlining and classification, and evidence of careful planning. The techniques of paragraph development found to be useful are definitions, comparisons, and contrasts, supplemented when useful with illustrative devices such as charts, diagrams, and photographs.

Exposition of a process deals with facts and operations in the order of their occurrence, that is, in a chronological step-by-step sequence. Occasionally, a certain stage in production may be performed by two or more alternate procedures, or two or more substages may proceed simultaneously. In these cases a flow chart, however simple or complicated, serves to keep the overlapping stages clearly before the reader. Transition from one stage to another is indicated as a new stage begins or as the preceding one ends. The exposition of a process is introduced by a preliminary sentence or paragraph to indicate its relation to other processes and to provide information on its economic and social significance. A summary sentence or paragraph will provide a sense of completion in terms of conclusions or recommendations.

Exposition of ideas usually deals with generalizations of beliefs and opinions and the introduction of specific examples. The exposition of a process, being definite and impersonal, is generally accepted by the reader. On the other hand, the exposition of an idea, being general and personal, may be, and usually is, challenged by the reader since concrete evidence is unavailable to both. In the exposition of a process the writer and reader depend on action and on principles that can be observed and proved. Whereas, in the exposition of an idea the writer and reader must have mutual confidence in each other's reasoning, judgment, and integrity, as well as skill in interpretation. The development of ideas depends upon the establishment of propositions (1) that can be tested and verified either by personal observations and experiences or by those of another authority; and (2) that can be reached by a logical process of reasoning. Thus, evidence, authority, and logic are the characteristics in the exposition of ideas.

Description. Reports deal to so large an extent with physical things that may not be known to the reader that the form of writing is definitely descriptive. The main function of description is to create an image in the mind of the reader who does not have access to the objects which are discussed in the report. Description gives written or oral equivalents of objects, shapes, relationships, qualities, and impressions. The techniques for paragraph development are the space and time sequences, comparisons and contrasts, and the citation of physical and chemical properties.

Argumentation. Many reports have as their ultimate purpose some action to be taken by an executive, an organization, or a governmental agency. Data are developed and arranged to convince the reader that he can base his decision upon the recommendations contained in the report. To achieve this end the writer should be factual, logical, direct, and convincing. Factual matter can be stated but debatable matter and policy need supporting evidence. Facts and principles are effectively employed when they lead the reader to conclusions that the writer strives to establish. To persuade, the writer should support statements with acceptable evidence, pertinent examples, and unquestioned authorities. Seldom are all the advantages on the same side of an issue. Therefore, the writer should indicate the instances which may cause negative action, and, at the same time, he should demonstrate the greater significance of his proposals.

Narration. Though seldom used in reports, narration can make the section on history of the subject effective. The story-telling characteristics of narration are personal references, conversation, and a sense of progress or motion. Of these, the use of the conversational method is seldom used in reports.

THE WHOLE REPORT—PARAGRAPHS IN ACTION

A person entrusted with the responsibility of preparing a report has a certain amount of firsthand contact with the elements which will contribute to the solution of the problem. His major concern is to anticipate the report as a whole and to assemble available and missing information to round out the final presentation. The well-qualified writer of a report has at his command technical knowledge, professional aptitude and experience, the knack of writing well, ability to think clearly, logically and creatively, and an intimate acquaintance with the methods of outlining, collecting data, tabular presentation and methods of preparing illustrations. Furthermore, his final product will be more attractive if he is acquainted with the production phases of report preparation; namely, format and arrangement, mechanics of style, punctuation, abstracting, and copyreading. Finally, he will achieve success if he visualizes the finished report in terms of its readers, its organization, and its content.

Only after having prepared several reports will the writer be in a position to anticipate the final product as a whole. In the meantime the chapters of this book will serve as reference and source material for each problem as it occurs in the preparation of the manuscript and final product.

READABILITY

Some compositions are easier to read than others. Two of the many elements which determine the level of readability are style or manner of writing, and subject matter or content. Complicated mathematical and scientific terminology makes some fields of thought difficult to communicate. The reader is in many cases not as far advanced as the writer. In other instances the writer is not as skilled in the art of communication as he is in the science of his technical specialty. Yet, in each field of thought some writers communicate their ideas more successfully than others.

Several factors inherent in the composition determine to what extent writing is easy to read and comprehend; in making this generalization it is assumed that the subject of the article is within the reader's field.

Readability may be defined as that character of writing that makes it effective — fully and exactly communicative with the minimum of effort on the part of the reader. Thus, a good readable passage needs to be read only once to gain the exact idea, impression, or feeling the author wishes the reader to get. Any passage that requires a second or third reading or concentrated study to gain its meaning has a low score on readability. The goal of every writer should be to produce a high level of readability in his compositions so that his readers may gain his ideas accurately with ease.

Readability Factors and Formulas

The factors in writing which control readability are many. They are found within the words, the sentences, the paragraphs, and the physical appearance of the writing. Among these many factors that affect readability may be listed the following few:

1. Factors related to words
   - Number of syllables per word
   - Number of letters per word
   - Percentage of long words in the composition
   - Sequential distribution of words according to their length
   - Percentage of words familiar to the reader
   - Repetition of words used in exactly the same sense
   - Consistency of use of words in the same sense
   - Use of active verbs
   - Use of root or prime word rather than derivatives
   - Use of nouns rather than pronouns
2. Factors related to sentences
   - Number of words per sentence
   - Sequential distribution of sentences according to their length in words
   - Percentage of long sentences — say over 40 words
   - Structural arrangement — order of subject, verb, and object
   - Kind and amount of punctuation
   - Complexity — number and length of phases and clauses
   - Place within the sentence of the key words
   - Place within the sentence of modifiers with respect to words, phrases, or clauses modified
   - Use of unnecessary or loosely used modifiers
   - Use of parallel construction and parallel units in numerical quantities
3. Factors related to paragraphs
   - Number of sentences per paragraph
   - Number of paragraphs per page or per column
   - Transitional words, phrases, sentences, and paragraphs introducing a change in subject
4. Factors related to physical appearance
   - Use of white space in margins, headings, and lines
   - Length of type line
   - Use of headings as guide markers
   - Size of type
   - Face of type
   - Page layout
   - Color of ink and paper

Formulas for computing readability have been under development since the 1920's.[2]

---

[2] The following references, presented chronologically, are selected from the extensive literature available:

Lively, Bertha A. and Pressey, S. L. "A Method for Measuring the 'Vocabulary Burden' of Textbooks." *Educational Administration and Supervision*. 9:389–98. October, 1923.

Burch, Mary Crowell. "Determination of a Content of the Course in Literature of a Suitable Difficulty for Junior and Senior High School Students." *Genetic Psychology Monographs*. 4:Nos. 2 and 3:265. August and September, 1928.

Vogel, Mabel and Washburne, Carleton. "An Objective Method of Determining Grade Placement of Children's Reading Material." *Elementary School Journal*. 28:373–81. January, 1928. See this reference for the Winnetka formula.

Lewerenz, Alfred S. "Measurement of the Difficulty of Reading Materials." *Los Angeles Educational Research Bulletin*. 8:11–16. March, 1929.

Dale, Edgar and Tyler, Ralph W. "A Study of the Factors Influencing the Difficulty of Reading Materials for Adults of Limited Reading Ability." *Library Quarterly*. 4:384–412. July, 1934.

Gray, William S. and Leary, Bernice E. *What Makes a Book Readable*. Chicago, University of Chicago Press. 1935.

Bryson, Lyman. "What Are Readable Books?" *Educational Forum*. 1:397–402. May, 1937.

Lorge, Irving. "Predicting Reading Difficulty of Selections for Children." *Elementary English Review*. 16:229–33. October, 1939.

Elliott, Catherine J. "Critical Analysis of the Objective Method of Measuring Reading Difficulty." *Pittsburgh Schools*. 15:201–9. May, 1941.

Walther, Cyrilla. "The Reading Difficulty of Magazines." *School Review*. 51:100–5. February, 1943.

Flesch, Rudolf. "Marks of Readable Style." *Contribution to Education*. No. 897. Teachers College, Columbia University. 1943. This reference gives a bibliography of 88 references.

Lorge, Irving. "Predicting Readability." *Teachers College Record*. 45:404–19. March, 1944.

Flesch, Rudolf. *Art of Plain Talk*. New York, Harper & Brothers. 1946.

Flesch, Rudolf. "A New Readability Yardstick." *Journal of Applied Psychology*. June, 1948.

Lorge, Irving. "The Lorge and Flesch Readability Formulae: A Correction." *School and Society*. 67:1730:141–42. February 21, 1948.

Dale, Edgar and Chall, Jeanne S. "A Formula for Predicting Readability." *Educational Research Bulletin*. 27: No. 1:11–20, 28. January 21, 1948: "A Formula for Predicting Readability: Instructions." 27: No. 2:37–54. February 18, 1948.

Flesch, Rudolf. *The Art of Readable Writing*. New York, Harper & Brothers. 1949.

Gunning, Robert. *The Technique of Clear Writing*. New York, McGraw-Hill Book Company, Inc. 1952. See this reference for the fog index.

Flesch, Rudolf. *How to Make Sense*. New York, Harper & Brothers. 1954.

Klare, George R. *Measurement of Readability*. Ames, Iowa State University Press. 1962.

The early work was directed primarily toward school children through the element of vocabulary. In 1935 Gray and Leary tested 82 factors, but reduced them to five in their final formula. These five factors are: (1) number of different hard words (words not in the Dale list of 769 easy words) ; (2) number of first, second, and third person pronouns; (3) average sentence length in words; (4) vocabulary diversity as measured by the number of different words expressed as a percentage of total words; and (5) number of prepositional phrases.

In 1943 Rudolf Flesch published the first of his series of formulas, followed by Dale and Chall in 1948. The fog index by Robert Gunning was published in 1952.

These past attempts involved several factors affecting readability, but principally sentence length, sentence structure, and choice of words. The hunt has been for a simple formula easily applied and yet reliable in measuring comparative reading ease.

The fog index by Gunning is a simple one. It is simply the sum of the average number of words per sentence and percentage of hard words (percentage of words having three and more syllables) multiplied by 0.4. This product supposedly approximates the public school grade level based on the readers and texts on literature used in the public schools. For instance, 20 words per sentence and 10 per cent words of three syllables and more would produce a fog index of $0.4\ (20 + 10) = 12$, corresponding to the reading level of the twelfth grade, or senior high school. This over-simplified formula fails to hold over the full range of grade levels as can be proved by calculating the grades from the data in Table 8.5.

Many of the earlier attempts to develop formulas for testing the readability of writing were based upon lists of familiar words. The use of uncommon words (words not in the list of common words) lowered the readability score. Many of the early studies were made in connection with writing and selecting reading texts for use in public schools. The goodness of the formulas was tested against the comprehension of the pupils.

For adult reading and for formulas to test a wide variety of business and professional writings the use of word lists and word forms cause needless effort. Further, the results, when applied to readings for adults, were not always valid because of widely different vocabularies.

Earlier formulas of readability included factors which created reader interest, such as references to persons. Here again for adult reading the creation of interest in what is read is not a suitable test for readability. It may be assumed that business and professional reading is done by readers who have an adequate vocabulary to understand the words read and an interest and motivation to read what they read. Ease of reading may, therefore, be reduced to three simple factors: (a) sentence length, (b) word length, and (c) sentence arrangement and complexity.

The formulas presented below measure sentence length and word length directly. Sentence complexity is measured indirectly by sentence length for the reason that short sentences are not easily arranged in an awkward manner, nor can they be complex or contain many useless words. The formula does not give weight to misplaced modifiers, loosely used pronouns, nor weak verbs. Although important to readability, these items are minor factors to sentence length and word length.

The fog index by Gunning would be an acceptable formula if it agreed more closely with the readers and texts used in the several grades in public schools. Gunning's formula has been modified by recourse to an analysis of the public school books listed in Table 8.1. The data assembled from this analysis are given in Tables 8.2 to 8.5.

The data in Table 8.5 on average words per sentence, syllables per word, and letters per word (see also Fig. 8.2) can be reduced to the following formulas, which hold well throughout the public school grades from 1 through 12:

$$G = 0.50\ (W + S) - 4.50$$
$$G = 0.58\ (W + L) - 4.60$$

in which,

G = public school grade
W = average number of words per sentence
S = percentage of total words of three and more syllables per word
L = percentage of total words of nine and more letters per word.

Both formulas give approximately the same result. Each is based on sentence length and word length, the two easily identified and measured factors which bear heavily on readability. These straight line formulas may be projected beyond the twelfth grade to give a comparison of any composition with the public school grade reading levels. The senior college level may be considered to be grade 16.

A test of readability is a useful tool for businessmen and professional men who have writing responsibilities. For use by business and professional men a readability formula needs to be easily solved and the input data must be easily and quickly obtained. Any formula that involves comparisons with a list of common words, identification of prepositional phrases, adverbs, parts of speech, or sentence structure is doomed to nonuse in business and professional writings.

The two formulas offered herein are such that they can be used with but little effort and with a minimum of uncertainty. The comparative scale — public school grades — is easy to judge. These formulas can be readily used by any writer to produce a reliable index of the level of readability of his composition.

A study of Tables 8.3 to 8.9 will afford a comparison for one's own writing. Technical and business reports should be held to a

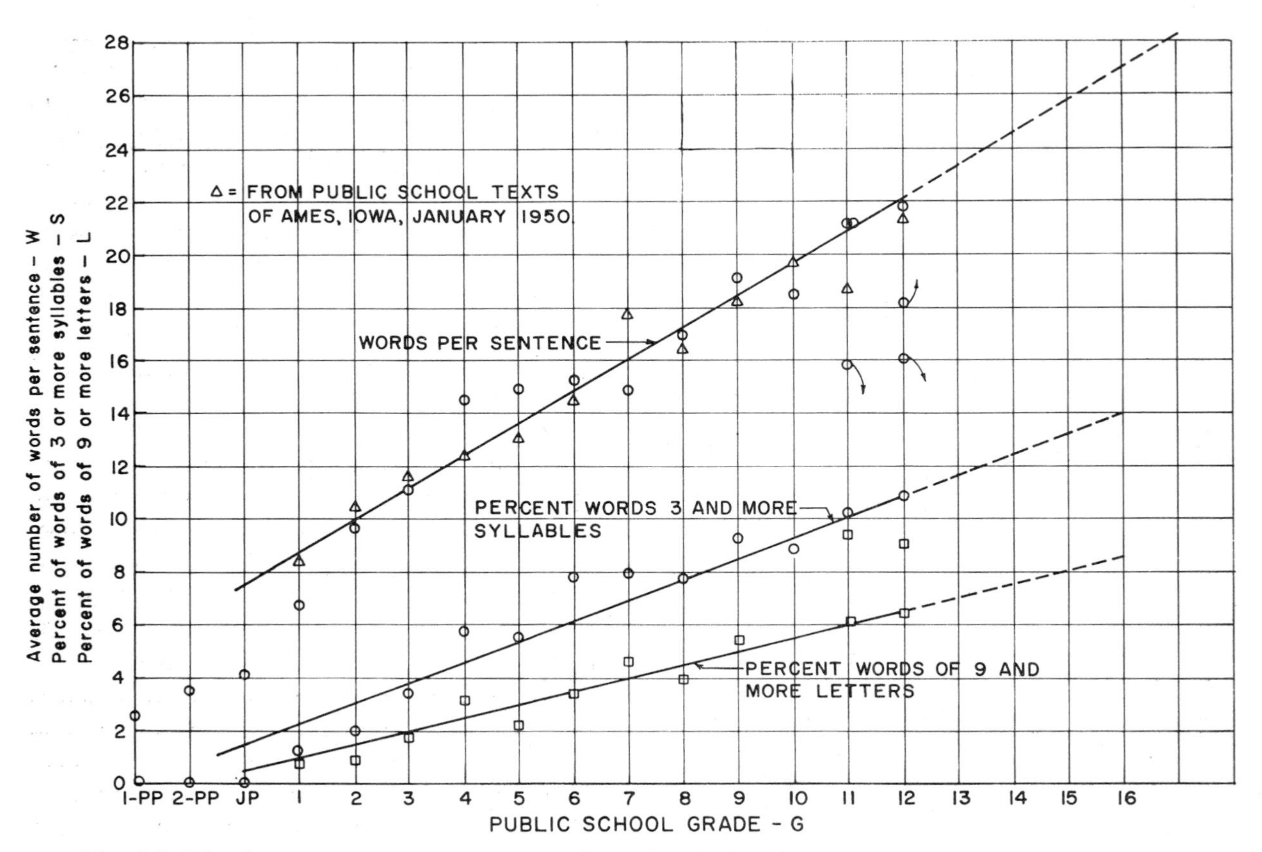

Fig. 8.2. Words per sentence, percentage of words of three or more syllables, and percentage of words of nine or more letters for the reading texts used in the public school grades in Arlington County, Virginia, 1960–61.

grade level of 12 to 14, corresponding to an average sentence length of 20 to 22 words and not more than 13 to 15 per cent words of three and more syllables, or 8.5 to 10 per cent words of 9 and more letters. Further it is advisable to keep all sentences to less than 50 words.

Guides for Counting Words, Syllables, Letters, and Punctuation For Determining Readability Factors

In developing the data in Tables 8.3 to 8.9 the following instructions and guides were used. They may be applied to all types of publications.

1. Adopt a random sampling scheme for the paper, magazine, or book that will yield at least 200 sentences from the pages throughout the publication. Avoid a system that will favor the beginning sentence of paragraphs. For distribution of sentences by words per sentence at least 300 sentences are required.
2. Omit advertising, tabulations, short statements, captions, recipes, dialogue, and the like. Wanted is the nonfiction, descriptive, feature type of composition.
3. Consider a semicolon as a period when it completes a full thought, i.e., end of a sentence. The words following the semicolon are to be treated as a full sentence if they make a complete thought. The words preceding a colon are to be considered a full sentence when they make a complete thought. Omit the words following a colon when they consist of itemizations not forming complete sentences.
4. Count compound words with a hyphen as two words.
5. Count numbers and abbreviations as written-out words in the form you would say them if reading aloud. Likewise count the letters in the words and the syllables you would use in expressing numbers and abbreviations aloud.
6. In counting punctuation, omit quotation marks, hyphens, semicolons (except when they are used as commas), periods, question marks, exclamation points, apostrophes, and contractions. Count only commas, dashes, colons (except when used as a semicolon or period), and parentheses (both).
7. Count 2,000 to 3,000 words for syllable and letter length. It is not necessary to count the syllables and words from the identical words used in the length of sentence count.

These rules are not the same as Flesch, Gunning, and others have proposed. They are simpler and devised to minimize the judgments to be exercised to include all material read, and to provide a method of handling abbreviations and numerals.

The above procedures were applied to a variety of published works as shown in Tables 8.6 through 8.9, and to the public school books used in developing the formulas.

Comments on Tables 8.1 to 8.9

Tables 8.1 through 8.9 give data bearing upon readability. This collection of data from the books and periodicals needs some explanation to make it better understood. The Scott, Foresman series of 12 readers (Table 8.1) from the first pre-primer through grade six were written to comply with rigid specifications as to vocabulary. Table 8.2 shows the syllables per word distribution of the new words introduced in each book and the accumulated vocabulary. The vocabulary begins with 17 words in the first pre-primer and reaches 5,748 words in the sixth grade reader. Each new word introduced was used on succeeding pages according to a predetermined pattern. Introduction of new words was scheduled throughout the book so the pupil would encounter the new words one at a time.

The percentage distribution of syllables per word and letters per word in Table 8.3 is not always smooth or consistent in trend. The introduction of a given word of syllable or letter length greater than those in use theretofore, and its repeated use, would tend to produce an unusually high frequency of use of that word. Some departure from a smooth distribution is also caused from lack of a stable sample, particularly in the low frequencies.

The high percentage of words of seven letters as compared with words of six or eight letters is a natural characteristic of the English language. This same high percentage of seven-letter words is found for the general publications in Table 8.7.

The maximum sentence length generally increases from the low grades through grade 12 (Table 8.4). There is a noticeable difference in grades 11 and 12 between the author's comments and the original literature. Within these books, composed largely

TABLE 8.1. LIST OF BASIC READERS AND BOOKS ON LITERATURE ANALYZED FOR LETTER, SYLLABLE, AND SENTENCE COUNTS

Note: These books were used in the public schools of Arlington County, Virginia, during the 1960–61 school year.

Book and Grade Designation	Title	Authors	Publisher	Year Published
1-PP (First Pre-Primer)	We Look and See	William S. Gray, Marion Monroe, A. Sterl Artley, May Hill Arbuthnot	Scott, Foresman & Co.	1956
2-PP (Second Pre-Primer)	We Work and Play	"	"	1951
JP (Junior Primer)	Guess Who	William S. Gray, A. Sterl Artley, May Hill Arbuthnot	"	1951
1¹	Fun With Dick and Jane	"	"	1951
1²	Our New Friends	"	"	1951
2¹	Friends and Neighbors	"	"	1952
2²	More Friends and Neighbors	"	"	1952
3¹	New Streets and Roads	William S. Gray, Marion Monroe, A. Sterl Artley, May Hill Arbuthnot	"	1956
3²	More Streets and Roads	William S. Gray, A. Sterl Artley, May Hill Arbuthnot	"	1953
4	Times and Places	William S. Gray, May Hill Arbuthnot	"	1951
5	Days and Deeds	"	"	1951
6	People and Progress	"	"	1951
7¹	Parades	William S. Gray, Marion Monroe, A. Sterl Artley, May Hill Arbuthnot	"	1956
8	Adventures for Readers	Jacob M. Ross, Mary Rives Bowman, Egbert W. Nieman	Harcourt, Brace & Co.	1953
9	Adventures in Reading	Jacob M. Ross, Blanche Jennings Thompson, Evan Lodge	"	1952
10	Prose and Poetry for Appreciation	J. Kenner Agnew, Agnes L. McCarthy	The L. W. Singer Co., Inc.	1955
11-AC (Author's Comments)	Prose and Poetry of America	Agnes L. McCarthy, Delmar Rodabaugh	"	1955
11-OL (Original Literature)				
12-AC (Author's Comments)	Prose and Poetry of England	Delmer Rodabaugh, Agnes L. McCarthy	The L. W. Singer Co., Inc.	1955
12-OL (Original Literature)				

of early literature, there is a noticeable difference in words and sentences between the works of the several authors.

Table 8.5 is a summary of the characteristics of the 18 public school readers and books on literature listed in Table 8.1. This table contains the data used to develop Fig. 8.2 and the readability formulas. The high number of words per punctuation point for first, second, and third grades as compared to higher grades, results from the heavy use of commas in the direct quotations of speech. Table 8.5 for public school books may be compared with Table 8.6 for general publications.

From Table 8.6 it is easily noted that the popular home type of magazine is control-edited to the level of grades 10 to 12. These publications have both a low word per sentence count, 17 to 18, and a low percentage, 10 to 13, of words of three and more syllables. The New Testament (J) is unusual with its 20.78 words per sentence and the low syllables per word, 1.32. The rather high percentage of long sentences (up to 112 words) makes part of the New Testament difficult to read. As a whole, though, it is high in readability, because of few polysyllables (23.89%) and high monosyllables (76.11%), the highest percentage in Table 8.7.

Table 8.8, for four publications, gives the letters per word distribution for different numbers of syllables per word. It will be noticed that the average number of letters per word of a given number of syllables is about the same for all four publications. The average number of letters per syllable decreases from about 3.20 for the one-syllable words to about 2.25 for the six-syllable words.

The percentage distribution of words per sentence in Table 8.9 is from the raw samples. Even the 2,880-sentence samples from several issues of the *Reader's Digest* is not sufficient to produce a smooth curve. This table gives some indication that certain authors may tend to follow a sentence length that produces a bimodal distribution, or a plateau top.

TABLE 8.2. NUMBER OF WORDS BY SYLLABLES IN THE VOCABULARY OF THE BASIC READERS OF THE SCOTT, FORESMAN SERIES

No. of Syllables	Grade and Book Designation											
	1-PP	2-PP	JP	1^1	1^2	2^1	2^2	3^1	3^2	4	5	6
	Number of Words Added in Book											
1	15	15	27	78	113	151	173	206	187	328	279	229
2	2	6	3	18	61	68	126	163	222	481	597	620
3				4*	3	10	15	28	83	210	345	452
4							1	4	5	43	117	183
5									1	2	26	45
6											1	11
7											1	0
Total	17	21	30	100	177	229	315	401	498	1064	1366	1540
	Total Vocabulary in Book											
1	15	30	57	125†	238	389	562	768	955	1283	1562	1791
2	2	8	11	29	90	158	284	447	669	1150	1747	2367
3				4	7	17	32	60	143	353	698	1150
4							1	5	10	53	170	353
5									1	3	29	74
6											1	12
7											1	1
Total	17	38	68	158	335	564	879	1280	1778	2842	4208	5748

* Includes animals, family, grandfather, and grandmother.
† Ten words not carried forward.

TABLE 8.3. PERCENTAGE DISTRIBUTION OF SYLLABLES AND LETTERS PER WORD IN ARLINGTON COUNTY (VIRGINIA) PUBLIC SCHOOL READERS

Syllables per Word	First Pre-Primer	Second Pre-Primer	Junior Primer	Book 1^1	Book 1^2	Book 2^1	Book 2^2	Book 3^1	Book 3^2	Book 4
	Percentage of Words of Given Number of Syllables Per Word									
1	90.15	82.30	86.18	84.46	80.08	75.88	74.62	74.03	69.85	68.91
2	9.85	17.70	13.82	14.10	18.75	22.16	23.25	22.95	26.36	25.35
3				1.44	1.17	1.96	2.06	2.93	3.66	5.21
4							0.07	0.09	0.09	0.49
5									0.04	0.04
6										
7										
Total	100.00	100.00	100.00	100.00	100.00	100.00	100.00	100.00	100.00	100 00
Letters per Word	Percentage of Words of Given Number of Letters per Word									
1	0.00	2.42	4.68	3.98	3.08	3.47	3.77	3.96	2.99	3.39
2	22.69	14.29	17.32	13.51	12.97	12.11	11.82	11.04	13.81	11.79
3	23.58	28.78	25.38	23.73	28.03	27.25	28.19	28.50	26.94	27.10
4	43.88	37.48	37.49	40.12	32.55	27.53	23.90	23.79	21.76	19.65
5	9.85	6.89	8.16	9.26	12.03	13.51	15.56	13.95	12.96	14.59
6		8.22	4.89	6.04	7.21	8.84	9.00	9.70	10.63	9.80
7		0.00	0.52	1.30	1.69	3.82	4.38	49.9	6.66	6.28
8		0.00	0.00	0.89	1.74	2.55	2.37	2.38	2.37	4.20
9		1.93	1.56	0.55	0.50	0.60	0.75	0.89	1.21	1.49
10				0.00	0.00	0.12	0.10	0.56	0.40	0.99
11				0.62	0.20	0.12	0.16	0.19	0.18	0.45
12						0.08	0.00	0.05	0.09	0.27
13										0.11
14										
15										
Total	100.00	100.00	100.00	100.00	100.00	100.00	100.00	100.00	100.00	100.00

TABLE 8.3. (*Cont.*) PERCENTAGE DISTRIBUTION OF SYLLABLES AND LETTERS PER WORD IN ARLINGTON COUNTY (VIRGINIA) PUBLIC SCHOOL READERS

Book 5	Book 6	Book 7	Book 8	Book 9	Book 10	Author's Comments 11	Original Literature 11	Author's Comments 12	Original Literature 12
Percentage of Words of Given Number of Syllables Per Word									
69.68	69.02	68.85	69.29	69.10	68.92	61.30	67.05	58.89	69.92
24.47	23.19	23.27	23.00	21.67	22.20	22.79	22.74	25.03	19.26
4.99	6.44	6.00	6.15	7.35	5.83	9.75	7.58	11.84	7.94
0.62	0.83	1.58	1.22	1.55	2.59	4.84	2.17	3.42	2.20
0.12	0.29	0.25	0.34	0.33	0.46	1.20	0.46	0.82	0.68
0.06	0.17	0.00				0.12			
0.06	0.06	0.05							
100.00	100.00	100.00	100.00	100.00	100.00	100.00	100.00	100.0	100.00
Percentage of Words of Given Number of Letters per Word									
3.40	3.96	2.89	3.69	3.79	4.09	2.69	4.56	3.08	4.44
14.45	13.31	14.40	15.60	16.64	15.07	17.10	15.98	16.80	19.20
25.58	25.36	24.64	24.09	24.28	23.81	21.71	22.78	19.82	23.29
18.91	19.33	20.64	19.28	19.27	19.72	14.77	16.91	14.33	16.47
14.88	13.95	12.53	12.02	11.58	13.21	9.93	11.51	12.41	11.52
9.56	8.19	9.38	10.31	9.27	9.40	8.97	8.80	9.72	7.85
6.56	8.08	7.76	7.00	6.58	5.30	9.03	8.11	9.06	7.00
4.46	4.33	3.04	3.95	3.11	3.81	6.28	5.25	5.71	3.75
1.40	1.85	2.74	2.40	2.90	2.88	4.13	3.09	3.35	2.47
0.32	1.00	1.12	0.80	1.26	11.04	2.51	1.54	3.19	1.88
0.32	0.42	0.56	0.64	0.74	1.02	1.02	0.93	1.43	1.36
0.16	0.11	0.20	0.11	0.26	0.37	0.84	0.31	0.77	0.60
	0.11	0.05	0.06	0.21	0.28	0.78	0.15	0.33	0.17
	0.05	0.05	0.05	0.11		0.18	0.08		
						0.06			
100.00	100.00	100.00	100.00	100.00	100.00	100.00	100.00	100.00	100.00

TABLE 8.4. SUMMARY OF ARLINGTON COUNTY (VIRGINIA) PUBLIC SCHOOL READERS

Percentage Distribution of Sentences by Words per Sentence

Words Per Sentence	First Pre-Primer	Second Pre-Primer	Junior Primer	Book 1^1	Book 1^2	Book 2^1	Book 2^2	Book 3^1	Book 3^2	Book 4	Book 5	Book 6	Book 7	Book 8	Book 9	Book 10	Author's Comments Book 11	Original Literature Book 11	Author's Comments Book 12	Original Literature Book 12
1	5.38	1.67	0.42	0.00	0.00	0.00	0.00	0.00	0.00	0.00	0.00	0.00	0.00	0.00	0.00	0.00	0.00	0.00	0.00	0.00
2	42.31	18.75	11.68	0.67	1.12	1.04	0.00	1.09	0.00	0.27	0.49	0.74	0.00	0.00	0.00	0.00	0.00	0.00	0.00	0.32
3	42.31	40.41	20.81	5.00	4.85	1.04	1.80	0.66	1.12	0.82	0.99	1.74	1.49	2.02	1.10	0.80	0.37	0.00	0.43	0.64
4	9.23	17.92	30.79	30.33	9.70	5.47	4.79	3.72	3.59	1.37	2.47	2.48	1.79	4.04	1.47	1.07	0.00	1.10	0.86	1.59
5	0.77	15.00	22.08	24.33	10.45	6.25	3.89	6.56	3.81	2.19	3.46	3.97	2.38	4.27	1.83	1.61	0.37	2.19	1.29	2.23
6		5.42	11.46	16.00	19.40	7.55	9.58	6.13	6.50	3.55	3.95	4.96	3.27	4.49	2.56	3.22	1.12	2.47	2.16	2.87
7		0.83	2.55	13.34	13.43	13.28	12.87	5.03	8.97	4.37	4.44	5.46	5.65	4.49	3.30	3.22	1.12	2.74	2.59	3.18
8			0.21	2.33	5.60	9.90	6.29	6.35	9.64	5.19	4.94	4.47	3.87	4.49	4.40	3.75	1.86	3.01	3.02	3.18
9				2.67	5.60	5.73	8.08	6.78	7.62	5.74	5.19	4.22	6.25	4.49	5.86	3.75	2.60	3.84	3.02	3.18
10				1.67	7.84	6.25	6.87	8.32	5.61	6.28	5.43	4.47	4.76	4.27	5.49	4.29	2.97	3.84	3.45	3.50
11				1.00	4.10	9.90	9.88	9.85	5.16	6.56	5.68	5.46	6.55	4.27	5.13	4.56	2.97	4.11	3.88	3.50
12				2.33	4.85	10.42	9.59	8.75	7.40	6.83	6.17	5.71	7.74	4.04	4.76	4.83	3.35	4.66	4.31	3.50
13				0.00	7.84	7.29	6.29	8.75	7.85	6.56	5.68	5.71	5.95	3.82	4.40	4.29	3.72	5.20	4.31	3.82
14				0.33	2.61	8.33	8.38	6.56	6.28	6.28	4.94	5.21	3.87	3.82	4.03	5.09	4.46	4.38	4.31	3.18
15					0.00	5.47	5.99	5.47	7.62	5.74	4.69	4.22	3.57	3.60	3.66	4.29	4.09	3.84	4.74	3.18
16					0.75	1.04	2.40	1.97	6.73	4.92	4.44	3.72	5.06	3.37	3.66	3.75	4.83	3.56	4.74	3.82
17					1.20	0.00	1.80	6.78	4.48	4.37	3.95	3.47	5.06	3.16	3.30	3.49	4.46	3.29	4.74	3.18
18					0.37	0.52	0.30	2.63	4.93	3.83	3.70	3.23	4.46	3.16	3.30	2.95	4.83	3.84	5.17	3.18
19					0.37	0.52	0.00	1.53	1.35	3.55	3.46	2.73	3.87	2.92	2.93	3.22	4.83	3.84	5.17	3.18
20							0.30	1.97	0.67	3.28	3.21	2.73	3.57	2.92	2.56	3.75	5.20	3.29	5.60	2.87
21							0.30	0.66	0.45	3.01	2.96	2.48	3.27	2.70	2.56	3.49	4.46	3.01	5.60	2.87
22							0.00	0.44	0.00	2.73	2.72	2.48	3.87	2.70	2.20	3.49	4.09	2.74	5.17	3.18
23							0.30		0.22	2.46	2.47	2.48	2.08	2.47	2.20	3.49	3.72	2.74	4.74	2.55
24							0.30			2.19	2.22	2.23	1.79	2.47	1.83	3.49	2.97	2.47	3.45	2.87
25										1.91	1.98	2.23	0.89	2.25	1.83	3.22	2.97	2.19	2.59	2.55
26										1.64	1.73	1.99	0.89	2.25	1.47	3.22	2.97	1.92	2.16	2.55
27										1.37	1.73	1.74	0.89	2.02	1.83	2.95	2.97	1.64	1.72	2.23
28										1.09	1.48	1.49	1.49	1.80	1.47	2.14	2.97	1.92	1.72	1.92
29										0.82	1.23	1.24	0.89	1.57	1.83	1.88	2.23	1.64	1.29	1.91
30										0.55	0.99	0.99	0.60	1.35	1.47	1.07	2.23	1.10	0.86	1.59
31										0.27	0.99	0.74	0.60	1.12	1.47	1.34	1.86	1.37	0.86	1.59
32										0.27	0.74	0.74	0.60	0.90	1.47	1.07	1.86	1.37	0.86	1.59
33											0.49	0.50	0.30	0.90	1.47	1.07	1.49	1.10	0.86	1.59
34											0.25	0.50	0.60	0.67	1.10	0.80	1.49	1.37	0.46	1.27
35											0.49	0.50	0.30	0.67	1.10	0.54	1.12	1.37	0.43	1.27

36											0.25	0.49	0.30	0.67	1.47	0.54	1.49	1.37	0.00	1.59
37												0.49	0.30	0.45	1.10	0.27	0.74	1.10	0.86	0.96
38												0.49	0.30	0.45	1.10	0.00	0.74	1.10	0.86	1.27
39												0.27	0.30	0.45	1.10	0.27	1.12	0.82	0.00	1.27
40												0.25	0.00	0.45	0.00	0.54	0.74	0.55	0.43	0.96
41												0.25	0.00	0.45	0.73	0.27	0.00	0.82	0.86	0.96
42												0.25	0.30	0.45	1.10	0.27	0.40	1.10	0.00	0.64
43												0.24	0.30	0.45	0.73	0.54	0.74	0.27	0.43	0.96
44												0.24	0.27	0.23	0.00	0.00	0.37	0.55		0.64
45													0.00	0.23	0.73	0.27	0.00	0.27		0.64
46													0.00	0.23	0.73	0.27	0.37	0.27		0.32
47													0.23	0.23	0.00	0.27	0.37	0.00		0.00
48														0.23	0.73	0.27	0.00	0.27		0.64
49														0.23	0.00	0.27	0.00	0.27		0.32
50														0.00	0.37	0.27	0.37	0.00		0.00
51														0.22	0.00	0.00		0.55		0.32
52														0.22	0.37	0.00		0.00		0.32
53														0.22	0.00	0.00		0.00		0.00
54														0.00	0.00	0.00		0.55		0.32
55														0.22	0.37	0.00		0.27		0.00
56														0.00	0.00	0.00		0.55		0.00
57														0.00	0.00	0.00		0.00		0.00
58														0.22	0.33	0.00		0.00		0.32
59														0.00		0.00		0.00		0.32
60														0.22		0.00		0.27		0.00
61																0.27		0.27		0.00
62																0.00		0.00		0.32
63																0.27		0.00		0.00
64																		0.00		0.32
65																		0.00		0.00
66																		0.00		0.32
67																		0.00		0.00
68																		0.27		0.32
69																		0.27		0.32
70																		0.27		
71																		0.00		
72																		0.00		
73																		0.55		
74																		0.00		
75																		0.00		
76																		0.00		
77																		0.00		
78																		0.27		
Total	100.00	100.00	100.00	100.00	100.00	100.00	100.00	100.00	100.00	100.00	100.00	100.00	100.00	100.00	100.00	100.00	100.00	100.00	100.00	100.00

TABLE 8.5. SUMMARY OF READABILITY FACTORS OF BASIC READERS AND BOOKS ON LITERATURE USED AS PUBLIC SCHOOL TEXTS

Note: See Table 8.1 for list of books.

Book and Grade Designation	Average Words per Sentence	Number of Words per Point*	Syllables per Word	Letters per Word	Letters per Syllable	Per Cent Words of 3 Syllables and More	Per Cent Words of 9 Letters and More
1-PP	2.58	1.19	1.10	3.41	3.10	0.00	0.00
2-PP	3.45	1.74	1.18	3.65	3.10	0.00	1.93
JP	4.08	1.66	1.14	3.53	3.10	0.00	1.56
1^1	5.52	6.34	1.17	3.73	3.19	1.44	1.17
1^2	7.79	17.12	1.21	3.79	3.13	1.17	0.70
2^1	9.53	23.16	1.26	3.96	3.14	1.96	0.92
2^2	9.97	20.42	1.28	3.99	3.12	2.13	1.01
3^1	11.07	22.00	1.29	4.05	3.13	3.02	1.69
3^2	11.16	25.93	1.34	4.11	3.06	3.79	1.88
4	14.43	14.59	1.37	4.28	3.10	5.74	3.20
5	14.96	13.61	1.37	4.19	3.08	5.54	2.20
6	15.23	14.24	1.40	4.28	3.05	7.79	3.49
7	14.84	15.27	1.41	4.42	3.13	7.88	4.72
8	16.94	13.88	1.40	4.26	3.04	7.71	4.06
9	19.11	14.88	1.42	4.26	2.99	9.23	5.48
10	18.45	16.56	1.43	4.30	3.00	8.88	5.59
11-AC	21.09	16.99	1.62	4.75	2.93	15.91	9.52
11-OL	21.08	14.97	1.46	4.42	3.02	10.21	6.10
12-AC	18.10	16.83	1.62	4.74	2.92	16.08	9.07
12-OL	21.74	12.04	1.49	4.28	2.87	10.82	6.48

* Includes only interior punctuation, such as commas and parentheses; colons and semicolons included only when they did not end a complete thought.

TABLE 8.6. READABILITY CHARACTERISTICS OF TYPICAL PUBLICATIONS AND THEIR EQUIVALENT PUBLIC SCHOOL GRADE

Publication and Letter Code	Average Words per Sentence	Average Syllables per Word	Average Letters per Word	Average Letters per Syllable	Average Points per Sentence	Per Cent Words of 3 Syllables and More	Per Cent Words of 9 Letters and More	Equivalent Public School Grade	
								Syllable Formula	Letter Formula
A. National Geographic	17.69	1.54	4.72	3.07	1.20	12.91	8.69	10.80	10.70
B. Changing Times	17.80	1.69	4.68	3.07	1.01	12.91	8.54	10.86	10.68
C. Reader's Digest	17.94	1.52	4.54	2.99	1.19	12.41	7.46	10.68	10.13
D. Fleet Owner	18.47	1.64	4.96	3.02	1.17	16.25	10.72	12.86	12.33
E. Better Homes & Gardens	18.56	1.50	4.56	3.04	1.28	10.59	6.35	10.08	9.85
F. U. S. News & World Report	18.77	1.57	4.89	3.11	0.86	15.30	11.25	12.54	12.81
G. Coronet	19.75	1.61	4.68	2.92	1.16	14.79	9.65	12.77	12.45
H. Holiday	20.70	1.47	4.51	3.06	1.42	10.30	7.14	11.00	11.55
J. New Testament, Rev. Standard Version	20.78	1.32	3.99	3.01	1.76	6.91	4.57	9.34	10.10
K. Engineering News-Record	22.36	1.61	5.03	3.12	1.33	15.58	10.74	14.47	14.60
L. Washington (D. C.) Post Editorials	23.06	1.60	4.72	2.95	0.79	16.64	9.63	15.35	14.36
M. Fortune	23.42	1.64	4.83	2.95	1.78	17.88	11.26	16.15	15.51
N. Time	23.71	1.61	4.84	3.00	1.51	15.38	10.18	15.04	15.06
P. Harvard Business Review	24.03	1.75	5.15	2.94	1.56	22.50	15.06	18.76	18.07
Q. New York Times Editorials	25.45	1.61	4.79	2.97	1.19	15.04	10.17	15.74	16.06
R. Bulletin of the Atomic Scientist	25.90	1.73	5.00	2.95	1.35	19.56	14.13	18.23	18.62
S. Harvard Law Review	28.94	1.74	5.09	2.92	0.68	22.07	14.38	21.00	20.53

TABLE 8.7. PERCENTAGE DISTRIBUTION OF WORDS BY SYLLABLES PER WORD AND LETTERS PER WORD FOR PUBLICATIONS IN TABLE 8.6

Samples are unadjusted.

Syllables per Word	Publication Letter (See Table 8.6 for name)																
	A	B	C	D	E	F	G	H	J	K	L	M	N	P	Q	R	S
	Distribution by Syllables per Word																
1	63.62	65.20	65.39	59.61	64.38	62.04	60.44	68.16	76.11	60.04	65.10	60.95	61.93	57.15	61.18	59.57	58.69
2	23.47	21.89	22.20	24.14	25.03	22.66	24.77	21.54	16.98	24.38	18.26	21.17	22.69	20.35	23.78	20.87	19.24
3	9.28	9.11	8.68	10.37	7.74	12.32	9.72	6.11	5.48	10.75	10.13	12.52	10.76	14.18	8.61	12.07	13.95
4	3.01	2.88	2.90	4.50	2.16	2.07	4.03	3.27	1.30	3.96	5.06	4.18	3.45	6.87	5.40	5.45	5.87
5	0.53	0.82	0.77	0.97	0.63	0.91	0.96	0.82	0.13	0.87	1.45	1.01	1.00	1.29	0.90	1.94	1.89
6	0.09	0.10	0.06	0.34	0.00		0.08	0.05				0.17	0.16	0.16	0.13	0.10	0.32
7				0.07	0.06			0.05					0.01				0.04
Total	100.00	100.00	100.00	100.00	100.00	100.00	100.00	100.00	100.00	100.00	100.00	100.00	100.00	100.00	100.00	100.00	100.00
Letters per Word	Distribution by Letters per Word																
1	4.48	2.87	6.27	2.98	4.28	2.07	3.11	3.49	2.57	3.47	3.09	3.85	4.05	2.46	2.91	2.40	2.52
2	15.38	16.45	15.00	13.62	14.52	20.26	14.91	15.64	18.55	12.60	18.35	15.61	15.05	17.33	18.80	18.27	18.23
3	19.19	20.37	19.18	18.53	17.99	17.70	20.64	22.19	29.80	19.07	19.64	20.47	17.67	16.50	19.11	19.71	18.14
4	15.79	17.55	17.14	16.87	19.26	12.41	16.31	17.11	20.66	15.26	17.09	14.42	16.37	14.94	13.87	13.40	12.54
5	11.34	11.13	12.57	12.93	13.77	11.66	11.85	13.41	10.18	12.43	9.09	12.42	11.94	9.83	11.86	10.30	10.77
6	9.52	9.27	9.19	8.30	11.22	7.61	9.50	8.88	6.22	9.66	8.00	8.47	9.49	7.85	8.94	7.40	8.36
7	8.93	7.97	7.57	9.20	7.98	9.02	8.43	8.12	4.42	10.26	10.00	7.26	8.85	8.11	10.01	8.10	8.18
8	6.68	5.85	5.62	6.85	4.45	8.02	5.60	4.03	3.03	6.51	5.09	6.24	6.40	7.92	4.31	6.29	6.88
9	4.13	3.61	3.01	4.63	3.70	5.95	4.28	3.16	2.42	3.53	2.36	4.22	4.53	6.19	5.24	5.10	4.86
10	2.55	2.50	2.32	2.77	1.16	2.73	2.71	1.74	1.57	2.88	4.00	3.30	3.01	4.44	2.31	4.02	4.08
11	0.94	1.20	1.15	1.86	1.02	1.24	1.29	1.36	0.54	1.79	1.27	1.78	1.25	2.39	1.39	2.57	2.62
12	0.70	0.57	0.51	0.69	0.35	0.58	0.76	0.44	0.00	1.95	0.73	1.02	0.88	1.12	0.62	0.86	1.57
13	0.26	0.38	0.36	0.35	0.06	0.58	0.53	0.22	0.04	0.16	0.91	0.47	0.32	0.70	0.46	1.12	0.64
14	0.08	0.19	0.09	0.21	0.00	0.17	0.05	0.22		0.27	0.18	0.32	0.12	0.16	0.00	0.30	0.51
15	0.00	0.09	0.02	0.14	0.06		0.03			0.16	0.18	0.15	0.07	0.06	0.15	0.16	0.05
16	0.03			0.07													0.04
17																	0.01
Total	100.00	100.00	100.00	100.00	100.00	100.00	100.00	100.00	100.00	100.00	100.00	100.00	100.00	100.00	100.00	100.00	100.00

TABLE 8.8. PERCENTAGE DISTRIBUTION OF LETTERS PER WORD BY SYLLABLES PER WORD

Letters per Word	Syllables per Word 1	2	3	4	5	6
	Grade 6—People and Progress					
1	4.71					
2	19.56	0.38				
3	35.67	1.53				
4	25.11	8.25	0.18			
5	12.48	21.03	3.68			
6	1.89	34.69	6.92	1.98		
7	0.50	21.95	20.77	4.68		
8	0.08	8.60	27.96	11.49		
9		2.76	24.10	23.97	20.74	
10		0.81	13.23	29.79	15.56	
11			2.28	17.87	20.74	
12			0.79	7.52	32.59	
13			0.09	2.13	8.15	
14				0.57	1.48	
15					0.74	
16						
17						
Total	100.00	100.00	100.00	100.00	100.00	
Average Letters per Word	3.29	6.07	8.15	9.73	10.99	
Average Letters per Syllable	3.29	3.04	2.72	2.42	2.20	

Letters per Word	Syllables per Word 1	2	3	4	5	6
	Grade 12 Author's Comments—Prose and Poetry of England					
1	3.95					
2	25.80					
3	34.81	0.30				
4	21.06	8.41	0.39			
5	11.59	17.36	2.24			
6	2.11	29.38	7.95			
7	0.63	28.32	20.16	6.70		
8	0.05	10.13	25.95	17.52		
9		3.67	22.78	17.76	2.36	
10		1.78	13.05	29.49	19.37	
11		0.65	5.71	16.99	25.40	7.69
12			1.62	8.43	30.10	15.38
13			0.15	2.57	15.71	31.73
14				0.48	4.71	28.85
15				0.06	1.83	10.58
16					0.52	3.85
17						1.92
Total	100.00	100.00	100.00	100.00	100.00	100.00
Average Letters per Word	3.20	6.35	8.29	9.71	11.62	13.38
Average Letters per Syllable	3.20	3.17	2.76	2.43	2.32	2.23

Letters per Word	Syllables per Word 1	2	3	4	5	6
	Reader's Digest					
1	8.06					
2	22.94					
3	28.91	1.24				
4	23.53	7.73	0.47			
5	12.10	19.72	3.18			
6	3.33	28.54	7.76			
7	1.13	23.09	18.00	4.87		
8		13.77	24.75	14.15		
9		4.70	26.76	21.58	2.62	
10		1.21	13.03	28.07	17.38	
11			4.42	19.95	18.81	5.49
12			1.47	6.50	25.71	13.19
13			0.16	4.18	20.48	27.47
14				0.70	10.95	31.87
15					3.57	15.38
16					0.48	4.40
17						2.20
Total	100.00	100.00	100.00	100.00	100.00	100.00
Average Letters per Word	3.23	6.31	8.28	9.84	11.94	13.60
Average Letters per Syllable	3.23	3.15	2.76	2.46	2.39	2.27

Letters per Word	Syllables per Word 1	2	3	4	5	6
	Harvard Law Review					
1	4.89					
2	31.76					
3	30.31	0.70				
4	18.20	6.59	0.44			
5	11.03	16.69	0.79			
6	3.41	28.65	4.39			
7	0.40	27.25	20.37	1.69		
8		14.64	27.92	9.23		
9		4.08	23.70	14.88	5.52	
10		1.28	13.26	27.87	16.02	
11		0.12	7.11	26.18	17.13	8.11
12			1.76	13.94	22.10	16.22
13			0.26	5.46	19.89	22.97
14				0.56	17.13	27.03
15				0.19	2.21	14.86
16						6.76
17						4.05
Total	100.00	100.00	100.00	100.00	100.00	100.00
Average Letters per Word	3.11	6.43	8.47	10.35	12.01	13.61
Average Letters per Syllable	3.11	3.21	2.82	2.59	2.40	2.27

TABLE 8.9. PERCENTAGE DISTRIBUTION OF WORDS PER SENTENCE IN POPULAR AND PROFESSIONAL PUBLICATIONS

Words per Sentence	Letter Code to Publication—Table 8.6								
	A,B	C	D,E,F	H	J	K,L	M,N,P	Q,R	S
1	0.12	0.14	0.12	0.00	0.00	0.00	0.00	0.00	0.00
2	0.00	0.17	0.23	0.30	0.22	0.00	0.07	0.00	0.00
3	0.35	1.42	0.46	1.21	0.68	0.00	0.20	0.19	0.00
4	1.75	1.49	0.35	1.52	1.24	0.16	0.60	1.49	0.38
5	1.63	2.40	1.28	2.27	1.46	0.32	0.79	1.49	0.63
6	2.10	2.78	1.74	2.12	3.04	0.95	0.93	1.30	0.63
7	2.21	3.54	2.09	2.88	2.36	2.54	1.65	0.74	0.89
8	3.96	3.89	2.67	2.27	3.37	2.23	1.46	0.93	1.14
9	3.14	3.78	4.06	3.64	3.15	1.91	2.18	1.68	0.89
10	4.54	4.10	2.44	2.88	3.26	2.07	2.05	1.12	1.01
11	5.36	4.37	4.18	2.88	4.27	2.07	2.38	2.23	1.14
12	4.54	3.54	4.87	4.55	4.72	2.23	2.91	2.42	1.27
13	3.96	4.83	4.41	4.55	3.71	2.54	3.38	1.86	1.90
14	4.77	3.96	4.64	4.39	4.50	4.13	2.98	3.17	2.28
15	5.47	4.41	6.26	3.79	4.72	4.13	3.24	2.42	2.03
16	5.82	4.51	3.94	4.24	3.94	3.50	3.64	3.72	2.15
17	5.24	4.97	5.34	3.18	4.39	2.54	3.84	3.35	2.41
18	5.12	4.37	5.57	2.73	4.39	3.97	4.10	3.54	2.53
19	4.89	4.24	5.22	2.27	4.39	5.55	3.77	2.23	3.04
20	3.96	3.06	4.18	3.18	3.82	4.13	4.17	2.23	3.04
21	3.84	4.10	4.52	3.94	3.49	5.55	4.17	3.35	3.17
22	3.03	3.02	4.06	2.73	2.36	3.02	3.38	3.91	2.79
23	3.26	2.78	3.60	3.33	2.36	3.50	3.31	5.59	2.92
24	2.79	2.78	3.13	2.27	2.92	4.61	3.38	2.05	3.68
25	2.56	2.19	2.67	2.88	2.81	3.18	3.18	4.10	4.06
26	2.56	1.84	2.09	2.73	1.57	3.66	2.98	3.17	3.68
27	1.51	1.81	2.09	2.12	1.57	3.34	2.98	2.79	3.30
28	1.05	2.26	1.86	1.82	2.14	2.23	2.65	1.49	3.42
29	1.05	1.81	1.16	1.67	1.35	2.54	2.18	2.05	3.04
30	1.51	1.25	1.16	2.42	1.80	2.23	2.32	2.42	2.92
31	1.28	1.42	1.16	1.52	1.12	2.23	1.85	2.61	2.53
32	0.35	1.11	1.04	2.27	0.79	2.07	2.12	3.54	2.53
33	0.58	0.56	1.04	1.52	0.67	2.38	1.65	2.23	2.53
34	0.35	0.80	0.93	1.36	1.12	1.75	1.85	1.12	2.28
35	0.70	0.94	0.93	1.06	1.12	1.91	1.99	1.68	2.28
36	0.93	0.87	0.58	0.61	1.01	1.75	1.65	2.79	2.28
37	0.23	0.45	1.04	0.91	0.68	0.95	1.59	1.49	2.15
38	0.00	0.49	0.23	1.21	0.56	1.27	1.26	1.68	1.77
39	0.58	0.59	0.46	0.76	0.67	1.11	1.26	0.56	1.90
40	0.58	0.45	0.58	1.97	0.34	0.64	1.19	2.42	1.90
41	0.23	0.42	0.35	1.06	0.22	0.48	1.26	0.74	1.52
42	0.00	0.28	0.35	0.30	0.56	0.64	0.99	0.74	1.52
43	0.00	0.14	0.35	0.76	0.68	0.95	0.86	1.12	1.39
44	0.58	0.14	0.12	0.00	0.11	0.48	0.60	1.12	1.27
45	0.00	0.24	0.12	0.61	0.34	0.48	0.60	1.30	1.14
46	0.23	0.14	0.11	0.15	0.67	0.00	0.53	0.56	1.01
47	0.12	0.21	0.00	0.46	0.45	0.64	0.46	0.74	0.89
48	0.70	0.24	0.00	0.30	0.34	0.00	0.40	1.12	0.76
49	0.23	0.10	0.00	0.15	0.56	0.32	0.26	0.74	0.76
50	0.00	0.07	0.11	0.00	0.34	0.16	0.26	0.93	0.89
51	0.00	0.10	0.00	0.46	0.34	0.16	0.20	0.37	0.63
52	0.12	0.07	0.00	0.00	0.12	0.32	0.20	0.19	0.76
53	0.00	0.07	0.11	0.30	0.22	0.48	0.33	0.19	0.51
54	0.12	0.03		0.15	0.00		0.20	0.19	0.38
55		0.14		0.15	0.12		0.33	0.37	0.25
56		0.00		0.00	0.45		0.33	0.37	0.38
57		0.03		0.15	0.00		0.20	0.56	0.38
58		0.03		0.15	0.12		0.07	0.19	0.25
59		0.03		0.15	0.12		0.20	0.00	0.25
60		0.03		0.30	0.22		0.13	0.19	0.00
61				0.00	0.00		0.07	0.19	0.25
62				0.15	0.00		0.00	0.00	0.25
63				0.15	0.12		0.06	0.19	0.25
64				0.15	0.12		0.00	0.00	0.13
65					0.22		0.06	0.19	0.13
66					0.12		0.00	0.18	0.13
67					0.00		0.06	0.19	0.38
68					0.12		0.00	0.00	0.25
69					0.00		0.06	0.18	0.13
70					0.12				0.16
—					1.12[a]				0.51[b]
Total	100.00	100.00	100.00	100.00	100.00	100.00	100.00	100.00	100.00
No. of Sentences	859	2,880	862	660	889	629	1,511	537	789

[a] Percentage for 10 sentences 71 to 112 words, averaging 88.1 words per sentence.
[b] Percentage for 4 sentences 71 to 80 words, averaging 77.8 words per sentence.

CHAPTER 9

Writing the First Draft and Revising

The discussion in Chapter 8 analyzed communication of thought through language. The process is usually one to be applied in stages if a high quality report is to result. These stages include writing and revising in a series of sequences until the writer is satisfied that he can no longer make improvements.

Many new products and processes begin in rough form on the drafting board, in field surveys, and in the development department. The method of successive trials or approximations is frequently desirable and, in many cases, necessary. Writing technical reports, letters, and papers is no exception because they improve by passing through stages in development from the first rough draft to the finished product.

THE PROCESS OF WRITING

Certain steps in the preparation of technical and business reports are directly comparable with those in the designing of a process, a machine, a building, or a bridge. The first step in designing is to determine the performance expected of the process or structure. The designer gains this information through study of the functions and objectives to be served. If there is a client, the designer confers with him to learn his ideas, requirements, and limitations. Likewise, in the preparation of technical and business reports, the author determines what the objectives are, who will read the report, and any specific limitations.

Having in mind the requirements to be met, the designer analyzes these in relation to the design possibilities, and plans a method of approach to the solution. He then begins to gather such facts as he may require. Similarly, one who is preparing a report, following a determination of the objectives and limitations, plans his approach by outlining the requirements of fact gathering, including necessary investigations.

Upon completion of the fact-gathering process, the designer organizes and analyzes his information and makes preliminary calculations. He also may put together certain minor parts of his process or structure in preliminary form. All of this is prior to making the first attempt to assemble a complete process or structure. Again, in the process of preparing a report the author thereof assembles and organizes his information in the manner which will best serve his purposes. He details his tabulations and illustrations. He makes preliminary calculations as required and fixes in his mind his completed report, just as the designer visualizes his completed process or structure.

The designer next sketches out his complete process or structure, without any attempt to be final, exact, or detailed. His objective in this preliminary draft step is to develop a picture of his complete solution.

He wants to see the component parts fitted to the whole. Is the plan wholly workable? Is the framework solid and functional? Technical and business reports are put together in the same manner. Rough draft writing is comparable to rough sketching in design. In each process, the details, the refinements, the artistic touches, and the blending together of all elements take place only after the basic parts are assembled into a workable whole. In preparing reports, the final creditable instrument of communication is achieved through painstaking revision of organization, sentence structure, grammar, spelling, diction, and style.

Report writing as an art of communication may be divided into eight steps:

1. Gaining an understanding of the objectives and purposes of the report, of the existing situation, and of the qualifications of the readers of the report.
2. Gathering and organizing the essential facts and information.
3. Analyzing the assembled data to the extent that proper solutions, convictions, applications, conclusions, and recommendations may be reached through reasoning and logic.
4. Outlining the report preparatory to writing.
5. Writing the rough draft.
6. Checking, revising, rearranging, and rewriting the early drafts.
7. Final review for arrangement, style, and mechanics.
8. Typing in final form, proofreading, assembling, and binding.

How well one succeeds with steps 4 through 7 depends first upon how thoroughly he has mastered steps 1 through 3, and second, upon his ability to express himself in writing. However, without mastery of the subject no writer, regardless of his excellence in composition, can prepare a satisfactory technical report. For the amateur or student, writing is frequently difficult because of a natural fear of not doing well. This fear may be largely replaced with confidence by learning the subject thoroughly and by having in mind all angles of its immediate application. Student-written reports, when they deal with subjects with which the student-author has had a firsthand contact, are usually better written than productions by the same writer on subjects for which the information is acquired at the moment. Writing becomes progressively easier as the writer becomes familiar with his subject, and as he gains experience in writing.

WRITING THE FIRST DRAFT

Having reached a decision on what material to include, the writer naturally develops in his mind several possible outlines of his report. From these preliminary outlines the writer eventually develops one that satisfies the particular requirements of the report under consideration. Once this outline is developed, rough draft writing begins.

If, in the course of analyzing the data, rough drafts of tables and illustrations were not prepared, the writer will save time and achieve better results by preparing all tables and illustrations before he starts on the composition. By having at hand these materials at the beginning, the process of writing will not be interrupted to arrange data, to determine relationships, to make calculations, or to prepare graphic elements.

Good writing is achieved by rapid writing, based on the presentation of ideas, followed by careful and detailed revising and checking of details, style, and mechanics. The first objective in writing is to record the main framework of ideas. This purpose may be achieved without stopping to create exactness in expression or finality in organization. Swift and continuous recording of the products of the mind may result in a rough composition lacking polish and emphasis, but including substance and vigor. The rough draft prepared in this manner is likely to be structurally sound, coherent, and serviceable. Writing which is produced under the strain of many starts and stops usually is jerky and lacking in continuity and transition. Such undesirable compositions result from trying to write in final form at the first sitting.

There are those who can write "final copy" in the first draft. These persons usually have excellent powers of expression and the concentration required to carry in mind several thoughts simultaneously. Most writers find that writing first in the rough is to be preferred to the process of endeavoring to be final the first time.

When writing swiftly to maintain the trend of thought, one may wisely delay the questions of mechanics until revision. Time out to look up words in the dictionary, to check spelling, grammar, or diction, to recast sentences and paragraphs, all interfere with the flow of thought. Notes or checks in the margin of the rough draft may be made as reminders of specific checking to be done later.

As writing continues it is often as difficult to focus one's thoughts upon the subject at hand as it is to give form to the particular expression being sought. Thoughts are elusive and frequently difficult to recall. To take advantage of stray suggestions which flash through the mind as one concentrates on another subject, the writer may make a note of the thought, or he may proceed to develop it in writing at the moment. If the latter course is followed, the paragraph can be fitted to its preferred location in the manuscript during revision. The important point is to record each idea before it is lost.

When stray ideas come to mind, one may have reason to question whether his outline was prepared adequately and properly. This question need not be a matter of concern. The results achieved when actively writing no doubt cover a wider and deeper field of thought than was stimulated in the first instance when preparing the outline. Thinking is somewhat of a chain reaction; one idea generates others. When writing, one is compelled to think accurately and logically. Thoughts then flow more freely than they do under forced thinking. Two persons, openly discussing a subject, can produce far more items of pertinent interest than can be achieved by each one separately. The action of writing, to some extent, serves the writer as a second person would; perhaps the writer unconsciously carries on a discussion with his reader and is stimulated thereby.

The writer need not be concerned because he departs from his outline when writing his rough draft. Outlines are but guides to be followed only as long as better ideas do not come to mind. They may be considered as suggesting the sequence and the minimum subject matter to be discussed, and, as such, are an essential step in the production of good reports.

For the same reasons that swift writing is advisable once the rough draft is begun, periods of three to eight hours or more in which writing can proceed without interruption, except for physical relaxation, are to be sought. The mind should not be allowed to take on any other important responsibilities until the rough draft has been completed. In the days of gathering and analyzing the information upon which the report is based, one's mind subconsciously works on the solution. Similarly, the mind continues to compose during the period of writing even though the writing is momentarily interrupted. Diversions to other matters and delays of hours should be avoided. A good plan is to complete at one sitting a given section or subject of the report, depending upon the complexity and length of the report.

While rapid composition without attention to mechanics or to finality of statement is perhaps the desired procedure in writing, each author will develop his own procedure according to his abilities, preferences, and experience. Always, however, revising and checking are not only desirable, but absolutely necessary to obtain good results.

REVISING THE FIRST DRAFT

After the rapid composition of the rough draft, careful revision is especially necessary if a well-written report is to result. The extensiveness of revision depends upon how well and how exactly the first draft was prepared and upon the time available. One who composes easily and with literary skill, probably will need to do but little revision as compared with the one who writes his first draft knowingly rough, under a plan of making three or four revisions.

Rewriting and revising of early drafts of a report or of any manuscript should be accomplished by plan. Five separate readings of the manuscript are desirable, each reading being for a specific purpose. The sixth step, the check for readability, does not require a reading of the manuscript. In order, these readings should be directed to:

1. Soundness of structure and organization
2. Clearness of expression and definiteness of meaning
3. Accuracy of facts
4. Styling and format
5. Over-all excellence after revision
6. Check for readability

Soundness of Structure and Organization

Even when written from a carefully prepared outline, the first draft of a report will need examination to see whether it is structurally sound and whether its organization follows a logical arrangement. A good means of checking the over-all organization is to reoutline by writing down the subject of each paragraph. Writing out the table of contents, perhaps in more detail than will be used in the completed report, is helpful in checking the organization. Specific items to detect are:

Subjects Out of Logical Position. While there is usually more than one satisfactory arrangement of the main and minor parts of a report, care should be taken to present subjects in a logical sequence. Decision should be based upon service to the reader. Generally, a subject is presented at the place it is first needed, even though an important use comes later in the report. Arrangements may follow in order of time, action and reaction, cause and effect, spacial or geographical location, special relations, or physical parts.

Duplication of Subjects. Unnecessary duplication of discussion easily finds its way into the rough draft. Seldom is outright duplication of composition desirable. The reader can be referred to the page where the subject is presented, if the occasion arises for a second use of the material. In some instances, minor references to, and discussion of, subject matter previously presented may be desirable. In such instances, the second presentation should be in a different wording and emphasis; the reader, then, will not be critical of the duplication. When unnecessary duplications are encountered, consolidation of the parts by rewriting is desirable.

Omission of Subjects. Failure to give full information is a natural tendency. During the process of organizing and analyzing the information the writer has become so thoroughly acquainted with his subject that in writing he unconsciously uses many items from his mind without realizing that he has not informed his reader. The best method of checking on omissions is to have the manuscript read by another person who understands the subject, but who is not familiar with its specific application. To err on the side of giving an excess of information rather than to omit material essential to an understanding of the discussion is good planning.

Unnecessary Material. Closely related to the insertion of omitted material is the deletion of unnecessary material. A natural tendency of some writers, particularly students, is to include details of procedures, scientific facts, theories, descriptions of processes, and historical discourses which are well-known to the reader. The facts may be presented briefly or merely mentioned. Again, the reader's state of knowledge of the subject is the key to the decision. In writing a report on whether or not to replace an existing motor-generator set with a new type of rectifier, it would be unnecessary to present a description of the operation and theory of the motor-generator set when the reader was the electrical engineer of the plant. On the other hand, the new type of rectifier probably should be described somewhat in detail.

Each subject should be examined to see that an adequate presentation has been made.

Introduction. Agreement between the introduction and the main body is essential. This should be checked when the report is in its final form with all parts fully developed. In revising the introduction, the writer should make certain that its first words are strong, positive, and appropriate.

Transitions. In subject matter that is presented in a logical order, transitional devices fit naturally. When transitions are difficult to compose, the adjoining subject matter should be examined for logical sequence.

The following words and phrases may be used to effect transitions, either sentence to sentence or paragraph to paragraph. Whole paragraphs may be used as transition devices between sections of a report.

Transition words:

First, second, third, finally, lastly
This, these, and those (should preferably be followed by a noun)
Nevertheless, however, thus, consequently

Transition phrases:

As a result of
In consequence
In spite of this loss
Next in order
To meet this additional difficulty
In a similar manner
Following these preliminary studies
Having investigated location and markets

Clearness of Expression and Definiteness of Meaning

The next reading of the rough draft should be to give the composition exactness of expression and to bring the English up to a high standard. Thoughts should be developed fully with complete and definite expression. Uncertain interpretations are to be avoided. All sentences should be direct and forceful. This may be achieved by a critical examination of each paragraph, each sentence, and each word. Particular items to consider are set forth in the following paragraphs.

Condensation and Expansion. Direct and forceful writing is achieved by making each word perform a necessary function. Omit words that can be deleted without affecting the meaning or readability. Adjectives and superlatives have less application in technical writing than in fiction and descriptive works. *Large, much, about, great, quite, big, very, actual, exactly, nice, of course,* and *interesting* are words that can be deleted 90 per cent of the time. Redundancy and jargon should be avoided and idioms should be used sparingly. Strive for the direct and concise form of sentence.

The following words and expressions illustrate the type of improvements that can be made by careful revision of expression:

Form to be Avoided	*Preferred Form*
Entirely satisfactory	Satisfactory
Proportioned out	Proportioned
Completely full	Full
Check up	Check
Drop down	Drop
Great variety	Variety
Very accurately, very large, etc.	Accurately, large
The amount of time saved	The time saved
In the evening at 7 P.M.	In the evening at 7; or, at 7 P.M.
The yellow interval should have a length of four seconds.	The yellow interval should be four seconds.
The structure was completely destroyed.	The structure was destroyed.
At the present time . . .	Substitute "now" or "at present" for this phrase.

An attempt was made to show an estimate of the value of . . .	An attempt was made to estimate the value of . . .
With regard to the specifications, the engineer will have them . . .	The engineer will have the specifications . . .
In respect of depreciation, it will be testified to by the next witness.	The next witness will testify on depreciation.
Due to the fact that the design was completed early . . .	Because the design was completed early . . .
Due to the heat, the work could not continue.	Because of the heat the work could not continue.
The actual facts are that . . .	The facts are that . . .
In case of failure of the lines . . .	If the lines fail . . .
In connection with the ordering of parts . . .	When ordering parts . . .
Monday was selected as an average day as far as business activity is concerned.	Monday was selected as a day of average business activity.

Excess words are frequently used in a second sentence which repeats the subject or condition of the preceding sentence. The two sentences may be combined to eliminate 10 to 35 per cent of the words.

Wordy	*Preferable*
Upon request, the data on power consumption and building volume were supplied by the physical plant department for the past 10 years. These data are tabulated in Table 2. In Fig. 3 is shown a curve of their relationship.	Table 2 and Fig. 3 show the annual power consumption in relation to cubic feet of buildings. The data, supplied by the physical plant department, are for the past 10 years.
The lines were a source of constant trouble last year. They were found to be broken before each game last fall, necessitating repair work.	Last fall it was necessary to repair broken lines before each game.
A conservative estimate of the number of families paying for garbage and rubbish collection would probably be around 2,500. When the present rate they are paying, $12 per year, is multiplied by 2,500 a total annual cost of $30,000 is obtained.	A conservative estimate of the number of families paying for garbage and rubbish collection is 2,500, which, at $12 a year, makes an annual cost of $30,000.

It is as essential to clarify writing by supplying words as it is to achieve clarity by eliminating words. A critical reading of the manuscript with the reader foremost in mind may disclose passages which omit essential information.

Uncertain Meaning	*Definite Meaning*
Domestic heating is seasonal; therefore, an increase in irrigation of agricultural land would be one solution of the seasonal load.	The generating capacity needed to provide for domestic heating requirements in the winter may be utilized in the summer by increased electrical pumping for agricultural irrigation.

Exactness of Expression. Vivid and graphic writing results from the use of words and expressions which have exact meanings. Critical study of each word and each phrase will do much to restrict the meaning and to eliminate ambiguities. Avoid using the words *small, large, few, many, several,* and *not often.* Substitute definite or approximate quantities.

General	*Specific*
The plant is located a few miles from town.	The plant is four to five miles east of town.
There are some very low areas along the Des Moines River where only a small amount of rainfall causes the banks to run full.	There are six to eight areas along the Des Moines River where rains of three to four inches cause the banks to run full.
A great percentage of the employees drive to work.	About 90 per cent of the employees drive to work.
This subject is discussed in a later section.	This subject is discussed on page 10.

The following words are typical of many that should be specifically checked to make certain that they are used correctly:

Much (great in bulk quantity) and *many* or *few* (in number)
Lower (position of elevation) and *less* (quantity)
Less (quantity) and *fewer* (number)
Large is preferred to *great* or *big* in referring to physical magnitude.
Price, cost, and *value* have different meanings when used technically. Price is the amount asked or paid in purchasing an article; cost includes purchase price plus other expense of acquiring article; and value is the worth of the article which may be more or less than its cost.
Cement (an ingredient) and *concrete* (a mixture of cement, coarse and fine aggregate, and water).

Case, project, problem, and *question* are words that should be used sparingly. These words not only lack exactness, but are too frequently used in a loose sense. When revising manuscript, these words may be eliminated by recasting the sentences or by using appropriate synonyms. *Plan, design, scheme, task,* and *proposal* may be used in the place of *project,* while *difficulty, situation, matter, subject,* and *proposition* may be substituted for *problem* and *question.*

Wordy and Colorless	*Improved*
Figures show that Virginia coal when shipped through the Panama Canal can be laid down on the Pacific Coast at a cost of $18.14 per gross ton.	Virginia coal shipped through the Panama Canal to the Pacific Coast would cost $18.14 per gross ton.
Take the case of diesel engines which were next considered.	Diesel engines were considered next.
He is undertaking a project of determining the most economical procedure.	He is trying to find the most economical procedure.
This problem was solved by installing an automatic spring control.	The difficulty was overcome by installing an automatic spring control.
The question of what type of lighting to use was referred to the engineer of design.	The type of lighting to use was referred to the engineer of design. Alternate: Selection of the type of lighting was referred to the engineer of design.
The forecasting will be based on the fact that the illumination problem can be solved without increasing the load per building.	The forecasting will be made on the basis that satisfactory illumination can be had without increasing the lighting load in the existing buildings.
The problem of overloading is one of the main troubles confronting the telephone company today.	Overloading of the lines is one of the main troubles confronting the telephone company.

Repetition and "Worn-Out" Expressions. The repetition of words and phrases usually results in awkward and colorless composition. In passages where parallel construction is desired, repetition is an asset. But generally it is better to reword the sentence or substitute synonyms. Certain phrases are so commonly used that they have become trite, and the careful writer will substitute other expressions for color and emphasis. Usually, reoccurring words result from continued use of the same sentence form. The remedy is to combine phrases, clauses, and sentences; to eliminate the multiple use of words; to recast the sentences; or to use substitute words of equal meaning.

Undesirable Repetition

Audio amplifiers are usually classed as two distinct types, the resistance-capacitance-coupled and the transformer-coupled. Since transformers are more expensive than resistors and capacitors the idea of an inexpensive design would automatically rule out the transformer-coupled amplifier. In certain applications, the transformer-coupled amplifier would be worth the extra cost. The voltage amplification in such an amplifier is much higher than that of a resistance-capacitance-coupled amplifier because of the voltage step-up in the transformer.

Repetition Eliminated

Of the two distinct types of audio amplifiers, the transformer-coupled type costs more than the resistance-capacitance-coupled because transformers are more expensive than resistors and capacitors. The transformer-coupled is ruled out in inexpensive designs, though it would be worth the higher cost in applications where its higher voltage step-up, as compared to the resistance-capacitance type, is a desirable feature.

Avoid hackneyed expressions such as the following:

In the last analysis
It stands to reason
It is interesting to note that
Last but not least
Referring to Fig. 4 it will be noted that
In accordance with
Attention is called to the fact that
Carried to the extent of
It follows that
Along these lines
As far as the supply is concerned
As in the case of
As regards to
Based on the fact that
Captain of industry
Doomed to disappointment
Equal to the occasion
Goes without saying

General Sentence Structure. For conveying exact sense, for ease of understanding, and for smooth reading, the parts of a sentence should be in their proper places. Modifiers are closely associated with the words or phrases they modify. Pronouns have quickly-recognized antecedents and parenthetical expressions are set off. No part of the sentence is allowed to dangle, and parallel construction is used in a series of statements of like usage and position. A sentence lacking in any of these requirements is likely to be awkward, or to lack positive sense. Any sentence which must be read a second time in order to understand it is a poorly written sentence. If the author, in revising his writing, even so much as hesitates on a sentence, he should take the hesitation as a signal of trouble, locate the weakness, and correct the sentence so he reads it without hesitation.

Poor Structure

In regard to the geographic limitation, it was found that only four counties could be adequately covered during the time allowable.

Good Structure

Geographically, it was found that only four counties could be covered during the time allowed.

As for these three basic testing instruments, it was found that the tube tester best suited for the shop should operate on the dynamic transconductance principle, and have a test incorporated in it for testing for gas content and for short circuits.

Of these three basic testing instruments, the tube tester best suited for the shop should operate on the dynamic transconductance principle and have incorporated in it the means of testing for gas and short circuits.

A number of letters were written to city officials in cities which generate their own power requesting information from them.

Fifteen letters requesting information were written to officials of cities which generate their own power.

Due to the high initial cost of such improvements, very few cities have undertaken to build them.

Because of the initial cost, few cities have built these improvements.

This use of statistics has also aided in helping the ability to forecast on a percentage basis.

This use of statistics has been an aid in forecasting on a percentage basis.

Three consulting engineering firms have submitted reports concerning the type of plant to be used, two of which are fairly good. However, the reports were made without very accurate knowledge of the existing conditions and cannot be relied upon very much.

Three consulting engineering firms have submitted reports on the type of plant to be used. Two of these reports are fairly good, though all three were made without complete knowledge of the existing conditions.

Progress up to the present time has been concerned with reading books and periodicals that relate to the subject as well as other helpful material.

The only progress has been the reading of books, periodicals, and other material relating to the subject.

The plan of attacking this problem is to use the information about the present water supply and calculate the cost of softening the water and compare it to the savings of soap.

This proposal will be analyzed by comparing the cost of softening the present water supply to the savings in cost of soap made possible with the softened water.

High-frequency heating is almost necessary in the case of polyvinyl chloride, which is sensitive to heat and has a small temperature range in which it can be heated, but at the same time has very poor heat transfer.

High-frequency heating is the desirable means of heating polyvinyl chloride, which, while sensitive to heat and low in heat transfer, has a small range over which it can be heated.

Parallel sentence structure and parallel word form are essential to smooth reading where more than one group of words or more than one word performs the same function within the sentence.

Faulty

Actuarial analysis of the retirement experience of public utility and industrial property is now widely practiced in the determination of depreciation in valuation procedures and in determining depreciation rates for cost-accounting purposes.

Probably, this is because governments have nothing to sell, earning profits for shareholders is not required, and income taxes are not required.

Among the 1,000 words E. L. Thorndike found to be used most often, only 36 are of more than two syllables. In Dale's list of 3,000 most familiar words, only one out of 25 is of more than three syllables. On the other hand, among words beyond the 20,000 most often used, two out of every three are of three syllables or more.

Parallel Construction

Actuarial analysis of the retirement experience of public utility and industrial property is now widely practiced in determining depreciation in valuation procedures and in determining depreciation rates for cost-accounting purposes.

Probably, this practice prevails because governments have nothing to sell, are not required to earn a profit for shareholders, and are not required to pay income taxes.

Among the 1,000 words E. L. Thorndike found to be used most often, only 3.6 per cent are of three syllables or more. In Dale's list of 3,000 most familiar words, only 21 per cent are of three syllables or more. On the other hand, among words beyond the 20,000 most often used, 67 per cent are of three syllables or more.

SPECIMEN PAGE OF REVISED DRAFT

The method of instruction was (next) considered. Most [of the] colleges, 86 percent, divide the time between classroom and laboratory; ~~work.~~ The other 14 per cent use laboratory instruction alone. In every school where shop ~~work is~~ [procedures are] taught, ~~some~~ [the classroom work is supplemented by] laboratory [exercises] ~~work is taught too.~~ At 93 per cent [of the colleges] a combination of theory and manual techniques ~~are~~ [is] taught. ~~It is interesting to note, however, that practically~~ all [but two] of the schools ~~thought~~ [stated] that some instruction in manual techniques is desirable.

Question 7 ~~on the questionnaire was an attempt to get at~~ [was introduced to obtain] the underlying reason for teaching shop courses. The question ~~is really asking~~ [called] for an expression of opinion, ~~and might also not have been~~ [because it was poorly worded, those replying may have mis-]interpreted ~~the same by all replying colleges.~~ [the question.] For instance, it is believed that some colleges ~~might have~~ marked "secondary" when there was ~~not any real~~ [no] objective in teaching the shop course for ~~that~~ [the] purpose marked. With ~~this~~ [these] conditions in mind, the results of ~~this~~ question [7] are presented. To teach mechanical skill ~~was~~ [is] a secondary objective with 65 per cent, while 97 per cent of the colleges considere~~d~~ [that the objective is] to provide a basic knowledge in mechanical processes. ~~as a primary objective.~~ One might conclude that the majority of colleges teach shop courses to provide a basic knowledge in mechanical processes; ~~and~~ [futhermore, they] believe that the best way to ~~do it~~ [achieve this objective] requires ~~some~~ instruction in ~~the~~ manual manipulation of machines. Shop instruction ~~was~~ [is] taught to provide a background for metallurgy by 32 per cent of the schools, while almost an equal number ~~said that~~ [consider this] objective ~~was~~ secondary.

Elements of Grammar and Composition. Errors in grammar are a natural result of rapid, rough draft writing. Ignorance is also a cause of grammatical errors. Careful revision of the first draft is required to correct the grammatical errors. Because the subject is too extensive for this manual, the reader is referred to authoritative books[1] on grammar and composition for an adequate treatment. A few comments only are included here.

Disagreement of subject and verb is a common error, particularly when collective nouns are used and when the subject may be separated from the verb by modifying phrases and clauses. Checking the agreement of subject and verb is easily accomplished by reading the sentence in skeleton form, which brings the subject and verb close together. Disagreement is then much more apparent.

Tense is also an element of grammar which gives frequent trouble. Here again a skeleton form of the sentence will indicate errors and inconsistencies. Past actions are stated in past tense, but the present tense is used for something that was true in the past and is still true. Something that is generally true without reference to time is stated in the present tense. Tense should not shift without making the reader aware of the need for the shift.

Disagreement of pronoun and antecedent can be overcome by direct comparison of the two words in each usage. Likewise, faulty reference of pronouns can be detected by direct comparison.

Careful checking of subject and verb, tense and pronouns will do much to eliminate the majority of errors in grammar.

Punctuation and Spelling. Because the writer alone knows the thought he wishes to convey, he alone can supply the correct punctuation. While certain uses of punctuation may be regarded as belonging to mechanics of style, punctuation so affects the meaning of the sentence that it deserves special attention. All punctuation which will be helpful to the reader needs to be supplied. The checking of punctuation is a logical operation when revising a manuscript for clarity of sentence structure. For a discussion of punctuation see pages 74 to 80.

Spelling is usually not an element of choice, even though certain phases of it may be optional. In revising a manuscript, the spelling of every word which the author may doubt should be looked up in the dictionary.

Accuracy

The third reading of the rough draft should be for the purpose of checking on accuracy of technical facts, arithmetic and mathematics, quotations, references (to figures, tables, and other parts of the report as well as to the literature), spelling of names, dates, and all statements in general. A thorough checking of these items is a painstaking but necessary procedure, if the final report is to be free from errors of fact. So far as possible, original sources should be referenced for the informational items. References within the manuscript can be verified by inspection, and all arithmetical and mathematical material should be independently recalculated.

Summary, conclusions, and recommendations should be checked to make certain that they agree with the conditions set forth in the introduction and with the results of analysis in the body. All terminal material needs to state accurately the results disclosed in the report.

Styling and Format

When the manuscript has been revised to achieve the best possible organization, clarity, and definiteness of expression, and made accurate in all details, it is ready for styling. In this fourth reading, attention should be first directed to consistent use of capital letters, abbreviations and numerals. Styling as affecting these elements must be chosen at the

---

[1] See the following:

Perrin, Porter G. *Writer's Guide and Index to English.* 3rd ed. Chicago, Scott, Foresman and Company. 1959.

Shaw, Harry. *Writing and Rewriting.* 4th Rev. New York, Harper & Brothers. 1955.

Skillin, Marjorie E. and Gay, Robert M. *Words Into Type.* New York, Appleton-Century-Crofts. 1948.

outset on the basis of the ultimate use of the report as to readership and publication. Final checking is for the purpose of obtaining conformity with the standards chosen for the particular report.

Format also should be indicated before the draft is released to final typing. The spacing, wording, and styling of headings, captions, and legends should be determined and indicated. It is important to select a complete schedule of headings so that they may be typed correctly. Likewise, the margins of the normal page and the layout of tabulations and illustrations need to be fixed ahead of final typing.

Over-all Final Examination

During the course of the four readings of the manuscript for purposes of revising, part of the first draft may be retyped several times. Certainly, if the writer's revisions are extensive he will find it desirable to start afresh with clean typing every so often. At the end of his revisions, he should have a manuscript that is clean enough for the typist to follow exactly. The writer will benefit by having another person give his manuscript a critical reading. By so doing the writer will have opportunity to see if his composition means to another what it means to him.

Whether or not a second person is available to read the manuscript before final typing, the writer should lay it aside for two or three days and turn to other duties. Later, the manuscript may be reread as a final check. During this waiting period the writer gains a new perspective and often sees his manuscript more realistically than he does when completely absorbed in it under the pressure of getting it written.

Test for Readability

Having revised the draft in the manner described in the preceding five steps, it is then well to make a check of its reading ease. As explained in Chapter 8, readability is that character of writing that makes it easy for the reader to gain the exact meaning intended by the author with ease and certainty. Either formula on pages 157–72 may be used to test the draft for reading ease. Try for an equivalent school grade of 12, certainly not higher than 14.

The average length of sentence is first determined. The sample for this purpose may vary from 100 per cent of the sentences in manuscripts of less than 200 sentences, to a systematically chosen sample of 200 or more sentences. Should the average sentence length be above 22 words, it would be well to make two sentences out of the longer ones, especially for those sentences above 50 words. The long sentences may be shortened by omitting conjunctions — and, but, however — and inserting a period, rewriting as necessary to give the second portion full meaning. In other instances, modifying clauses often can be rewritten as independent sentences. In shortening the over-all average sentence length, work particularly on the sentences that express two or more separate thoughts. Try to get each thought into a separate sentence.

The other factor in the formula is either percentage of words of three and more syllables or percentage of words of nine and more letters. The factor for syllables should be held to about 13 per cent, and for letters 8.5 per cent. Should the draft run too high in word length, try reducing the number of long words by substituting shorter ones. Often a book of synonyms is helpful in finding shorter words. Changing to the active voice shortens the word — "contradiction" to "contradict," "operation" to "operate." This change will not only shorten the word length, but will improve the sentence structure too.

Reports on certain subjects may run to a high word length because of the frequent use of a particular technical word. A report dealing with the subject of "depreciation" must of necessity make repeated use of this long word. Similarly, for a report on some subject related to cities, the words "municipal" and "municipalities" are frequently used. In such reports, these words may be omitted from the length of word count, or an allowance made for them by permitting a slightly higher grade level in the solution of the formula.

There need not be a specific effort to write

in words of one syllable, but the effort should be to use short words when they will do as well as long ones. In fact, much can be said with words of one syllable, as illustrated by the following passage:

SAY IT IN WORDS OF ONE SYLLABLE

When you come right down to it, there is no law nor code that says you have to use big words when you write or talk.

There are lots of small, good words that can be made to say all the things you want to say quite as well as big words would do. At first, it may take a bit more time to find the small words. But it can be worth the time for all of us know what they mean. Some small words, more than you might think, are rich with just the right feel, the right taste, as if made to help you say a thing the way it should be said.

Small words can be crisp, brief, terse — go to the point, like a knife. They have a charm all their own. They dance, twist, turn, sing. Like sparks in the night they light the way for the eyes of those who read. They are the grace notes of prose. You know what they say the way you know a day is bright and fair — at first sight. And you find, as you read, that you like the way they say it. Small words are gay. They can catch large thoughts and hold them up for all to see, like rare stones in rings of gold, or joy in the eyes of a child. Some make you feel, as well as see: the cold deep dark of night, the hot salt sting of tears.

Small words move you with ease where big ones bog you down and get in the way of what you want to say. There is not much, in all truth, that small words will not say — and say quite well.

Use small words and those who read what you write will thank you for the time you spent to find those small words. And they will not come back with "what do you mean?" for you will have meant what your small words say.[2]

PREPARING TABLES AND ILLUSTRATIONS FOR FINAL TYPING OR REPRODUCTION

When preparing the manuscript in form for final typing, attention to the exact location and sequence of all tables and illustrations is desirable. Decisions about form, location, and reproduction of tables and illustrations are important to the typist in arranging page lay-outs, page numbers, and cross references.

Beginning in the early stages of the preparation of tabular work and illustrations it is important to consider the following: number of copies required, methods of duplication and production, and the manner and process of publishing the report.

Even though the author of a report is responsible for the production of only the original ribbon typescript plus a carbon copy or two, he should give proper consideration to the ultimate handling of his report. Duplication by any process — mimeograph, multilith, offset, letterpress, or by one of the many trade name "fast copy" chemical processes — requires particular preparation of the several parts of the report. The author, and those who assist him, should seek early decisions on the number of copies to be prepared and method of producing them before advancing into final form, content, and arrangement of the parts of his report. See Chapter 16 for a description of duplicating processes.

---

[2] Ecclesine, Joseph A. "Big Words Are for the Birds," *Printers' Ink* 247:7:72. February 17, 1961. This article was modified by *Reader's Digest* and published on page 45 of the issue for July, 1961. The version above includes additional modifications.

CHAPTER 10

Correspondence

Although a formal report may contain only one letter, the letter of transmittal, a considerable amount of correspondence takes place during the planning of the investigation and report as well as during the collection of information.

This chapter on correspondence deals with the essential requirements of business letter writing. Specific applications of business letter writing techniques may be found in the discussions on questionnaires, letters of transmittal, and letter reports. These discussions are presented elsewhere because they preserve the unity of treatment at the places where they serve most effectively as illustrations of their respective functions.

FUNCTIONAL CLASSIFICATION OF LETTERS

A letter may be considered as the written equivalent of one side of a conversation. Letters are used because two parties are at a distance. When the communication of ideas, that is, procedures, knowledge, experiences, and opinions, becomes extensive other forms of writing become more suitable than the letter.

Letters may be classified on a functional basis into social letters, business letters, and letter reports.

A. The social letter
   1. Narration
   2. Congratulation
   3. Condolence
   4. Issue, acceptance, or declination of invitations both formal and informal

B. The business letter
   1. Inquiry, reply, and follow-up
   2. Personnel functions: introduction, application, reference, recommendation, appointment
   3. Business: sales, orders, acknowledgments, credit and collection, claims and adjustments, testimonials, making reservations and appointments, and confirming telegrams
   4. Legal

C. The letter report
   1. Periodic
      a. Regular intervals
      b. Special intervals
   2. Inquiry
      a. Informational
      b. Action

The social letter is beyond the scope of this discussion.

Regardless of the function that a letter is to serve, special attention is given to the form, the tone, and the content.

FORM OF LETTERS

The form, including the arrangement and appearance, of a letter has assumed a certain degree of conventional rigor. Yet, even with this imposed formality there is plenty of opportunity to exhibit initiative, resourcefulness, and originality. Form is a matter of established custom, and arrangement is a matter of fundamental design. Form and arrangement blend into a harmonious unit to produce a pleasing effect when each is employed according to established principles.

The form of a letter consists of the principal elements which serve definite and essential functions. It is this form that streamlines the information a letter conveys effectively and efficiently. This book contains many specimen letters; they should be critically reviewed as the text is studied.

The accepted conventional elements of the letter are discussed in the sequence: letterhead, inside address, salutation, body, and closure.

1. The letterhead contains the name of the firm, organization or agency writing or sponsoring the letter, its principal type of business, its address, and the date of writing. The letterhead, like a title to a book or report, should be pleasingly designed. Ornate and overly illustrated letterheads detract from their principal function. The specimen letters in this chapter and the letters of transmittal in Chapter 12 illustrate several possibilities in the content, design, and styling of letterheads.

2. The inside address contains the name, professional status, or responsibility of the recipient, and the address of the recipient or the company employing him. Open punctuation and the block form, as illustrated in the specimen letters, is now almost always used in business letters.

3. The salutation personalizes the communication. Whenever possible, the personal form is used. The personal or impersonal salutation may be formal or informal in tone.

A. Impersonal

Official
Sir:
Madam:

Business
Dear Sir:
Dear Madam:
Gentlemen:
Ladies:

Formal
My dear Sir:
My dear Madam:

B. Personal

Informal and Business
Dear Mr. Compton:
Dear Mrs. Perkins:
Dear Miss McHenry:

Formal
My dear Mr. Black:
My dear Mrs. Green:
My dear Miss White:

4. The body contains the message from the writer to the recipient. The development is characterized by sentences and paragraphs that are direct, brief, and factual. The subject matter is governed by the type of information to be conveyed.

The opening sentence or paragraph should be so planned that it will gain the attention of the reader quickly and favorably. The objective of the message should be given first consideration. Then the writer could present his facts, reasons, and explanations.

The closing sentence or paragraph should call for the action or the decision of the recipient.

5. The communication terminates with a formal complimentary ending, the signature of the writer and his official position. The closure contains such supplementary information as the initials of the stenographer, names of the persons receiving copies, and a list of enclosures accompanying the letter.

Yours very truly,

Ernest Hartford
Executive Assistant Secretary

Very truly yours,

National Slag Association

____

H. J. Love, Manager

Respectfully submitted,

POWER DEVELOPMENT COMMITTEE

Elmer B. Stevenson
W. Ronald Abbott
Joseph Kingery
John A. Merkle, Secretary

By ______________________________

Howard K. Olson, Chairman

Yours very truly,

John A. MacDonald

STATE HIGHWAY COMMISSIONER

By ______________________________

Lyle K. Abbott
Deputy Highway Commissioner

The usual complimentary closure phrases are employed more by habit than by intent; they are:

Very truly yours
Yours very truly
Sincerely yours
Cordially yours
Respectfully submitted

Interorganizational Correspondence

Correspondence within an organizational unit, between departments and plants is written on special forms. The body of these letters or memoranda (memos) as they frequently are called remains unchanged in arrangement and tone; but the inside address, salutation, and closure are made quite informal. In place of the inside address and letterhead the following three lines are used:

To: W. Bronson Guernsey
From: Frank M. Highly
Subject: Interplant Production Reports

In place of the usual closure, a signature of the writer or initials after his typed name at the beginning is sufficient. The form, tone, individuality, and quality of interplant, interdepartment, or intradepartment letters should equal that required for outside letters.

TONE OF LETTERS

The tone of a letter expresses the personality of the writer and reflects the subject matter discussed in the letter. The characteristics of a good letter are completeness, correctness, clearness, conciseness, conviction, and courteousness.

The opening sentence should state the purpose of the letter effectively and engagingly to gain the immediate interest and attention of the reader. The opening paragraph should establish confidence, good will, and respect between the writer and the recipient. The vocabulary should conform to the professional attainment of the reader. Length of sentences, paragraphs, and letters is an academic matter; the important factor is that only as many words should be used as are required to convey the ideas clearly. A few extra, well-chosen words frequently make the difference between understanding and ambiguity. The essence of a letter is brevity, but not brevity at the expense of maturity and completeness.

ARRANGEMENT AND CONTENT OF LETTERS

The form and tone of the body are closely related to the subject matter of the letter.

A single paragraph letter should be well centered. The margins at the sides are wider than in longer letters, the inside address starts lower, and the body of the letter is placed so that its center is slightly above the center of the sheet. Quality of the content, evenness of typing, correctness in spelling and grammar, and punctuation that does not destroy the sense are the points the reader notices quickly. But the first impression of the letter as a whole is determined by harmony among the various elements, evenness in weight of the typing and printed letterhead, good proportion of each element, a sense of unity among the elements focusing attention on the body. These are the characteristics possessed by well-arranged letters of distinction.

The individual, his department, even the company for which he works should strive toward distinctive appearance in correspondence. The letter should be neat, attractive, economical, courteous, and correct. The writer can develop respect among the recipients of his letters by exercising consistency in style, tone, and arrangement.

The ability to write good letters depends upon the mastery of the generally applicable fundamentals of English and psychology. The illustrative specimen letters which follow should not only be read but they should be studied critically in terms of the suggestions contained in the text as a whole and this chapter in particular. Notice the following items:

1. Location of date with reference to the right-hand margin and position with reference to letterhead and inside address
2. Content and arrangement of the inside address
3. Style of the punctuation in each element of the letter from beginning to end
4. Methods of securing attention by arrangement and typography rather than by underscoring
5. Effectiveness of various arrangements for the paragraph considered as a unit, and the relative attractiveness of the block paragraph and the indented paragraph
6. Lack of oddities, obtrusive ornaments, and distractive features so that the recipient is not distracted by blatant make-up

Business firms recognize the benefits arising from letters that represent them favorably. The make-up of these letters follows company custom, standards, and policy regardless of the individuals assigned to write them. Nevertheless, it is possible and essential to individualize business letters.

The person who affixes his signature to a letter should check for correct transcription by the stenographer. The writer, when he signs a letter, should realize that he is responsible for it and will get credit for the bad features as well as the good.

The paragraphs in a letter should be arranged to read easily just as in any other writing. When many items are involved, the continuous prose arrangement creates a confusing image in contrast with an orderly tabulation. The following example from an instruction form letter issued by The American Rolling Mill Company brings this point out effectively.

Hard to read:

If you will look at this customer's orders, you will find that there are 66 sheets still due against their C1942, our 1047–98B; 82 sheets still due against their C1944, our 1047–100B; 165 sheets due against their B1945, our 1047–101; and on their C1946, our 1047–102B, there are still 49 sheets due.

Easy to read:

If you will look at this customer's orders, you will find that there are still due against:

C 1942	Our 1047–98 B	66 sheets
C 1944	Our 1047–100 B	82 sheets
B 1945	Our 1047–101	165 sheets
C 1946	Our 1047–102 B	49 sheets

In this chapter and by the specimen examples throughout this book, it is shown that the writer of letters can communicate his ideas, whether they be simple or complex, in an original and effective manner by mastering form, tone, arrangement, and development of the paragraph. With these fundamentals in letter writing at his command and a thorough grasp of the subject he can write a good letter regardless of the functional classification of the message.

Brown Engineering Company

TELEPHONE 2-8141

CONSULTING ENGINEERS

REGISTERED
PROFESSIONAL ENGINEERS

K. R. BROWN J. V. GEBUHR G. C. HAVENS
E. F. BEHRENS R. A. SCHREIBER W. E. NICHOLS
L. B. ECKLES M. T. McDONALD C. D. GIBBS
E. S. BOUDINOT J. S. VETERSNECK H. E. KELSO
G. P. PRICHETT J. M. FAIRALL

322-334 K P BUILDING
DES MOINES 9, IOWA

January 23, 19..

Prof. Harold M. Siedell
College of Engineering
Iowa State University
Ames, Iowa

Dear Professor Siedell:

Since Mr. Behrens is to be out of the office for approximately a week, we are writing to let you know that your letter of January 22 has been received, but is being held for Mr. Behrens' attention.

We are certain your request for material for classroom use will be taken care of as soon as he returns.

Yours very truly,

BROWN ENGINEERING COMPANY

Grace T. Hawes

Grace T. Hawes
Secretary to Mr. Brown

gh

Specimen 10.1.
Secretary's acknowledgment

Lansdale Incorporated

DIVISION OF THE ROCKFORD CORPORATION

3212 OAKMAN BOULEVARD
DETROIT 32, MICHIGAN

March 8, 19 . .

Mr. Weston Williams, President
Williams, Nelson, & Hardaway
1066 Foster Avenue
Oak Park 10, Illinois

Dear Mr. Williams:

As requested in your letter of March 6, I have enclosed a copy of "What is Industrial Hydraulics?" as delivered at the recent Annual Meeting of the National Conference on Industrial Hydraulics.

Actually, I believe there is little difference between the original and the condensation as it finally appeared in the Techniscope, although the latter was originally intended to be considerably abbreviated.

We are, of course, pleased to have you use the talk in connection with your work and if you should want additional copies we would be pleased to supply them. The National Research Foundation has requested that its sponsorship of the conference at which the talk was given be mentioned whenever the material is used.

Yours very truly,

LANSDALE INCORPORATED

R. E. Eschback
General Sales Manager

RE:vvr
Encl.

Specimen 10.2.
Reply to request for information

COLLINS RADIO COMPANY CEDAR RAPIDS DIVISION

May 18, 19 . .

Cedar Rapids, Iowa telephone: EMpire 5-8411 cable: COLINRAD

Mr. L. R. Hillyard
Engineering Personnel Officer
Iowa State University
Ames, Iowa

Dear Mr. Hillyard:

This refers to our previous arrangements made by telephone early this year for recruiting dates on your campus during the school year. We appreciate the opportunity of talking to your graduates and, as you know, have always experienced a strong interest from them regarding employment opportunities with our company.

We would like to interview fall quarter graduates on October 9 and will have two interviewers available to handle separate schedules for EE, ME and IE graduates. Please place IE graduates on one schedule and EE and ME graduates on another. On January 24 and 25 we would like to interview winter and spring quarter graduates and will have three interviewers available each handling a separate schedule on both of those days. Set up two schedules for EE's and ME's and one schedule of IE's on each day of this visit. We would like to have you reserve three single rooms at the Memorial Union on the night of January 24 in connection with this visit.

As we discussed on the phone, we feel it would be advisable to arrange a separate date for interviews with summer applicants who have completed three years or more of college course work. Therefore, we would like to have you set up two schedules on March 19 for summer applicants majoring in EE, ME or IE work. A special bulletin pointing up details of our requirements and areas of work offered on our summer training program will be forwarded to you not later than March 1. Literature for our visits to interview graduating seniors will be sent at least thirty days prior to each visit.

Thank you for the opportunity to again visit and interview your students.

Sincerely yours,

L. R. Nuss
Manager of College Relations
bw

Specimen 10.3.
Arrangement for interviewers' appointments

CARBIDE AND CARBON CHEMICALS DIVISION

UNION CARBIDE AND CARBON CORPORATION

CARBIDE AND CARBON BUILDING
30 EAST FORTY-SECOND STREET
NEW YORK 17, N. Y.

October 11, 19..

Prof. Lyman P. Young
Chemical Engineering Department
University of Minnesota
Minneapolis 14, Minnesota

Dear Professor Young:

Mr. W. F. Reich, Jr. has asked me to thank you for your letter of October 7, to which you attached Mr. Robert H. Lamb's letter of application. We are attaching a copy of a letter we have addressed to Mr. Lamb suggesting that he fill out one of our qualification records and forward it to us.

At this time we do not know what our requirements for men will be in January, but we shall keep this man's application in our active file and arrange to interview him as soon as possible.

We appreciate your calling good men to our attention. Mr. P. G. Horecka has done very well and is now handling the affairs of our San Francisco office.

Very truly yours,

CARBIDE AND CARBON CHEMICALS CORPORATION

E. E. Fogle

Assistant Sales Manager
Industrial Chemicals Division

EEFogle/el
Enc.

Specimen 10.4.
Reply to reference letter

FROM OFFICE OF SECRETARY-TREASURER
AMERICAN CONCRETE INSTITUTE
18263 WEST MCNICHOLS ROAD
DETROIT 19, MICHIGAN

February 1, 19..

Memorandum to ACI Technical Activities Committee

From William A. Maples, Associate Editor

Subject: "The Patent Status of Prestressed Concrete and the Relationship of Prestressed Concrete to Building Codes," a manuscript by Curzon Dobell, Preload Enterprises, Inc., submitted for consideration as a convention contribution and as JOURNAL material.

Synopsis: Patents relating to prestressing are traced from that issued to Ostrander in 1862 to those still pending in this country. A brief discussion of the more important patents is summarized by a table listing licensees. The second part tells what has been done so far in developing codes relating to prestressed concrete and closes with a plea that because thought and practice in this field are still in a state of flux, no action be taken now to rigorously channelize design and construction.

Length: 18 double-spaced typed pages

Estimated Platform Time (in shortened form): 10 minutes

Estimated JL space: 10 pages

Remarks: Mr. Dobell treats a difficult subject in an interesting manner and leads the reader easily through the intricate maze of patents affecting prestressed concrete. His manuscript is recommended for the convention program and for JOURNAL publication.

Chester L. Post is being asked to serve as critic reader. TAC members will be sent copies of the manuscript upon request.

WAM:bb

Specimen 10.5.
Routine memorandum

WILLIAMS POWER & LIGHT COMPANY

WILLIAMS, WEST VIRGINIA

March 3, 19..

Allis-Chalmers Manufacturing Company
Box 512
Milwaukee 1, Wisconsin

Attention: Centrifugal Pump Department

Gentlemen:

Please send us a quotation on a motor-driven centrifugal pump which is to supply condenser circulating water at the rate of 6000 gallons per minute against a total dynamic head of 60 feet. The water is clear and noncorrosive.

The pump must be of horizontally split casing construction, standard bronze fitted and capable of a 15-foot suction lift.

The motor is to be drip-proof construction, suitable for 3-phase, 60-cycle, 2300-volt operation. No control to be included.

The pump and motor are to be directly coupled and mounted on a common bedplate of fabricated steel or cast iron.

Please include in your quotation the price, weight and delivery time of this unit. Also, attach two copies of pump performance curves and specifications.

All bids will be opened at 11:00 a.m. March 22. Therefore, your quotation must be in our hands prior to that time.

Yours very truly,

WILLIAMS POWER & LIGHT COMPANY

W. O. Bennett

W. O. Bennett/rj   Chief Engineer

Specimen 10.6.
Request for quotation

ALLIS-CHALMERS MANUFACTURING COMPANY

MAIN OFFICE • BOX 512 • MILWAUKEE 1, WIS.

June 12, 19 . .

Mr. W. O. Bennett, Chief Engineer
Williams Power and Light Company
Williams, West Virginia

Dear Sir:

We are pleased to submit the attached quotation, specification sheets, and proposed curves of our 16 x 14 inch, type SD, centrifugal pump with motor drive. We are certain that its construction and performance conforms in every respect to your requirements as outlined in your letter.

The price of the unit including pump, motor, coupling and bedplate is included in the enclosed proposal. We will be able to ship within 45 days after the order is received at our West Allis Works.

We are pleased to submit this quotation to you and if we can be of further service in regard to your pumping requirement, please consult Mr. J. M. Days, Manager of our office at Charleston, West Virginia.

Yours truly,

John Doe, Manager
Fluid Dynamics

JD/sh

Enc.

Specimen 10.7.
Quotation

CHAPTER 11

Letter Reports and Short Reports

Letter reports are business letters that deal especially with the answers to problems arising in commerce, science, business, industry, engineering, government, or any other area of human activity. Thus, the application of the principles of correspondence developed in Chapter 10 holds insofar as "form" is concerned. However, the tone, arrangement, and content reflect the specific function of the letter report. The principal point of departure lies in the nature of the subject matter of the letter report as compared with the broader scope and classification of business letters. Letter reports resemble business letters closely (1) in principal parts, (2) in form and layout and (3) in typographical arrangement. Letter reports differ from business letters (1) in development and content and (2) in style of writing.

THE LETTER REPORT

The usual development of the body of a letter report includes all the principal units of a "formal report." The scope and treatment of subject matter are usually so limited that they lend themselves readily for presentation in letter report form. Therefore, the opportunity to write frequent letter reports provides excellent experience for the writing of the longer and more comprehensive formal reports. A functional organization for the body of letter reports is suggested in Specimen 11.1, page 203.

Organization Units

Unit 1, usually a brief paragraph, is used to establish "contact" between the recipient and the writer, to make reference to other correspondence, and to present the manner in which the data were acquired.

In response to your request of August 10, I herewith submit this report on my investigation of methods of controlling snowdrifts along highways. The drifting characteristics of snow . . . (Specimen 11.3)

One of your initial requests to this Bureau was to conduct a study of the various activities of the sanitary division. Since such an investigation . . . (Specimen 11.4)

This brief report is arranged so that you may conveniently study the summarized factual data collected to provide you with essential information relating to the present status of residential vacancies.

The "Statement of Problem," constituting Unit 2 may be one or two paragraphs in length. The problem is stated completely, yet concisely. Reasons are given for writing the report. Questions that existed before the study or arose during the study are defined. The general characteristics of the subject under discussion are explained. The method of developing the report is briefed.

Impending problems upon which this preliminary information will have definite bearing are the forthcoming vote upon incinerator bonds and the expiring of a contract with the Los Angeles By-Products Company for the sale of salvageable rubbish. (Specimen 11.4)

In addition to the summarized survey data there are presented the schedule of operations, the summary of findings, the explanation of procedures, vacancy factors, and . . .

The "Abstract or Summary of Findings" is placed near the beginning of the letter report and usually serves as Unit 3. One or more paragraphs may be used to digest the conclusions reached and the essential recommendations offered. The outline form of presentation is frequently employed in order to emphasize each of the conclusions or recommendations.

In order to facilitate the operation of the Printing Service, it is recommended that:

1. The number of duplicating machines be increased from four to five by the purchase of one new offset press, and
2. A uniform system of issuing and handling orders for duplicating work be set up for all departments of the college. (Specimen 11.2)

With the solution of the problem and the recommendations out of the way the writer proceeds with the "Development of the Report" as Unit 4. This unit of the letter report presents the bases upon which the conclusions and recommendations have been developed. To make his solution of the problem convincing the writer includes essential facts, related theories and arguments, and a brief interpretation so that the recipient's attention is directed toward the acceptance of the solution. The evidence is presented concisely; therefore, the material may be outlined or briefed. Specimens 11.2 to 11.6 illustrate the manner employed by each of the writers for backing up his solution of the problem, his conclusions, and his recommendations.

The final paragraph contains Unit 5 "Concluding Statements." Above all, whenever some action should be taken the writer of the report should clearly indicate the nature and extent of action required in order to make the solution effective. The closing sentence should be firm and contributory rather than an admission of incompleteness in subject matter or inferiority in confidence and treatment. "I hope that you will find the information satisfactory" or "I trust that the matter will be of use to you" are examples of indecision. Good closing sentences:

We would be pleased to give more thought and study to this problem of material handling. At our next meeting in Toledo, I would appreciate an opportunity to discuss this problem further with Messrs. Brown and Sewell. (Specimen 11.5)

The complimentary "closure," Unit 6, is an adequate and recognized method of "signing off." Original data, tabulations and graphic presentations, and interpretations are usually added to the letter report as "Enclosures" designated as Unit 7 in Specimen 11.1.

Content

The content of the letter report is based upon the inherent function that a report fulfills in providing the answer to a problem. The answer is based upon recorded data, upon observation of human behavior or activities, upon experiments or upon investigations. The writer knows that the recipient wants the answer. He knows, too, that the recipient will value the answer in terms of the manner in which the answer is reached and, finally, that the recipient wants an answer that is based upon factual data, experimental data, or authoritative opinion and judgment. For these reasons the organization of a letter report follows a scheme that is especially adaptable to the presentation of the subject in the sequence that suits the recipient. A suggestion for organizing the letter report is presented in Specimen 11.1. A study of this form reveals that the major elements are those used in the business letter. The principal difference arises in the content and development of the body of the letter. The underlined and numbered headings in Specimen 11.1 correspond, in general, with the principal elements of a formal report. The title of a formal report is represented by the usual contents of the letterhead, date, inside address, salutation, subject line, and closure. The body is represented by Items 2 through 5 including statement of the problem, abstract of findings, development of the report, and concluding statements. The illustrative matter is represented by Item 7 which lists the enclosures — other letters, tabulations, and illustrations.

The letter report is used when the scope of the subject is limited so that the entire matter can be written in a few pages. Generally speaking, about three pages of single-spaced typescript should be the limiting length of the letter report with a few additional pages for the supporting data contained in the enclosure. Some excellent letter reports of many pages have been written, but a careful analysis indicates they would have been more effective if they had been written as short reports.

THE MEMORANDUM REPORT

In subject and treatment the memorandum report is equal to the letter report. The one distinctive difference is the use of the "to-from-subject" form of beginning. This informal form, therefore, restricts the memorandum report to interoffice, intercompany, or within the family situations where writer and recipient are in close working relations. There should be no essential difference in the outline and the treatment of the subject because of using the memorandum form instead of the letter form.

The informality and simple physical form of the memorandum report make its use well adapted to temporary, preliminary drafts which may later be incorporated in short or formal reports. Fundamentally, however, the memorandum report was developed as a single and informal form to use within the organization.

Specimen 11.6 is an example of a memorandum report used by the U.S. Bureau of Reclamation to transmit results of a simple research study. By employing the outline form with headings, this report makes available in brief space a great deal of information, including Table 1 and Figure 1. The presentation in this direct and concise report illustrates effective use of the elements of reports.

THE SHORT REPORT

As the treatment of the subject of a report grows in number of pages and involvement, the letter and memorandum report forms become cumbersome. Further, the more voluminous and involved a report becomes, the less need there seems to be for outward evidence of personal relationships. Thus, the short report has been developed to bridge the space between the personalized letter report and the formal, or long report, with its many special parts. The short report is preferred when the contents require about four or more pages in total.

Preliminary Parts of Short Reports

The form of the short report may include any combination of the following parts, depending upon the situation and local preferences:

1. Separate cover
2. Inside title with full identification
   a. On separate sheet
   b. On upper portion of first page
3. Table of contents
4. Letter of transmittal
5. Attachments

The short report is suitable for internal or external reporting. When the report is sent outside the organization in which it was prepared, a title page and letter of transmittal would be required.

Some companies which use the short report extensively have developed a printed form for the title page. Specimen 11.8 is one such form. Note that this form has two distinct features, other than the usual identifying items of title, author, recipient, and date: (a) the abstract and conclusions, and (b) the small size which can be folded to the size of a filing card.

Cover and Title Page

In the short report, either a cover or a title page is used, occasionally both. The function of the cover or title page is to provide the information usually contained in the heading, salutation, and closure of letter reports, or the preliminary parts of formal reports.

The cover and title page will show:

The subject of the report
The author and his position
The sponsoring unit of organization
To whom the report is directed
Place and date

Certain of these items of information will be repeated on the title page, should both a cover and title page be used. As with formal reports, the function of the cover and title page is to give identification to the report. The cover, in addition, provides a physical protection for the report and aids in handling and filing the report.

In the short report of three or four pages, when prepared primarily for internal use and when accompanied by an attached letter of memorandum of transmittal, the essential identifying information may be placed on page 1 of the report, above the first, or introductory section.

Development of the Text

The text or body may constitute the entire short report, although original data and supplemental material may be placed in an appendix. In the letter report practically all tabulation, curves, diagrams, charts, and illustrations are relegated to enclosures. In the short report these items are developed as summary tables, curves, diagrams, charts, and illustrations, and are placed in the text at appropriate places to assist in the interpretation of the report and in substantiating the conclusions and recommendations. Original laboratory test data and field observations are used when they are essential to the report. When not necessary to an understanding of the discussion, the original data are placed in an appendix in order not to interfere with the smooth flow of thought in the report proper.

As a rule the short report deals with a single purpose or objective with restricted scope. The formal report deals comprehensively with a problem of major significance and broad scope.

The essential characteristics of the short report are directness and conciseness. And these reports should be correct, clear, complete, and convincing.

A suggested detailed outline or pattern to follow is shown as Specimen 11.9. The introduction to the report contains a treatment of the following items: object, nature of work, definitions, and related facts. The attainment of the objective is developed in terms of the following items: method, procedure, equipment and apparatus especially devised for this study, results, conclusions, and recommendations.

THE STUDENT LABORATORY REPORT

The short report lends itself well to the writing of the student laboratory report. In general the tests and experiments performed by college students are of limited scope and short duration. The principal functions of the laboratory experiment are usually to verify fundamental theories, to study the basic characteristics of energy-producing and energy-consuming machines, and to learn about physical and chemical properties of engineering materials.

The purpose of an experimental engineering course is to train the student in methods of observing, recording, analyzing, and presenting the behavior of machines, materials, and processes. These experiences may include the analyses of theoretical performance, measurement of actual performance, description of characteristics, and an evaluation of performance compared to machines, materials, and processes which perform similar or related functions.

Laboratory tests and experiments are planned to be completed in two to six hours. Thus, it becomes evident that these tests offer useful data for the writing of short reports. In writing these reports the student gains the experience in observation and expression which later enables him to write good reports on the job. See Specimen 11.11 for an illustrative example of a student laboratory report.

Writing the Report

Writing the student laboratory report begins long before the experiment is over or even commences. First, each student should review the underlying theory to be verified and acquaint himself with the equipment to be used. He should plan the conduct of his experiment or test just as carefully as the professional man plans for his investigation and report. A review of this kind will enable the student to handle the equipment with assurance, to anticipate the precautions he should take in making observations, and at the same time to grasp the relationship of the concepts and phenomena which he is studying.

Skill in designing form reports will enable the student to record his observations clearly, accurately, and efficiently. He will utilize the help afforded in Chapter 6, *Tabular Presentation*. Frequently a student will be better prepared for the experiment if he designs or creates his own tabular form than if he fills in spaces and columns designed by someone else. The recorder can often detect irregularities in a test by alert attention as to how the data should vary. He can then call for a check reading while it can be made promptly and easily. After the test is over it may be impossible to obtain these corrected check readings. The tabulation of observed data should be arranged so that further computations can be readily made and added. Whenever possible these calculations should be independently checked.

With the experiment and calculations completed the student is ready to write the report. The primary purpose of these reports is to arrive at conclusions which can be substantiated by the data and facts obtained in the experiment or test. In addition, the student develops skill in the presentation of his data so that others will not only understand his report but will be convinced by his interpretation, reasoning, conclusions, and recommendations.

Organization of Report

The pattern for developing the student report may follow that recommended in Specimen 11.9 or the one employed in Specimen 11.6.

Title. A brief but fully descriptive title provides sufficient information for reference and filing purposes. The title sheet should also include the date and the name of the person performing the test.

Object. The purpose and limitations of the test are stated concisely.

Apparatus. This section describes *with what* the experiment, test or investigation was conducted. It includes a description of the machine tested, the material studied, or the process investigated. Descriptions are also given of the equipment and instruments used. Reasons for particular arrangement of apparatus should be stated. Where a technical name adequately describes a piece of apparatus, equipment or instrument, a lengthy description is unnecessary. However, any new, unusual, or nonstandard equipment or other item should be described completely. Drawings or diagrams should be used if they increase clarity and eliminate lengthy descriptions. The description of the apparatus, its arrangement, and of the instrumentation should be so clear and complete that any competent engineer might reproduce the test setup.

Procedure. This section describes *how* the test data were collected. It should include:

a. Condition of the test
b. Length of the test
c. How and when observations were made
d. Statement of what was held constant, and how
e. Statement of what was varied, and how
f. Special precautions taken
g. Trouble encountered
h. Safety considerations
i. Standard test procedures identified by titles.

Given the description of procedure, a competent engineer should be able to duplicate the test in all its essential features.

Discussion. The results obtained (the results called for by the objective) are concisely set forth. Specific values should be stated. A statement regarding the accuracy of the data should always be made. Wherever possible, the test results should be compared with published values for similar conditions, citing literature consulted, and explaining variations. Any additional comments regarding conditions of testing, explanation of interesting phenomena, and personal ideas of the writer are important *but they should be placed following the discussion of the results.*

Curves. Graphical summaries, curves, charts, and diagrams help to visualize the major results of the project. Include any statement that will enable the reader to use the curves. Every curve sheet should carry sufficient information to relate it to a particular test:

1. Under specified conditions
2. On a given piece of equipment
3. At a certain place and time
4. By a certain test group or individual

Tabulations. In the text use tabulations to summarize and generalize important data and findings. Carefully planned summary tabulations are an important part of the report. Tabulations in the body of the report should aid the reader to interpret the data and to grasp quantitative trends and relationships. Just as good presentation, analysis, and interpretation aid in determining good conclusions, good summary tables aid in grasping the significance of the numerical data collected during the tests or observations.

Calculations. Sample calculations of all but obvious values are made, using test data. When more than one calculation of a kind must be made, the data used in the sample should be identified. All but obvious formulas should be derived or their source indicated. Symbols should be explained and units specified.

Supplemental Data. Calibration or correction factors for instruments should be included on the data sheets.

Name of Firm
Professional Status
Address of Firm

Date

Name of recipient
Professional status
Address

Subject: Identifying short title

Salutation:

1. *Contact*: Authorization for writing the report.
2. *Statement of Problem*: Reasons for the report; questions defined; nature of report fully indicated; one or two paragraphs in length.
3. *Abstract or Summary of Findings*: Digest of conclusions reached; statement of recommendations offered; concise treatment; a paragraph or two.
4. *Development of the Report*: Includes facts, theories and arguments that lead to the conclusions; evidence usually concise; arrangement may be outlined or briefed; use as many paragraphs as are necessary.
5. *Concluding Statements:* Suggestions, requests, opinions, proposals follow the evidence presented in the body of the report; a paragraph or two.
6. *Closure*

Complementary closure
Signature
Typed name of person signing letter
Official position of signer

Name or initials of person writing letter
Initials of stenographer
List of enclosures
Copies to:

7. *Enclosures*: Identified as "Enclosure 1," "Enclosure 2" or as "Exhibit 1," etc.; consists of drawings, laboratory report sheets, tabulations of original observations, letters, or other pertinent documents.

Specimen 11.1.
Organization of letter reports

Charles B. Winslow & Company
Industrial Consultants
531 La Salle Avenue
CLEVELAND 17, OHIO

22 April 19..

President Donald K. Mattern
214 Creighton Hall
Universal College
Lenox, Missouri

Dear President Mattern:

This report on the operation and management of the Universal College Printing Service is submitted in accordance with your request dated February 4. The following major recommendations are based upon observations made during the time available for the study, and might be altered as the result of a more extensive survey.

In order to facilitate the operation of the Printing Service, it is recommended that:

1. The number of duplicating machines be increased from four to five by the purchase of one new offset press, and

2. A uniform system of issuing and handling orders for duplicating work be set up for all departments of the college.

Difficulties in the management of the Printing Service can be traced to personnel problems; two recommendations to relieve this situation are submitted:

3. If possible, the general level of wages paid to full-time employees should be increased. Consideration should be given to the desirability and possibility of changing the basis of such wages from an hourly rate to an annual salary.

4. Although the employees of the Printing Service, in general, are industrious and efficient, there is evidence that some are not suited for the type of work they are doing. Such employees should be assigned to other duties.

The observations which led to these recommendations are discussed in the following pages.

As a service organization, the Printing Service performs a large number of functions for college departments and other organizations on and off the campus. Centralization of such functions is a logical arrangement necessary

Specimen 11.2.
Letter report

for economy of operation. As indicated on the accompanying organization chart, the types of work performed by the Printing Service are many and varied, ranging from addressing and mailing to multigraphing and offset printing. The major part of the work consists of a large volume of many types of duplicating for other departments.

(The development of the report is accomplished by a discussion, omitted in this specimen, of the following items: Operating Problems, Space Limitations, Handling of Orders, Charge for Work and Personnel Problems.)

In our opinion intelligent direction is being given to the operation of the Printing Service; the manager's efforts deserve encouragement. It is believed that the adoption of the recommendations presented at the beginning of this report will eliminate many of the criticisms leveled at the Printing Service during past months and will make this service department more effective and useful at a lower cost per unit of work.

Respectfully submitted,

CHARLES B. WINSLOW & COMPANY

John H. Godfrey

John H. Godfrey
Project Manager

JHG:bm

Enclosures:

1. Organization Chart
2. Table of Costs and Charges at Other Midwestern Colleges
3. Table of Tenure for Employees
4. Wages in other Midwestern College Printing Service Departments
5. Monthly Volume of Duplicating Service
6. Amount of Ink Consumed

Specimen 11.2 (continued)

WILLIAM A. GRIFFITH,
Student in Civil Engineering
407 Welch Avenue, Ames, Iowa

August 23, 19..

Prof. R. J. Miller
Professor of Civil Engineering
Iowa State University
Ames, Iowa

Dear Professor Miller:

In response to your request of August 10, I herewith submit this report on my investigation of methods of controlling snowdrifts along highways. The drifting characteristics of snow are discussed; and methods of controlling the drifting by artificial barriers, natural barriers, and highway design are summarized. Costs are not reported upon because reliable figures were not available in the limited time allowed for this report.

SUMMARY

Each of the three methods of preventing the drifting of snow on highways--artificial barriers, natural barriers, and highway design--has its advantageous applications. Snow fence is universally used and is a satisfactory method in most locations. Its disadvantages of unsightliness and seasonal expense of erection and removal are overcome by the use of natural plantings. When combined with roadside development and where farming operations permit, the natural plantings are proving to be a desirable method of snow control. The drifting of snow on the roadway may be prevented in many locations by proper geometric design of the highway, which also results in desirable safety features.

Perhaps the best control of snow may be achieved through consideration of all three of these methods of drift prevention during the design and construction of the highway. Each method may be used at those locations where it is advantageous. When the existing highways are modernized, the remodeling plans should include provisions for snow control based upon the experience at each location.

BEHAVIOR OF DRIFTING SNOW

To understand the methods of controlling snowdrifts, it is first necessary to understand the behavior of drifting snow. Snow is carried along the ground by the wind in the same manner that sand and soil are transported by water. Whenever the velocity of the wind is lowered, its snow-carrying capacity is lowered, and some of the snow is deposited as a drift.

Specimen 11.3.
Letter report by a student

On the leeward side of every barrier to wind movement there exists an eddy area in which the wind loses forward velocity. This ichthyoidal eddy area is where the drifting occurs. On the leeward face of the barrier, the air moves upward in a circular motion about a horizontal axis parallel to the face of the barrier. In the portion of the eddy area farthest from the barrier, the air moves in a similar manner, but opposite in circular direction to that near the barrier. Both of these circular movements of the air carry snow to the area between them where it is deposited to form a drift. The drift may grow to fill the entire eddy area.

The width in the direction of the wind and the shape of the eddy area are dependent upon the shape of the barrier, rather than the velocity of the wind. For barriers of identical shape, the width of the eddy area in the direction of the wind is proportional to the height of the barrier; a 6-foot high barrier causes an eddy area 39 feet wide. The slope of the ground on the windward side of the barrier may affect the width of the eddy area. The eddy area caused by a 4-foot high barrier with a 2:1 downward slope on the windward side is 19 feet wider than that caused by the same barrier on level ground. The ground slope on the leeward side of the barrier affects the boundary lines of the eddy area and the drifting characteristics within the area. The wind velocity may affect the drifting characteristics. A strong wind will cause maximum sweeping action in the outer portion of the eddy area, with the result that the heaviest drifting will occur close to the face of the barrier.

METHODS OF SNOWDRIFT CONTROL

All methods of snowdrift control are based upon one of two general principles. The object is either to remove the snow from the lower air strata before it passes over the highway, or to shape all barriers so that the air currents can flow smoothly over them without creating eddy areas.

Artificial Barriers. The use of artificial barriers such as permanent or removable snow fences to remove the snow from the lower air strata before it passes over the highway is probably the oldest and most generally recognized method of snowdrift control. The snow fence is placed on the windward side of the highway to create an eddy area between it and the highway. The result is that wind passing through the openings and over the fence is slowed sufficiently to cause most of the snow to be deposited in a drift between the fence and the road.

Locating snow fence, a matter of experience and experiment, depends upon the contour of the land, wind velocity, and cross sectional design of the road. The fence is placed sufficiently far from the road so that the eddy area formed by it does not extend to the right of way. The usual distance from the snow fence to the right of way line is 50 to 150 feet. Standard snow fence is made in heights up to 5½ feet with posts of 7, 7½, 8 and 8½ feet in length. The posts are generally set 3 feet deep and 10 to 15 feet apart with the bottom of the fence on the ground. The fence itself consists of 3/8-by 1½-inch wooden slats set vertically and spaced 2 inches apart. These are wound between five double strands of 13-gauge galvanized steel wire, the strands being twisted three times between slats and spaced 10 inches apart. The slats should be well seasoned; free of knots, cracks and decay; and should be treated with preservative.

Specimen 11.3 (continued)

While effective in controlling the drifting of snow, the artificial barriers are unsightly, require erection in the fall and removal in the spring, and at times interfere with farm operations. The slat-type of snow fence is widely used and is considered satisfactory from both its cost and effectiveness.

Natural Barriers. Closely related to artificial barriers is the use of specially designed plantings of trees and shrubs for snow fence. Plantings consisting of single and double rows of trees or shrubs, or both trees and shrubs in various combinations have been used with varying degrees of success.

To be suitable for natural snow barriers, a tree or shrub should be low growing, dense near the ground, frost resistant, drought hardy, free from serious insect and disease pests, adaptable to various soils, long lived, resistant to snow breakage, ornamental, and reasonably priced. Suitable species of shrubs include chokecherry, honeysuckle, American plum, lilac, Russian olive and Buffalo berry. Trees may be either conifers or deciduous and include Rocky Mountain red cedar, Eastern red cedar, Colorado blue spruce, Ponderosa pine, Box elder, Hackberry, Chinese elm, American elm and Burr oak.

The use of natural barriers is limited to locations that do not interfere with farming operations. While their seasonal cost is low, their initial cost is high, and some years are required for the plantings to become effective.

Highway Design Methods. The second general method of snowdrift control finds its application in the proper design of highways. In a number of localities, especially on the western prairies, the snowdrift may be prevented through highway design. With this method the sweeping power of the wind blows snow from the roadway, and the cross section is designed so that it presents no breaks which will form eddy areas.

To prevent drifting, highways should be designed to take advantage of the prevailing winds. The grade line should be from 6 inches to $1\frac{1}{2}$ feet above the level of the adjacent ground to present the roadway surface to the sweeping action of the wind. The cross section should be streamlined with wide, flat, shallow ditches and flat slopes. The ideal slope for both sideslopes and backslopes is 4:1. The design of cut sections is especially important for it is here that drifting is most severe. Borrows may be taken at hill tops to reduce the cost of flat backslopes. On high fill sections it is impractical to make sideslopes as flat as 4:1, but care should be taken that they are not too steep or an eddy area will be formed on the roadway.

Permanent and effective snow control can be designed into the highway. Many of the features of geometric design of the highway which are desirable for control of snow are also desirable for reasons of safety. These features are becoming prominent in recent designs. Improvement in the methods of earth moving has so reduced the cost of grading that it is now practicable to streamline the highway cross section to make it self-cleaning and nondrifting.

Respectfully submitted,

WG:WG

William A. Griffith

Specimen 11.3 (continued)

CITY OF LONG BEACH

Long Beach 2, California

December 30, 19..

To: C. B. Wirsching

City Manager

From: J. B. Wentz

Bureau of Budget
and Efficiency

Preliminary Report of an
Investigation of the Sanitary
Division of the Department of
Public Service

Dear Mr. Wirsching:

One of your initial requests to this Bureau was to conduct a study of all of the various activities of the sanitary division. Since such an investigation to insure reliability and sufficiently detailed results must cover a considerable period of time, it is thought wise to submit a preliminary report at this time.

Impending problems upon which this preliminary information will have definite bearing are the forthcoming vote upon incinerator bonds and the expiring of a contract with the Los Angeles By-Products Company for the sale of salvageable rubbish.

Listed below are determinations already made and presented herewith plus those items still under consideration.

A. DETERMINATIONS MADE TO DATE

1. Cost per ton to collect and dispose of each type of refuse.

2. Cost of operating the city dump.

3. Analysis of income from the sale of refuse.

4. Advisability of making collection of unsegregated rubbish. (Comparison of the saving to the city plus convenience to the taxpayers with the income now realized from sale of rubbish collected as now segregated.)

5. Analysis of rubbish as to source and combustibility.

Specimen 11.4.
Letter report within department

6. The most desirable incinerator site.

7. Time left at present dump site.

B. <u>ITEMS STILL BEING STUDIED</u>

1. Scientific time study of truck operation and routing.

2. Advisability of equipment modifications.

3. Advisability of city owned and operated salvage facilities.

4. Possible improvement of personnel administration and record system.

For convenience of treatment and orderly presentation the final report has been planned to include the following three principal parts, each of which will be summarized at the beginning of each subdivision.

I. Comprehensive Analysis of Sanitary Division Activities.

II. Investigation of Rubbish Collection and Salvage Methods.

III. Consideration of Proposed Incinerator Site and Related Matters.

During the entire study of the subject this Bureau has received the highest type of cooperation from members of the Public Service Department and Sanitary Division contacted for information. These men are to be commended for their interest in improving efficiency and sincere willingness to exert their own energies to this end.

Respectfully submitted,

John B. Wentz

Specimen 11.4 (continued)

McKINSEY, KEARNEY & COMPANY

ESTABLISHED IN 1926 AS JAMES O. MC KINSEY & COMPANY

135 SOUTH LA SALLE STREET

CHICAGO 3

TELEPHONE STATE 2868

March 18, 19..

Mr. P. W. Lorimer
Executive Vice-President
The Toledo Insulation Company
Toledo, Ohio

MATERIAL HANDLING

Dear Mr. Lorimer:

We discussed briefly some passing observations of the material handling problems at the Mansfield Plant. You introduced me to Mr. Brown, Mr. Sewell and the Chief Industrial Engineer. In this brief discussion, it was properly pointed out, by those of your organization, that there are many problems in this field which are peculiar to your materials which are not apparent in passing.

We were all agreed that there is a great potential saving to be made in material handling at the Mansfield Plant.

Following are some of the suggestions which came out of that discussion.

We suggest that the use of unit loads with the special adaptations of power fork trucks be further considered. We suggest the following to further stimulate the development of a practical solution:

1. The use of unit loads in well-organized packing stations with some form of the accepted practice of providing sufficient accumulation of unit loads to make the operation practical.

2. Stabilize the unit loads by gluing the bags or cartons together.

3. Using a top screen, either a typically stationary screen or a special vertically movable top screen, on a fork truck to provide slight compression and stability of load in transit.

Specimen 11.5.
Letter report

4. Consider the special development of side gripping frames to secure unit loads in transit.

5. Consider placing unit loads directly in railroad cars, without manually handling packages as at present, although the unit loads may only partially fill the car perhaps to 66% of capacity. The balance of the car volume could be filled manually as at present.

6. Consider the use of vertical frames of 2 x 4 inch lumber or steel members to stabilize stock piles in storage areas.

7. Consider convenient special methods of handling finished products as was suggested by your Mr. Green at Mansfield. His suggestion was to use sharp forks of small diameter on a power fork truck which would be extended directly into the finished product. This solution could not be used on all products. You are handling some items with "pitch-forks" at present, which is a manual demonstration of Mr. Green's suggestion.

We would be pleased to give more thought and study to this problem of material handling. At our next meeting in Toledo, I would appreciate an opportunity to discuss this problem further with Messrs. Brown and Sewell.

Yours very truly,

Seth L. Winslow

SLW:D

Seth L. Winslow

Specimen 11.5 (continued)

U.S. BUREAU OF RECLAMATION
Denver, Colorado

January 6, 19..

Memorandum for: C. L. Conner
From: H. J. Kahn and H. B. Phillips
Subject: Electrical resistance between cone and cylinder

I. INTRODUCTION

At your request an experiment was performed in order to determine the electrical resistance of a system consisting of a right circular cone within a right circular cylinder.

II. RESULTS

Table 1 lists the resistances obtained for the two cones used in the experimental determination.

TABLE 1

Height of cylinder (L), in.	Diameter of cylinder (2b), in.	Diameter of base of cone (2a), in.	Total resistance of system (R), ohms	Specific resistance of electrolyte (ρ), ohms
12.0	17.8	4.5	114.45	3971.4
12.0	17.8	3.0	139.49	3971.4

III. RECOMMENDATIONS

None.

IV. BASIC DATA

The system under investigation consisted of a right circular cone of base radius (a) and height (L) and a right circular cylinder of radius (b) and height (L). It was desired to determine the electrical resistance that exists between the cone and the cylinder when the axis of the cone is placed coincident with the axis of the cylinder and the space between the two is filled with an electrolyte of specific resistance (ρ). Refer to Figure 1 which shows a cross section of the setup, together with basic dimensions.

Specimen 11.6.
Memorandum interoffice report

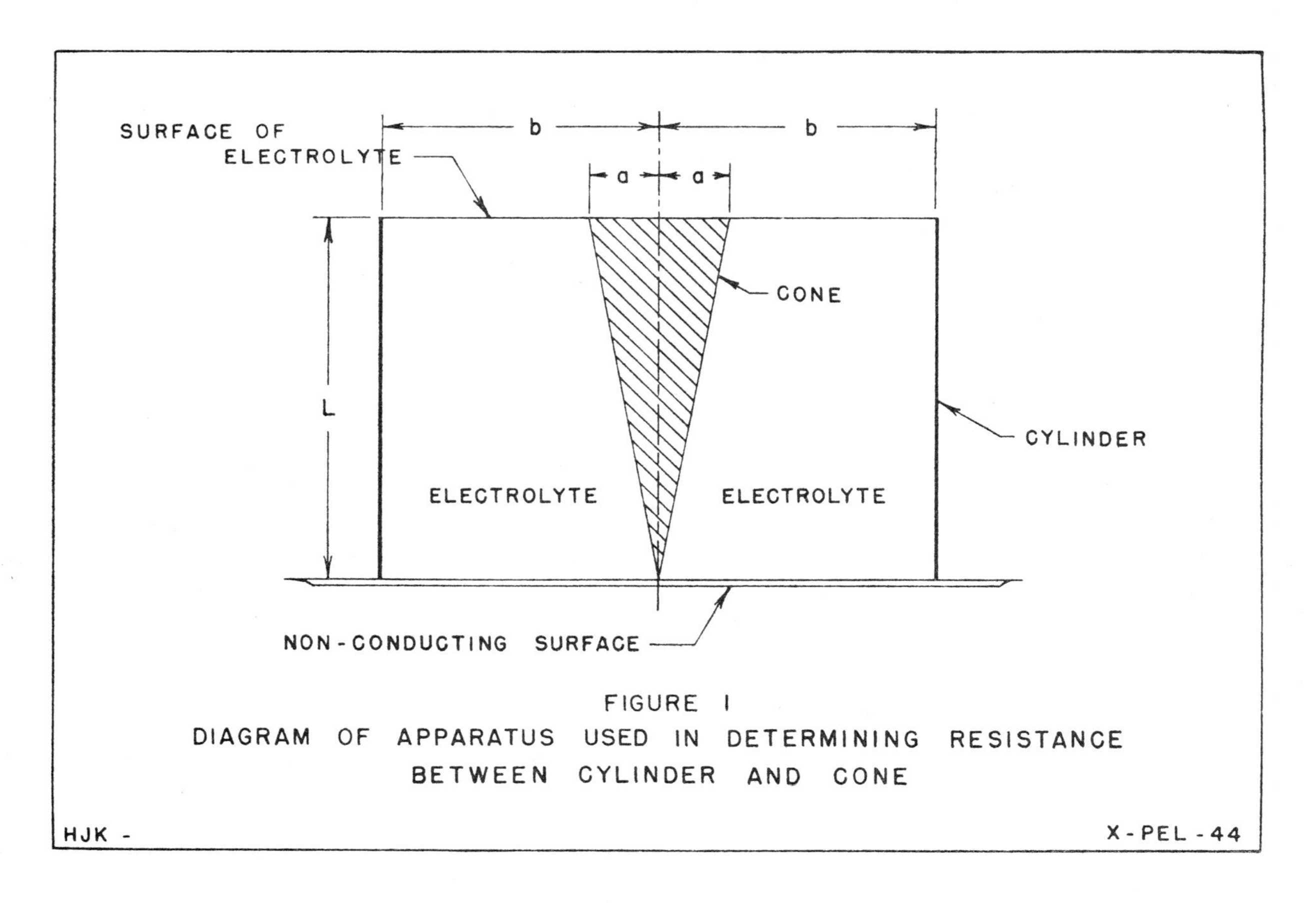

FIGURE I
DIAGRAM OF APPARATUS USED IN DETERMINING RESISTANCE BETWEEN CYLINDER AND CONE

V. TECHNICAL DETAILS

The cones and cylinder used in the resistance determination were constructed from sheet metal to the dimensions as shown in Figure 1. These were then placed in their proper relative positions in a tank of sufficient size to accommodate them and the tank was filled with tap water which served as the electrolyte. By connecting the system into a Wheatstone bridge circuit the resistances shown in Table 1 were determined.

The specific resistance (ρ) of the electrolyte was determined from the relation $\rho = 1/K$. The procedure for determining K was the same as described in Section 7, Basic Data, of the Memorandum sent you July 10.

VI. REFERENCES

Memorandum for T. P. Ahrens from C. N. Zangar and H. B. Phillips. Subject: "Electric analogy conductivity for percolation out of wells," August 16, 19..

VII. PERSONNEL

C. N. Zangar, H. J. Kahn, and H. B. Phillips participated in this study.

H. J. Kahn   H. B. Phillips

H. J. KAHN   H. B. PHILLIPS

Specimen 11.6 (continued)

MINUTES OF MEETING ON BUILDING 77

THURSDAY, FEBRUARY 19, 19.., PLANT MANAGER'S CONFERENCE ROOM

Attending:	H. J. Marshall	J. P. Holloway	M. V. Yohn
	F. M. Frantz	A. C. Perry	H. R. Grable
	R. R. Clark	F. S. Kline	L. A. Darmstaetter

The Engineering Shops have conducted a study which shows that adequate space for storing of mobile equipment for both the Floor Plant Yard Department and the Engineering Shops does not exist in the present garage building 21A. This building is used as both a work area for repairing mobile equipment and for storing some of it overnight. They have therefore prepared an "M" request to remodel building 77.

Building 77, which was formerly the storage garage, is of wooden construction and is in poor condition with the exception of the roof.

The Floor Plant opposes any remodeling of building 77 at this time because of the following reasons:

1. This space has been reserved as the only remaining spot for future tank installation.

2. It is currently required for raw materials storage; no other plant area exists to store material now absorbed there.

3. As soon as additional space is found for raw materials this building should be destroyed.

Inasmuch as Shops need additional garage space and building 77 is objectionable as far as the Floor Plant is concerned, H. R. Grable presented two plans for additional garage space. The first plan would be to construct a garage on the ground north of the print stores and west of building 22. The second plan would be to extend the present garage building 21A northward along the print stores. Both of these plans would provide adequate storage for mobile equipment and allow building 21A to be used as a repair area only.

Following a lengthy discussion of all the plans it was decided that building 77 would not be used or remodeled as a garage and that Shops would request a new building. The plan selected was the one to extend building 21A northward. The Architectural Department is to design the building and come in with a cost estimate and an "M" request.

L. A. Darmstaetter

LAD:DMW
Copies to: Those attending meeting and
D. G. Yentzer, J. R. McCray
R. D. Mayhew, C. M. Swarr

Specimen 11.7.
Report of minutes of meeting

SUBJECT FILE CLASS		NO.
AUTHOR		DATE
TITLE		
ABSTRACT (Fold along this line)		
RECIPIENT	MASTER FILE LOCATION	NO. PAGES
PRINCIPAL FINDINGS		

Specimen 11.8.
Inside title page

DETAILED OUTLINE FOR BODY OF SHORT REPORT

Object

State the purpose of the work covered by the report and the situation or events that make the study desirable.

Nature of Work

Indicate how the work was accomplished — whether by development of a theory, by research and investigation of one or more phenomena, by tests, by compiling data and drawing comparisons, or by making a survey.

Definitions

Define as concisely as possible such factors as the limitations of the report, the scope of investigation, and any special words or terms used.

Related Facts

Cite earlier work used as basis or as supporting material.

Method Used

Describe the method chosen to develop the facts and to arrive at a solution of any phase of the problem in hand. Discuss various methods that were considered and indicate why the method used was given preference.

Procedure

Outline step by step the work done; describe the theories and assumptions applied, the calculations performed, and the experiments and tests made.

Equipment

Describe in detail any special or unusual equipment, devices, or instruments used in developing the solution or in obtaining data.

Specimen 11.9.
Outline of body of short report

Results

Summarize pertinent data; attempt to anticipate and answer questions that may be raised regarding them. For ease of comparison and interpretation present the data in tabular or graphic form whenever practical. Indicate the range of accuracy of various results and point out any known agreement or divergence from other similar data. Analyze the facts developed and the results obtained, and translate the findings into their proper bearing on the problem.

Conclusions and Recommendations

Set out concisely without discussion the conclusions and recommendations which follow from the results and analysis.

Appendix

Present in the appendix any details of secondary nature that would tend to make the body of the report voluminous or to distract attention from the primary contents. It might be well to present in appendices the derivation of formulas or equations used for calculations in the report, statistical data, detailed test information, full method descriptions, and the like. But put nothing in the appendix which must be read or referred to in order to understand the report.

Specimen 11.9 (continued)

CULVERT INSPECTION FIELD REPORT FORM

Culvert Type Corrugated Galvanized Iron   Railroad Ft. Dodge, Des Moines and Southern

Division ____________

Near Just East of Fraser, Iowa   42.86   18 Feet

(Town) (State) (Culvert Number) (Mile Post Plus) (Fill Height)

Size Twin 48" Length ________ Gauge 14 Installed 1933 Base Metal ________

CULVERT PROTECTION		SERVICE CONDITION		SOIL & WATER	
Plain Galvanized	☑	Scouring ☑ or Filling	☐	Normal	☐
Bituminous Coated	☐	Continuous Flow	☐	Organic	☐
½ Coated & Paved	☐	Frequent Flow	☐	Alkali	☐
Full Coated & Paved	☐	Intermittent Flow	☑	Mineralized	☐
Asb. B. Coated Only	☐	Fill Normally Dry	☑	Cinders	☐
Asb. B. Coated & Paved	☐	Fill Normally Damp	☐	Sea Water	☐
Field Paved	☐	Fill Normally Swampy	☐	Sewage	☐
Paving Width	☐	Water Standing in Pipe	☐	Spring	☐

STRUCTURAL PERFORMANCE

Installed too close together
Deflection in East pipe about 1"
Deflection in West pipe 2" to 3"
Pipes silted half full of sand.

Photo No. ______

MATERIAL PERFORMANCE

Galvanizing: Intact where visible except at flow line above sand. Spots gone and rust showing. Also outside where cinder fill contacts pipe. Spots of spelter gone.

Coating:
None

Pavement:
None

Base Metal: Tight rust where galvanizing gone. No scale - little loss of metal.

Date 10/10/61

By J. L. Cooper R.Y. Barham

Specimen 11.10
Form report

The following specimen, 11.11, is printed on both sides of the sheet in order to conserve space in this book. The student laboratory report would be submitted by the student author, typed double space on one side of the sheet only.

E. E. 201

LABORATORY TEST 4

JOULE'S LAW

by

Howard R. Smith

Partners: John R. Waite and Fred P. Johnson

May 18, 19..

Specimen 11.11
Student laboratory report

JOULE'S LAW

PURPOSE OF TEST

Test 4 demonstrates the relation of power to current and resistance in an electrical circuit as defined by Joule's law.

PRINCIPLE

Joule's law may be stated thus: The rate at which heat is developed when an electric current flows in a resistance is proportional to the square of the current and to the resistance. As an equation, Joule's law may be written:

$$P = I^2R$$

in which P is the power in watts, I is the current in amperes, and R is the resistance in ohms.

The usual expression for power as the product of current and voltage, $P = EI$, is developed from Ohm's law, $R = E/I$ by substituting E/I for R in the equation, $P = I^2R$.

In these tests, P was calculated from readings of voltage and current in a controlled circuit operated under known loadings of resistance.

INSTRUMENTS AND APPARATUS

The test was run on ISC load rack 1120, rated at 1.5 to 150 ohms, 120 volts, and 10 kw. Instruments used were a 10-ampere ammeter, a 150-volt voltmeter, and a carbon pile rheostat. The laboratory 120-volt, direct-current supply was used.

PROCEDURE

The wiring diagram of Fig. 1 shows the circuit used.

The circuit was protected with a 10-ampere fuse in the line switch.

Two runs were made: the first, with a constant resistance of 12 ohms and a varying current; the second, with a constant current of 6 amperes and a varying resistance.

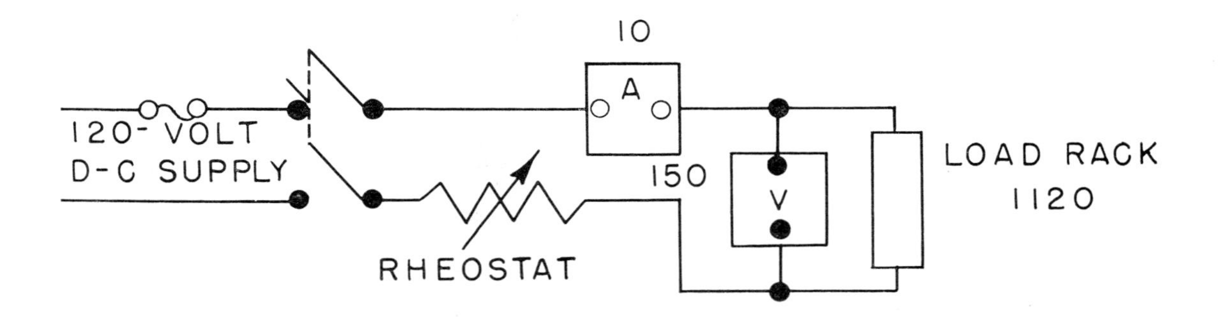

Fig. 1. Wiring diagram.

Specimen 11.11 (continued)

In run 1, the switches of the load rack were set to give a constant resistance of 12 ohms, while the current was varied from 0.0 to 9.2 amperes by adjustment of the rheostat. In run 2, the switches of the load rack were changed to vary the resistance from 1.5 to 20 ohms in a series of readings. After each change of resistance the current was adjusted to 6.0 amperes for each reading.

The same readings were taken in both runs--switch positions, current, and voltage across the load rack. Resistance was determined from the switch position assuming 15 ohms per unit of the load rack. Power was computed for each reading as the product of the current and voltage.

RESULTS

Table 1 gives the observed readings and the calculated results. Graphical comparison of results is presented in Fig. 2.

DISCUSSION OF RESULTS

In run 1, R was held constant at 12 ohms. For this case the equation of the power-current relation takes the form

$$y = ax^2$$

which is a parabola with the vertex at the origin. The

Specimen 11.11 (continued)

Electrical Engineering Laboratory

Title of Test JOULE'S LAW No. 4

Test made by HOWARD R. SMITH

FOREMAN

Apparatus tested: ISC LOAD RACK No. 1120 Set

Rating 1.5 TO 150 OHMS, 120 VOLTS, 10 KW.

Date MAY 18, 19 Wiring Checked by B. S. W. Data Checked by

	1	2	3	4	5	6	7	8	9	10	11	12	13	14
INSTRUMENT NO.														
SHUNT OR C.T. NO		TABLE 1. OBSERVED READINGS AND CALCULATED POWER												
MULT. OR P.T. NO.														
RANGE USED														
SCALE READ			RESISTANCE			CURRENT		VOLTAGE		POWER				
FACTOR			R, OHMS			I, AMPS		E, VOLTS		P, WATTS				
1			RUN 1. RESISTANCE CONSTANT											
2			12			0.00		0.0		0				
3			12			0.50		10.0		5				
4			12			0.95		14.5		14				
5			12			1.90		21.0		40				
6			12			2.75		31.0		85				
7			12			3.60		45.0		162				
8			12			4.85		56.5		274				
9			12			5.85		67.0		392				
10			12			6.50		76.5		497				
11			12			8.15		96.5		786				
12			12			9.20		109.5		1007				
13														
14			RUN 2. CURRENT CONSTANT											
15			1.50			6		8.5		51				
16			2.37			6		13.5		81				
17			3.00			6		18.5		111				
18			4.50			6		27.0		162				
19			6.00			6		37.0		222				
20			7.50			6		43.0		258				
21			10.00			6		57.5		345				
22			13.12			6		79.0		474				
23			18.00			6		108.0		648				
24			20.00			6		118.0		708				
25														
26														
27														
28														
29														

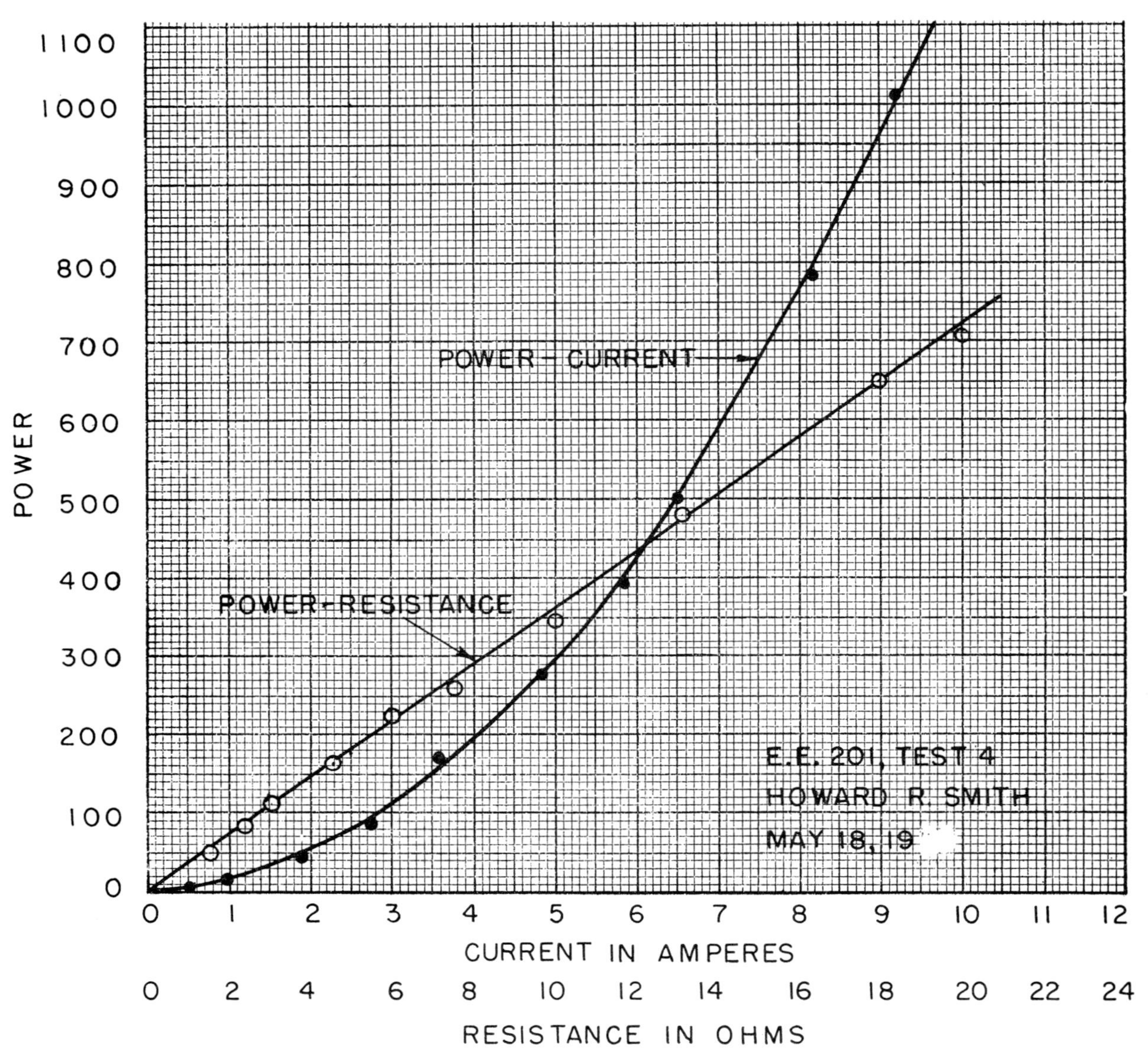

Fig. 2. Relation of power to current and resistance for ISC load rack 1120.

Specimen 11.11 (continued)

power-current curve of Fig. 2 is seen to follow this equation. A definite check on the shape of the curve is obtained by observing the ratios of the power at equal increments of current. At 2, 4, 6, and 8 amperes (Fig. 2) the power is 48, 190, 420, and 770 watts, respectively. Since these readings of the current are in the ratio of 1:2:3:4, the values of the corresponding power should be in the ratio of 1:4:9:16. Actually, they are 1:3.96:8.75:16.02, which is a reasonable check.

The power-resistance curve of Fig. 2, obtained from run 2, is a straight line of the form

$$y = ax$$

This straight line passed through the origin. The slope of the line should be I^2, or 36 watts per ohm because I was held constant at 6 amperes. From Fig. 2, the line having a slope of 36.0 is seen to fit the calculated points quite well.

Joule's law is one of the fundamental laws of electrical engineering. It is the defining equation for the unit of resistance, the ohm. The law applies to alternating- as well as to direct-current circuits. It is

Specimen 11.11 (continued)

usually associated with losses, such as the I^2R, or copper loss, in a machine or transmission line.

Of significance, however, is the fact that in many applications of electricity the heat developed is desirable rather than undesirable. Examples of desirable heat losses are thermal fuses, flat irons, ovens, and all other electrical devices used for heating.

The second-degree equation relation between power and current is of great practical importance. The fact that losses increase with the square of the current, while power developed or transmitted varies with the first power, accounts for the use of the high voltages in electrical equipment. A consideration of this relation will also emphasize the importance of operating heating devices at their rated voltage.

CONCLUSION

Joule's law is one of the simple, fundamental laws of electrical engineering. At the same time it is a law of great importance--one which has application in every problem concerned with electricity in motion.

The tests conducted confirm the basic relation of power, current and resistance as stated by Joule's law.

Specimen 11.11 (continued)

CHAPTER 12

Formal Reports—Preliminary and Supplementary Parts

Reports are prepared in many different forms, covering a wide variety of topics. Any attempt to standardize completely the form of the report would have the effect of placing more emphasis upon form than upon content. Stereotyped reports are the result of overemphasis upon form, and the careful writer will devote his energies to collecting information, solving problems, and presenting ideas. However, any writer can benefit from a rational approach to preparing reports. There are certain fundamentals of report writing which will aid in producing better reports.

RELATION OF FORMAL REPORTS TO LETTER AND SHORT REPORTS

In practice, the use of the various report forms varies widely. The choice of any particular form seems to depend more upon the author's judgment than upon any set procedure.

Generally speaking, when a report exceeds three pages of single-spaced typewritten matter plus illustrations, the writer should consider using the short report or the formal report. The formal report may be considered an expansion of either the letter or short report.

For example, instead of lumping all the material together in a letter report, the writer may divide it into logical components of the short report form. If these various sections need considerable elaboration on the work done, the conclusions and recommendations proposed, then the formal report form should be used.

ORGANIZATION OF FORMAL REPORTS

The elements of a formal report are well established. However, it is not always desirable or even necessary to employ all of these elements. Judgment must be used in selecting those elements which will present the information to the best advantage. The following tabulation lists the sequence of elements as they usually appear in formal reports:

1. Cover and outside title page
2. Flyleaf
3. Frontispiece (on a verso)
4. Inside title page
5. Copyright notice
6. Letter of transmittal
7. Dedication
8. Foreword
9. Preface
10. Acknowledgments
11. Table of contents
12. List of tables and list of illustrations
13. Symbols and notations
14. Abstract or summary
15. Body of the report
    a. Introduction
    b. Discussion
    c. Terminal section
16. References
17. Appendix
18. Index

Preliminary sections of formal reports consist of informational and reference materials which identify the report and explain the conditions under which it was prepared. Specific material in the preliminary sections varies according to the purpose, size, and character of the report. By custom, these parts are similar in name and function to those used by book publishers.

Preliminary parts of reports should be included according to the following plan, provided that the parts indicated apply to the particular report.

Class A. Reports prepared in fulfillment of formal or official requirements of high order where high quality appearance is essential.

Class B. Reports not too official in purpose and use, more than 25 pages in length and retained within the organization where economy of time and expense is a factor in their preparation.

Class C. Reports of committees and organizations, and reports that are to have a wider circulation than classes A and B. Perhaps issued in mimeograph or "fast copy" form.

Class D. Interoffice and memorandum type of reports of 5 to 15 pages, of perhaps temporary value.

This suggested schedule for preliminary parts of formal reports is a rough guide for typewritten reports. Printed reports and reports of wide circulation should be prepared with greater attention to permanency and identification.

COVER AND OUTSIDE TITLE PAGE

Covers of leather, buckram, cardboard, or other suitable flexible material are appropriate for reports. Many commercial covers with special fasteners for loose-leaf binding are available. Class D reports may be prepared with only a heavy backing rather than a complete cover, in which case the inside title page becomes the front cover and title page combined.

Outside titles serve the purpose of identification, rather than of giving information. Hence they need contain only the title of the report, author's name, and date. The cover title may be shortened from that on the inside title page to conserve space. The title may be lettered directly on the cover in

Preliminary part	Class of report*			
	A	B	C	D
Cover and outside title	r	r	r	r
Flyleaf	r	o	o	u
Frontispiece	o	o	o	u
Inside title	r	r	r	o
Letter of transmittal	r	r	o	o
Foreword	n	n	o	n
Preface	o	o	o	n
Acknowledgments (separate part)	o	o	o	n
Table of contents	r	r	r	o
List of tables	n	o	r	u
List of illustrations	n	o	r	u
List of symbols and notations	o	o	o	o
Abstract or summary	r	r	r	r

* The "r" indicates that the part should be required, the "o" indicates that it is optional if appropriate, the "u" indicates that the part is unnecessary, and the "n" indicates that the part is not appropriate.

colored ink, or typed or lettered on a paper label of suitable color. The outside title is usually centered right and left on the page just above the geometric center of the page. Other pleasing covers may be made by off-center arrangements which retain balance and unity of the page. Usually several trials are necessary to achieve a satisfactory arrangement of the title on the cover.

FRONTISPIECE

A frontispiece is not a requirement of a formal report. It is used primarily as an item of added interest and for the purpose of giving prominence to a special feature of the subject reported upon. If a frontispiece is to be used, its informational value and attractiveness are both important considerations. Maps, aerial photographs, photographs of special equipment and scenes, organizational charts, and other types of over-all elements are suitable subjects. The frontispiece faces the inside title page.

INSIDE TITLE PAGE

The inside title page gives complete identification to the report. The important elements are those which identify as well as distinguish the report from others. Identifying items usually included on the inside title page are:

Title of report (and subtitle, if any)
Author and official position
Name of recipient to whom the report is directed
Name and address of the organization through which the report is issued
Date and place of issue or preparation
Serial designation if in a series

The title should be complete, limiting, and fully descriptive of the report. Although brevity is desired, frequently it must be sacrificed in favor of longer titles which are required to describe the report accurately. A good title tells the reader what the report contains. Suitable restrictive words and phrases are used to convey the exact description of the subject. Such phrases as "report on," "a preliminary investigation of," "a survey of the feasibility of," and other combinations of words which do not add essential meaning to the title are unnecessary. The examples at the bottom of this page indicate the characteristics of good titles.

There is little opportunity for variations in the wording of the title page except in the title itself, because the other elements are the names of the parties thereto, the place and date. These elements in combination

Original title	*Improved title*
A Brief Report on the City of Harlan	Taxes and Expenditures for Public Works in Harlan, Iowa, for 1957 to 1962 (Original title does not state the subjects which are discussed.)
The Electrical Engineering Graduate in Sales Work	Opportunities for the Electrical Engineering Graduate in Engineering Sales (Original title is not specific.)
Report to the Portville Bridge Commission of the Survey of Cross-River Traffic in July, 1960, and a Schedule of Toll Rates With an Estimate of Annual Income for the Proposed Frontier Memorial Bridge	Toll Rates and Estimated Annual Income Based on July 1960 Traffic for the Proposed Frontier Memorial Bridge (Original title is too detailed, though it is fully restrictive.)
Enlargement of the Power House and Extension of the Distribution System of the Rockhill Electric Properties	A good title as written.

with the title are arranged to effect a pleasing combination of type mass and white space. Artistic layouts are obtained by attention to symmetry, balance, unity, climax, and harmony. Slender, wide, and square effects should be avoided. Pleasing proportions result from rectangles of about a 3:5 ratio. The type mass should appear to be balanced about the optical center of the page, and the several parts of the page should be arranged to support one another. Uneven vertical spacing between the several parts is more pleasing than even spacing. Two- and three-line parts are given unity by close spacing of the lines.

When only typescript is available, there is little opportunity for contrasting sizes, styles, and weights of letters. Contrast and emphasis are achieved by the use of capitals, capitals and lower case, underlining, and letter spacing. Printer's type provides a wide variety of faces, permitting a number of variations and effects in the design of the title page.

An effective procedure of laying out a title page, is to type each item of information in several arrangements, cut these into slips of paper and then try different arrangements until a good one is found. It sometimes becomes desirable to alter the wording of the preliminary title in order to achieve a desired balance in the lines.

Good principles of title page design are shown on the following pages of specimen titles.

EXPANSION AND MODERNIZATION OF THE FORGE SHOP

of

MC NEELEY AND CORWITH METAL WORKS

Submitted by

HOWELL, HOLDEN and ASSOCIATES
Engineers and Contractors

January 6, 19. .

2490 Liberty Building
214 East Michigan Boulevard
Chicago 6, Illinois

Specimen 12.1.
Title page

THE ENGINEERING PROFESSION IN TRANSITION

A Report of the EJC Committee

on its

Survey of the Engineering Profession

Prepared by
ANDREW FRASER, CONSULTANT

ENGINEERS JOINT COUNCIL
33 West 39th Street, New York 18, N. Y.
November 19..

Specimen 12.2.
Title page

The Harrington Manufacturing Company

Engineering Division

METHODS OF IMPROVING THE MOTOR MAINTENANCE

at the

IOWA MEMORIAL UNION

Report 169

St. Louis, Missouri
January 5, 19..

Specimen 12.3.
Title page

W I D E-B A N D A M P L I F I C A T I O N

by

Nathan J. Downey
Electrical Engineering Student

to

Raymond G. Patenhill
Associate Professor of Electrical Engineering

Purdue University
East Lafayette, Indiana
March 18, 19..

Specimen 12.4.
Title page

LETTER OF TRANSMITTAL

The letter of transmittal, a business letter, serves as the official medium through which the report is passed from the author to the recipient. In addition to taking the place of words which would be spoken if the report were handed to the recipient, the letter of transmittal is a permanent and official record of the transaction. This "delivery ticket" is the only medium that bears the official signature of the author and the date of delivery.

Subject Matter

In the letter of transmittal is a reference to the original authority or request under which the report was prepared. This thought and a statement of the subject are the minimum essential items of the letter. The letter of transmittal may contain any selection from the following items:

Reference to authority or request under which the report was prepared
Report title or general statement of subject
Scope and limitations of report, if not indicated in statement of subject
Reasons, need of report, or immediate application
Conclusions, summary, or findings
Discussion of principal findings
Methods used in preparing report
History or background of subject
Recommended disposition of report
Acknowledgments

Which of the above items to include in a particular letter of transmittal is determined on the basis of the character of the report, the relationship of the author and recipient, and the situation at the moment. Probably no report would necessitate the inclusion of all these items in the letter of transmittal. The first three items — authority, subject, and scope — are found in practically all letters of transmittal and are among the first subjects mentioned. Reference to authority and subject are the first two items, usually.

Whether the results of the study are stated in the letter of transmittal depends upon the particular report and its arrangement. A report giving a summary of results in a preliminary section, hardly needs to repeat the information in the letter of transmittal. However, it is advantageous to the reader if the letter of transmittal indicates whether the answer is positive or negative. A sentence, or even a paragraph, to indicate the general findings, when included incidentally in the letter of transmittal, is usually appropriate for all question-solving types of reports.

The letter of transmittal is an appropriate place to acknowledge the assistance of others in the preparation of the report, provided that the acknowledgments can be brief and simply stated. A statement of acknowledgments, if lengthy, should be included as a separate preliminary section.

Characteristics

The letter of transmittal is the author's only place to be personal; the report is always strictly objective. There are reports in which the author desires to give something of his personal contact with, or attitude toward, the subject. Such material is out of place anywhere except in the letter of transmittal or preface. In this same field of information, it is sometimes desirable to point out in the letter of transmittal certain policies, considerations, or assignments which are more appropriately omitted from the body of the report, and yet helpful in giving the reader the proper understanding of the basis upon which the report was prepared. There is close similarity between the letter of transmittal and the preface or foreword. Each serves as the outlet for personal contact between the author and reader. For this reason few reports contain both parts. When both are appropriately used, the letter of transmittal should be brief and formal.

The letter of transmittal may be considered as a separate, somewhat detached part of the report. For this reason it follows the inside title page rather than following the table of contents or other preliminary part. All reports, regardless of length and character, contain the elements of the letter of transmittal. In letter reports, the information is given in the opening paragraph of the letter; in memorandum reports for use wholly within the organization sponsoring the report, the information may be incorporated within the title page or first paragraph of the introductory section. In formal reports a separate sheet is used.

Specimen letters of transmittal follow.

Specimen 12.5.
Letters of transmittal for periodic reports

Dear Sir:

In accordance with the statute, I am transmitting to you herewith the Twenty-fifth Biennial Report of the Michigan State Highway Department for the fiscal years ending June 30, 1960, and June 30, 1961.

Very truly yours,

Dear Mr. Mayor:

Complying with the ordinance of the City of Portville, I herewith submit my annual report, showing a complete abstract of the books of this office for the fiscal year ending March 31, 1961.

Respectfully submitted,

Gentlemen:

We submit herewith the Fifty-first Annual Report of the City of Des Moines for the year ended March 31, 1961, as required under Section 5677 of the Code of Iowa.

Respectfully submitted,

2122 Lincoln Way
Ames, Iowa
November 28, 19..

Professor Frank E. Jensen
Chairman, Publication Board
College Annual
213 Beardshear Hall
Ames, Iowa

Dear Professor Jensen:

In compliance with the instructions you gave me October 10, I am submitting this report, "Plans for a Photographic Darkroom for the College Annual."

The objective is restricted to presenting an outline of the needs for darkroom facilities and a general plan which will satisfy these needs. No attempt has been made to provide detailed working drawings.

Yours very truly,

Alfred B. Bardner
General Engineering
Student

Specimen 12.6.
Letter of transmittal

THE MIDWEST ENGINEERING CORPORATION

220 Wacker Drive, Chicago 6, Illinois

January 6, 19..

Honorable Mayor & City Council
Municipal Building
Falls River, Nebraska

Gentlemen:

Pursuant to instructions contained in your letter of November 30, 19.., signed by Mayor L. K. Randall, we submit herewith the results of our studies to determine the possibilities of developing power by the municipality for use within the city of Falls River and vicinity.

We have also included an analysis of a proposal for power development submitted to you by Mr. Randolph Jester.

Acknowledgments are due the officers of the Nebraska Power Company for supplying the necessary information on their properties within your territory.

Respectfully submitted,

Frank Marshall

Frank Marshall
Electrical Engineer

FM:bym

Specimen 12.7.
Letter of transmittal

NEWHOUSE ENGINEERING COMPANY

INVESTIGATIONS—APPRAISALS—SURVEYS—PLANS

645 WEBSTER AVENUE, CLEVELAND, OHIO

December 20, 19..

Northern Light & Power Company
575 Euclid Avenue
Cleveland, Ohio

Gentlemen:

In accordance with our agreement signed August 16, 19.., we have completed an appraisal of the light and power properties operated by you in the town of Lakeside. Our detailed report is submitted herewith.

This appraisal is based upon inventories submitted by you plus our own field checking and examination of the property. The date of appraisal is December 1, 19...

We find that the property has a value of $865,980, including working capital but omitting intangible items.

Very truly yours,

K Martin Landis

K. Martin Landis
President

KML:vw

Specimen 12.8.
Letter of transmittal

RIENHARDT HEATING ENGINEERS

UNITED LIGHT BUILDING

INDIANAPOLIS, INDIANA

DOMESTIC AND
INDUSTRIAL HEATING

TELEPHONE
CH 3-7156

January 10, 19..

Webb, Miller & Crawford
268 Professional Building
Harrison, Illinois

Gentlemen:

Your letter of November 20, 19.., instructed us to make a comparative study of the costs and advantages of various heating systems that could be installed in the Grant Hill Hospital which you are now designing. The accompanying report is submitted in fulfillment of this assignment.

We are recommending panel heating with forced hot water circulation. This arrangement will give adequate heat with minimum air movement, and there will be no exposed piping or radiators. The annual heating cost is the lowest of any method we investigated, though the cost of installing the heating system is about 15 per cent higher than standard steam systems with cast-iron radiation.

The cooperation of your staff in furnishing us with the essential information relative to the general design and the requirements set forth by the hospital officials is appreciated.

We will be pleased to work further with you in preparing the final design of the heating system for this hospital.

Very truly yours,

RIENHARDT HEATING ENGINEERS

H. J. Berkel

HJB:jk

H. J. Berkel, vice-president

Specimen 12.9.
Letter of transmittal

FOREWORD

The words *foreword* and *preface* as applied to preliminary parts of reports, bulletins, and books have not always been used with consistent distinction. The discriminating author and publisher use the term foreword to apply to a statement written by someone other than the author, and the term preface to apply to the author's statement. The president or other official of the company or association sponsoring the work, an outside authority interested in furthering the knowledge developed in the report, the immediate teacher or supervisor under whom the work was performed, or a long-time professional colleague of the author are typical of those who write forewords. These persons are particularly qualified for writing the foreword to a report because they have the background for the evaluation of the material; namely, a personal knowledge of the author and a keen appraisal of the significance of the report.

The content of a foreword usually includes comments which are more appropriately said by someone other than the author. Qualifications of the author, the merit of his work, the over-all value of the subject, history of the work, and timeliness of the objectives are subjects for treatment in a foreword. Forewords tend to produce a better understanding of the subject and a wider readership. Thus, they are appropriate for reports directed to general readers rather than to a small group of technical, administrative, management, or financial executives. A foreword would be appropriate in a report on a phase of the company's business which after being submitted to the management was later reworked for distribution to prospective customers.

Common practice in technical periodicals is for the editor to give a few words of comment and evaluation about the subject and author of feature articles. This advance evaluation on the article and author gives the reader opportunity to know the objectives and relative importance of the article before beginning to read. In much the same way, a foreword to a report or, on occasion, a preface to a book is an aid to the reader.

PREFACE

Text and reference books usually contain an author's preface rather than a letter of transmittal, because these publications are not addressed to specific persons. Hence, the author places his personal message to his readers in the preface. Because reports are usually written for specific readers and are sent with a letter of transmittal, a preface is not generally included. There are reports, however, that appropriately include both, such as a report submitted by an employer to his chief on a subject of private investigation unknown to the chief. Research and committee reports are often better suited to the use of a preface than a letter of transmittal.

A preface to a report may include the author's explanation of why the report was written, something of his background of experience or thinking that led to the writing of the report, how he hopes the report will be used, and some details of history. Acknowledgments may be included also, but as with the letter of transmittal, if they are extensive, a separate section should be used.

ACKNOWLEDGMENTS

It is courteous and considerate on the part of an author to extend credit to those individuals and organizations particularly helpful to him in the preparation of his report. This help includes assistance and co-operation in the gathering of information as well as in the writing and preparation of the typed report. Footnote references to the literature are usually considered proper credit to the authors of other works that have been used, but if extensive and direct use is made of a previously published work, additional credit should be given in the acknowledgments. As a matter of practice it is better to be liberal in mentioning the assistance of others than to have someone disappointed by not being mentioned.

Specimen 12.10.
Foreword

FOREWORD

We as older engineers, either suffering or profiting from long years of experience and observation, need to read at least once each year something along the order of the accompanying report of "How the Young Engineer Looks at Engineering and Engineers." The young authors, Harold F. McCarran and George G. Howard, have contributed a valuable paper to our professional lore. This report is one that will stand repeated readings by the employers of young engineers and the college professors who have it within their responsibility to mold the thinking and professional attitudes of the college students, who tomorrow will become the practicing engineers.

McCarran and Howard have done a remarkable job because they have covered the bridge from college student life to the first years of professional life, not only within their own thinking and interpretation, but in terms of what some 50 other graduates have to say.

On the one hand they readily admit that they found the young engineers too ambitious to achieve rapid advancement and initial responsibility. On the other hand, their findings clearly charge the older engineer with failure to extend to these young engineers the types of responsibilities that will enable them to mature and reach sound judgments much earlier than is customarily considered proper. Part of this difference of thinking, I am certain, comes from the changed profession. The real work of the engineer is not in performing manual skills but in directing and conceiving engineering works. Thus, there is a changing attitude within the field of practice, which some engineers have not yet realized or admitted, but which has found its way into the curricula and into the art of teaching.

As a former, privileged professor of McCarran and Howard, I am elated to say these words in behalf of their report. A performance of this type by graduates is one of the compensations we professors sincerely enjoy. The Society is enriched by having these two juniors on the rolls. Their thinking and their findings are giving us new life which we old codgers really need.

Professor Bart W. Hazelton

Specimen 12.11.
Preface

PREFACE

Three years ago when developing a thorough report on the mineral geology of Lake County, Colorado, I had occasion to study the records, public and private, of the mining operations of this mountainous area. Upon completion of this report on geology, my files contained a mass of information on the mining history of Lake County not previously assembled. Much of the information, although not pertinent to my final report on geology, was valuable historically and of possible value to current and future mining operations.

As time permitted I extended my study into the older mining operations with the objective of preparing this book on the Mining Operations and Mineral Extractions in Lake County, Colorado.

This book is presented from the viewpoint of the mining engineer. Though based on historical records, I do not consider this work a history. Neither is it regarded as a text on the subject, though the student of mining will find herein many a lesson to be learned, applicable today as well as in the pioneer days of Colorado.

This enjoyable work uncovered the trails of many noted - and unnoted - personages. If there is indication of too much biographical material, the reader should excuse it on the grounds that, after all, the mining successes and failures are just reflections of the individuals responsible therefor.

An endeavor has been made to give credit to individuals and sources of information through liberal use of footnotes. Should credit be omitted it is unintentional. May those forgotten be recognized by my general thanks and appreciation to all who contributed to my efforts in any way.

Hugh D. Hutchins

Acknowledgments may be stated in the letter of transmittal, in the preface, or in a separate section of the preliminaries. The space required to extend proper credit to all those whose assistance should be mentioned, determines whether a separate section should be used. Acknowledgments in the letter of transmittal should be limited to a comparatively simple statement not exceeding four or five lines.

TABLE OF CONTENTS

The table of contents is a topical outline of the report together with page numbers. The entries in the table of contents are the exact headings which appear throughout the body of the report to mark the various parts, divisions, and sections of the text. The table of contents has two functions: First, from it the reader can learn what subjects are treated in the report, the relative value of related topics, and the order in which they are developed. Second, the table of contents is a reference device by which the parts of the report may be located by page number. In this latter function, a detailed table of contents is particularly desirable in a long report which does not have an index.

The typographical arrangement of the table of contents is important. Entries subordinate to the main and subsections of the report are indicated in the table of contents by indentation and style of type. It is not essential that the lines of the table of contents be typed in the same arrangement of capitals and lower case typescript as used for the same headings in the body. Relation of the several subjects into which the report is divided is shown mainly by indentations, but the relation is emphasized in certain outlines by contrasting type.

The table of contents is generally a complete assembly of the headings used in the report for the parts and sections which follow the table of contents. When it is desirable to conserve space and when the minor subdivisions of the sections are numerous and relatively unimportant, they may be omitted from the table of contents. The contents page should be arranged as a separate part. Its composition and position on the page deserve careful planning, and its typography is selected on the basis of pleasing effect and functional merit.

The following pages contain specimens of tables of contents.

LISTS OF TABLES AND ILLUSTRATIONS

Longer reports containing tables and illustrations to which reference may be necessary should have a list of tables and a list of illustrations following the table of contents. These lists are prepared directly from the table captions and figure legends, according to their numbered sequence. The page number is given, and no break in the sequence should be made for material which may be in the appendix.

SYMBOLS, NOTATIONS, AND GLOSSARY

A list of the letter symbols and notations used in the report is a convenience to the reader of a report containing extensive mathematical or scientific analyses. The system of letter symbols and other notations should conform to the standards of the subject field as recommended by the American Standards Association,[1] other official body, or as commonly practiced in the subject field.

In addition to symbols and notations, the reader will benefit from a glossary of technical terms, should the report deal with terms whose meanings might be subject to question or be unfamiliar to the reader.

---

[1] See American Standards Association, 70 East 45th Street, New York 17, N.Y., for complete listing of standards for letter and graphical symbols.

Specimen 12.12.
Acknowledgments

ACKNOWLEDGMENTS

The successful completion of the studies herein reported was made possible by the splendid cooperation of many individuals and organizations. To all those who in any manner aided in the work, the author expresses his sincere thanks. He is especially grateful to Dr. H. D. Berging for supervising the chemical analyses; to Prof. Chester R. Enger for preparation of the photomicrographs; and to Mr. Baker W. Bolton, of the Eastern Lakes Steel Company, for furnishing the special steels.

Acknowledgment is made to the General Electric Company for loaning many of the special instruments used in making the laboratory measurements. The painstaking care with which H. S. Meyer and Carl A. Jones conducted the laboratory tests for the physical characteristics and with which H. H. Lands machined the specimens is appreciated.

The sympathetic interest and wise counsel of Dr. M. Q. Koeller, director of the Institute, considerably encouraged the author to overcome the many difficulties encountered.

Specimen 12.13.
Table of contents

TABLE OF CONTENTS

LIST OF ILLUSTRATIONS

Specimen 12.14.
Table of contents

TABLE OF CONTENTS

Specimen 12.15.
Table of contents

TABLE OF CONTENTS

Specimen 12.16.
Table of contents

TABLE OF CONTENTS

ABSTRACT

The element immediately preceding the introductory section of the report is called the abstract. In report writing, the abstract is confined to a summary of the findings plus such additional information as is necessary to make the summary of the findings understood. The abstract is primarily for the purpose of setting out the main results, whether they be facts, conclusions, or recommendations, rather than for the purpose of describing the report or giving an over-all summary of it.

Instead of placing an abstract of the findings ahead of the introduction as a preliminary part of the report, the practice of some writers is to move forward the terminal section, or at least a summary of it. When this is done any one of three arrangements is used: (1) The summary section is placed as a preliminary element ahead of the beginning of the body as stated above for the abstract, (2) the summary is placed immediately ahead of the introductory section but as the first section of the body, or (3) the summary is placed immediately following the introductory section.

There is an increasing tendency toward using the abstract of findings, the complete terminal section, or a summary of the report in a forward position. This arrangement is particularly good in the long report because it places the findings before the reader at a convenient location. Executives who wish to read at once the answers, and read at a later time the details of how the answers were obtained, particularly favor an abstract or summary at the beginning. In reports of less than about 10 pages, the summary may be incorporated within the introductory section, so that reading it gives one both explanatory background and findings.

Content of Abstracts

When the terminal section or a summary of it is moved forward, when a summary type abstract is used, or when a combination of the two is used, the contents thereof require careful selection. This is because statements of objectives and findings may be properly included in the letter of transmittal and introduction as well as in a forward summary. A certain repetition is natural within these parts of formal reports, though the subject matter need not be unnecessarily duplicated. Effectiveness of the arrangement and of the contents is achieved when the letter of transmittal, abstract, introductory section, and terminal section are planned to supplement each other. However, regardless of arrangement of preliminary sections, the body of the report is complete and not dependent upon other parts of the report.

The report abstract may be regarded as somewhat different than the usual abstract which accompanies technical papers, articles and proceedings, or the abstracts contained in publications which are devoted entirely to abstracts. An effective arrangement of a report abstract is to include the following information in a direct and concise statement:

1. Statement of the assignment
2. Statement of the findings
3. Principal factors which support the findings
4. Recommendation for action to take

Types of Abstracts

In scientific and technical papers and proceedings the abstract may be given the name of synopsis, summary, or epitome. But regardless of name, the objective is either (1) to state the facts found in the original article together with sufficient explanatory material to enable the summary of facts to be understood, or (2) to describe the contents and limitations of the article without giving the findings. These two types of abstracts may be referred to as (1) the factual abstract and (2) the descriptive abstract.

The factual abstract also is used in publications which in themselves are collections of abstracts. Here the abstract serves in place of the original and, because it does not accompany the original, the reader must be given facts or else he has gained little from reading the abstract. Publications for this particular purpose include Ceramic Abstracts, Chemical Abstracts, Highway Research Abstracts, Public Health Abstracts, and others. The factual abstract also gives sufficient general information so that the conditions upon which the results were obtained and are to be applied are understood by the reader. The factual abstract is the type usually written by one for his personal use during his study of the subject or for later reference.

The descriptive abstract is used apart from the original material only in the brief statements that are often given in bibliographies. The descriptive abstract has only the function of describing the article so that the reader may judge whether he is interested in reading the original. This type of abstract states the area of the subject covered, objective, and how the objective was reached, without presenting factual information which may be used in lieu of reading the original. The descriptive abstract is occasionally used with a report prepared for general circulation among a wide range of readers who are not informed of the character of the report ahead of receiving it.

Rules of Abstracting

A few rules of abstracting may be mentioned, though each abstract must be prepared for its own probable uses and readers. One who is gathering information for his own personal use or for another's use in a particular application is guided by these uses, and will record in his abstract only that information which appears to serve the specific purpose. When abstracting for a wide readership, selection of the material is based upon the relative importance for all applications rather than on limited applications. Extreme care is taken that the abstract sets forth an accurate statement of facts and the original author's views. The abstracter, in writing an abstract for another to read, does not allow his own views to discolor those of the original author. Further, he gives the author's relative emphasis to the subjects and ideas expressed in the original. The abstract does not need to follow the sequence of the original, though it usually will. Three general types of information should be given in the factual abstract:

1. Statement of the subject, its scope, and its applications
2. Main facts and their sources upon which the analysis is based, and something of the method used by the author in his analysis
3. An accurate statement of the facts, conclusions, and results

In those instances when the abstract does not accompany the original article, special attention is given to the inclusion of the complete reference.

The length of an abstract is controlled by the length and subject matter of the original paper or report and the purpose for which the abstract is written. Longer original material calls for a shorter abstract in percentage of original. Perhaps 1 to 10 per cent of the original number of words is a reasonable range for abstracts. This brevity is obtained by eliminating the minor and descriptive material of the original and by writing in a concise and condensed style. Complete sentences should be used and every effort made to produce a smooth reading abstract.

There follow three examples of abstracts which illustrate the general types discussed.

APPENDIX

Whether material should be placed in the body of the report or in the appendix is answered by the question: Will the reader of the report need to read the material in order to understand the report? Whether the material needs to be included at all is answered by the question: Is the material desirable as supporting material for the critical reader, as reference material in connection with current use of the report, or as reference material for future use of the report?

The appendix is the proper place to include material that is unnecessary to read in order to gain the proper understanding of the report, but which may need to be available either as reference or as supporting information. Tabulations, illustrations, and analyses which are important findings are

Specimen 12.17.
Abstract

ABSTRACT

The contents of this report indicate that the erection and operation, at the Gary Refinery of the Republic Refining Company, of a catalytic polymerization plant, which is patented by the Universal Oil Products Company, is desirable.

Further indications are that the earnings derived from this installation will be increased greatly if a new vapor recovery system is erected to operate in conjunction with the polymerization plant, which will embody the following desirable features:

1. It will enable processing of all of the unsaturated refinery gas which is the potential polymer gasoline, thereby greatly increasing the polymer gasoline yield.

2. It will save tetraethyl lead because of the high blending value of the polymer gasoline.

3. It will allow handling and storing the blending butane under pressure, thereby reducing the loss from storage.

4. There will be practically no butanes in the treated gasoline, thereby reducing pumping losses.

5. It will allow making a light pressure gasoline cut which can be inhibited and will not require acid treating or rerunning.

6. It will result in an improved product which will have a value in (a) customer acceptance, (b) storage stability, and (c) advertising purposes. (These items have not been included in the realization because of their indeterminate nature.)

The initial cost of installation of a polymerization plant using the present vapor recovery plant will be $125,000, the operation of which will return the investment at the rate of 68.5 per cent a year.

The total initial cost of the polymerization plant and the proposed vapor recovery plant will be $475,000. The operation of this assembly should return 80.5 per cent a year on the investment.

The immediate erection of the proposed vapor recovery system and the polymerization plant is recommended.

placed in the body of the report. Original data or reference material upon which the findings are based may be placed in the appendix provided that the reader need not read this material in order to understand the discussion. The body of the report should provide all information which is essential to gaining full understanding of the report.

When over-all content of the report is such that it becomes desirable to segregate the tables or illustrations from the reading text so that the reading sequence is not too broken, such material may be grouped at the end of chapters or sections.

Appropriate matter to be arranged in sections of the appendix consists of the following:

1. A bibliography when added strictly as supplementary matter not containing references essential to the proper reading of the report.
2. Plans and specifications which may be included as a convenience to the reader.
3. Extracts of statutes, city ordinances, contracts, patents, and similar reference material which may be the basis of discussion or interpretations within the text.
4. Compilations of original data obtained by research or by survey which are included for use by a reader who wishes to undertake his own critical analysis of the data. When information of this type is included in the appendix, essential summaries or graphs of it should be presented in the body of the report.
5. Copies of standard forms, collection sheets, and other working papers which are supplementary to the text.
6. Theoretical analyses and mathematical derivations not necessary to an understanding of the text, but which may be desired by some of the readers as a basis of checking the theoretical development in the text.
7. Specimen materials, such as sample calculations or applications of suggested procedures.
8. Documentary papers, including letters, legal papers, affidavits, and instructions.

INDEX

An index is not to be confused with the table of contents. An index is an alphabetical listing with page numbers or other means of reference of all the topics, subjects, phrases, and names mentioned in the report. By custom the index is always the final section of the report.

Few reports include an index because the subject matter covered is of limited scope, and the table of contents suffices for all ordinary use in locating a particular subject in the report. Reports which may extend into a hundred or more double-spaced pages of typescript and which cover a wide range of topics that may need to be looked up frequently, perhaps should have an index. Otherwise a detailed table of contents will serve the reader in locating specific subjects.

Seldom is an index prepared for a typewritten report or for any report of limited circulation. Reports which are printed for general circulation should contain an index if readers are likely to use the reports for frequent reference. Many a report or reference book fails to give its full value because of the lack of an index or because of not having an adequate one.

The preparation of an index is a difficult and painstaking process to be undertaken only by one who is familiar with the subject as well as with the steps in indexing. The objective in preparing an index for a report or book is primarily to see that all subjects and their subdivisions are indexed. Indexing is a process of classification. The procedure may be handled by first carefully reading through the report (page proof if it is being printed) and underlining in color all words that are to be indexed. Subentries may be indicated at the same time by use of a different colored underline. When all key words are underlined the words and their corresponding page numbers are written on cards about 3 by 5 in. The next step is to sort the cards into alphabetical order by main entries and subentries. The final step is to type the listing in suitable typographical arrangement. The final typing should be verified by checking the original colored markings in the report or page proof with the typed index.

Specimen 12.18.
Factual abstract

ABSTRACT

Engineering educators face the problems of including the training required by the technician, the professional engineer, and the executive in one curriculum; adding the technical material that has been made essential by recent technical advancement; and maintaining a balance with the humanities and social sciences.

The solution presented in this report is a combined four- and six-year course as follows:

1. Two years of pre-engineering study corresponding to the first two years of the present conventional four-year curriculum.

2. Two years of general training composed of the following:

Social sciences	14.0 per cent
Communications	8.4 per cent
Fine arts	3.0 per cent
Technical fundamentals	74.6 per cent

3. Two years of intensive training in engineering for those students who show exceptional ability in the four-year course.

The special features of this proposed curriculum are:

1. It provides for training of technicians, professional engineers, and "executives" in one curriculum.

2. It postpones the choice of a major field until the student has had greater educational experience and has reached greater intellectual maturity.

3. It relieves the engineering school of the problem of adjusting the curricula downward to meet the varying and inferior standards of high school preparation.

4. It allows the engineering school to concentrate on its primary function, engineering education.

Educators should cooperate in drawing up their curricula under the direction of some large organization, such as the American Society for Engineering Education. Individual schools must abandon competition for enrollment.

Specimen 12.19.
Descriptive abstract

ABSTRACT

The Collegiate Specialty Manufacturing Company desires to relocate its main office and plant from the concentrated area of northern New Jersey to a less populated area. This report covers the survey of possible locations along the Eastern coast. The considerations pertaining to five cities are presented in detail.

Factors considered are raw material supply, transportation, labor supply, housing, educational facilities, and public attitudes toward a new industry. Brief discussion is given of the probable reaction to existing employees of Collegiate Specialty toward moving to another city.

Specimen 12.19A.
Factual abstract. Compare with Specimen 12.19.

ABSTRACT

Lynchburg, Virginia, is recommended as the future location of the main office and plant of the Collegiate Specialty Manufacturing Company. Lynchburg is preferred on the basis of the stipulations of the company with respect to source of textiles, light metals, wood, finishing materials, labor, transportation, and housing.

Detailed comparisons of Lynchburg with five other cities along the Eastern section of the country, New York to Georgia, are given in the report. Some dozen other cities were considered, but in less detail. Two features, more than others, clearly indicate Lynchburg as the first choice. The sincere and friendly attitude of the public officials and citizens at large toward expansion of industry and a new labor force to be moved in is wholesome and refreshing. The community does not offer special tax benefits or other financial inducements. It offers its high spirit of community life and tradition of maintaining a highly respectable, clean, and nonpolitical community. The other favorable situation is the adequate supply of good, modern, and well-located housing at reasonable cost.

In view of the attitude of the local citizens and the fine physical facilities available, including public schools, the present employees of Collegiate Specialty are most likely to accept the move to Lynchburg with but little objection. They will find it easy to adjust to their new environment quickly.

CHAPTER 13

Formal Reports—Body

The complete development of the report is placed in a section called the body of the report. This development may follow either the natural sequence in which the investigation took place or the psychological sequence by which the reader's decision for action may be obtained most effectively. The main divisions of the body will be designated in terms of the functions they perform. Thus these terms will serve as guides in writing reports under any of the classified types. As indicated in the discussion on outlining, Chapter 2, the tone of any report will be personalized by using divisional headings or terms that vividly relate to the particular field of thought represented in the report under consideration.

OUTLINE FOR THE BODY OF REPORTS

The development employed in this chapter will be the natural sequence by which the body of the report is prepared under functionally designated divisions or headings as follows:

The Introduction
- Statement of subject, objectives, and scope
- Clarification of reasons for the preparation of the report
- Explanation of general methods employed
- Statement of the plan or organization of the report

The Discussion
- Presentation of the essential information collected
- Analysis and interpretation of the data
- Solution of the problem

The Terminal Section
- Summary
- Conclusions
- Recommendations

The reader of a report, especially if he is a client, employer, or an executive representing management or administration, will be anxious to know what the findings of the report are and what conclusions and recommendations may be derived from the preparation of the report. Even though the writer follows the natural sequence in the development, he will satisfy the major interest of the reader by placing the abstract or summary, the conclusions and the recommendations ahead of the introduction and the development.

Acknowledgments and other formal matter are introduced whenever desired.

The formal report in the Appendix illustrates the use of the major elements recommended in this chapter.

THE INTRODUCTION

Across the table from the chief sits one of his key assistants, who has just been summoned for conference.

"Bill," he says, "I have a fine assignment for you. You remember that about a month ago I mentioned the possibility of our acquiring the old Riddle plant which might be made suitable for our new foundry. Well, the Board is interested, and I want you to look the plant over, and if you find it suited to our needs, report on the cost of rehabilitating, equipping, and operating it. Use whatever personnel you desire, and call on other departments for such help as needed. We will want your report by February 10."

Here is an over-the-table conference. One-sided to be sure, but no doubt the chief gave opportunity for a few questions, so it can be called a conference.

Later, a second over-the-table conference, also one-sided, will be held. This conference will come February 10 when the chief reads the introductory section of the report. The words written there must do for the chief what his brief, specific, and concise instructions to the assistant did toward giving him an understanding of the assignment. The written introduction to a report should give the chief (and members of the Board) an understanding of the objectives of the investigation, how they were accomplished, something of the findings, and a plan of the report which follows the introductory section.

Importance and Content of Introductions

On the introduction to a business or technical report depends whether the remainder of the report will be understood easily, whether the pages which follow provide that which the reader expects, and whether the reader gains the proper concept of the subject. A good introduction sets up for the reader an orderly path to follow, it co-ordinates the subject matter, guards against digression, and provides a check on the scope of the conclusions. The introduction is a descriptive preview of what is to follow.

Each introduction should be custom-built for the particular report of which it is a part. Few introductions will discuss all of the following items, but this list is suggestive of the subject matter from which selections may be made:

1. Subject of report, objectives, or purpose
2. Present situation giving rise to need of study
3. Writer's understanding of the assignment
4. Writer's point of view or attitude toward subject
5. Limitations, scope, or extent of treatment, what report is and is not
6. History, background, and review of previous reports
7. Basic theories, principles, or policies involved
8. Methods used to reach conclusions
9. Sources of information
10. How information was gathered
11. What information was used
12. Findings briefly and incidentally stated
13. Concepts and definitions of terms
14. General plan followed in developing the solution
15. Plan and content of the report.

If the above items were developed in detail, the introduction would become a lengthy treatise; in fact, the report itself. But such development is not intended. Introductions to reports should be brief, concise, and helpful. The history, background, and definitions, when these items become too long for the introduction, may be placed in separate sections. The other items suggested need only be mentioned. The reader does want to know at the outset, however, whether the report is based on laboratory experiments, field surveys, questionnaire results, or "armchair" deductions. Also, the introduction should state early what elements of the problem are included, what excluded. Does the plan and estimate of cost include building and equipment, or only the building?

The introduction should be written as a presentation of the report itself, and as such it will be about the same as would be stated in an oral hearing with the chief. On this basis there should be no trouble in holding the introduction to a brief yet complete statement of the essential items. Discussion of the general subject or established science on which the report is based should be left to text books.

Each report will require its own selection of items to be mentioned in the introduction. A committee that spends ten months studying the possibilities of industrial development of an urban community may have occasion to write an extensive introduction for benefit of the executive board of the chamber of commerce, while the production manager of the ABC Manufacturing Company, reporting to his chief on the same community as a possible location of a branch plant, could appropriately dispose of the introduction in 200 words.

Opening Sentence

While a strong introduction which sets the goal for the remainder of the report is desirable, of equal importance is a forceful opening sentence to the introduction. Because reports are written on specific proposals or questions for specific readers, no space should be wasted on beginnings with a "far away" approach. The first sentence should state the specific subject and objective. If the history of the subject or recent technological development needs to be mentioned, it may be used at some point following the first paragraph of the introduction to show the situation, the reason why the question arose, or as background information.

A beginning such as, "The objective of this report is to determine whether or not it is economically desirable to purchase water from the Taylorville Water Company rather than to supply the ABC Company from private wells," is a strong beginning containing the subject and objective. No words are wasted in informing the reader about the contents of the report.

"In considering whether to replace the motor-generator sets of the Street Railway Company with ignitron converters, it was thought best to determine first the probable future of streetcar service, because of recent trends to gasoline bus service." Here is another opening sentence that gets to the heart of the report in a hurry.

Compare the two foregoing opening sentences with the following two alternates:

A manufacturing company frequently has the choice of purchasing its water from the local water utility or establishing its own supply from wells. Which method is to be adopted must be determined by each individual company on the basis of local conditions. Cost, quality of water, and available supply are important items to consider. . . .

Engineers are ever trying to improve equipment and methods, and the electrical engineer has made notable advances in power supply in the past few years. One advancement is in the methods of supplying direct current. Recently, the ignitron converter has become available and it is now being used as replacement for the motor-generator set. . . .

These "essay" or "theme" types of openings are to be avoided in favor of the direct start in full force.

Selection of Subject Material

Once a good beginning is made, the writer must strike a reasonable middle ground between being deficient or too detailed in his introductory information. The decision of what information to give is based upon knowing the reader of the report. What does he need? How much does he already know? How much of what he already knows needs to be repeated to make certain he has it in mind? How much is needed for other possible readers, or for the sake of making the report complete in meaning when read by one not currently acquainted with the subject? How much is needed to make the report understandable to the current reader when he rereads it at a later date or to the successor of the boss, should there be one within a few months?

While it is not good writing practice to cause a person to read through introductory material with which he is familiar, such readers will, no doubt, recognize the value to the report of a well-rounded and descriptive introduction which gives a comprehensive preview of the report concisely and directly without detail. Material well-known to the reader and essential (in the opinion of the writer) to a proper understanding of the report may, nevertheless, be introduced and its possible unfavorable reaction on the reader softened somewhat by the use of such phrases as:

It will be recalled that

Briefly in review

It must be kept in mind

From the previous itemization of the possible contents of an introduction it might seem that the introduction is a complete discussion of the subjects contained in the body of the report. Actually, it is intended that the introduction be brief, but descriptive. Thus, its minimum contents need contain only:

1. Statement of subject and objective
2. Clarification of the situation or circumstances making preparation of the report desirable
3. Explanation in brief of the general methods used to reach the desired answers
4. Statement of the plan or organization of the report

These four items, for reports of 10 to 30 pages (250 to 300 words per page), could be covered in as few as four to ten sentences. Certainly, two pages would be maximum. Whenever the introduction runs too long because of the development of the details of history, definitions, theories, or concepts, these items should preferably be placed in sections other than the introduction.

A well-written introduction is of material aid in writing the remainder of the report. It serves the reader by telling him what is to follow, and aids the writer in clarifying the subject and in setting up for him a plan for the development of the remainder of the report. The discussion and terminal sections are developed in harmony with the objectives and scope presented in the introduction.

Specimens 13.1 and 13.2 are illustrative of the essential characteristics of introductions.

THE DISCUSSION

Following the introduction is the development of the body of the report containing the essential discussion for solving the problem and for arriving at sound conclusions and practical recommendations as a basis for action. The functional procedure for achieving these objectives may be developed as follows:

Presentation of the essential information

Analysis and interpretation of the data in relation to the problem

Solution of the problem

Skills involved in making the discussions effective in each of the foregoing functional divisions are presented in the preceding chapters. At this stage it is reasonable to assume that the writer is proficient in the use of English, in the preparation of an effective outline, in the sorting and assembling of the applicable portions of the information he has collected, in the tabulation of numerical data, and in the judicious use of illustrations.

Presentation of Essential Information

From the abstract and introduction the reader already possesses a clear idea of the principal findings and background features of the report. In the development of the report the writer's first task and responsibility are to present those facts which will lead directly and convincingly to the proposed solution, conclusions, and recommendations.

The terms *directly* and *convincingly* are the keynote to effective and interesting presentation of factual and qualitative information. The writer needs to exercise good judgment in retaining only that information which contributes to the acceptance of the solution. He is expected to discard mercilessly all information unrelated to the major purposes of the report even when this information is a logical part of the subject as a whole. Each body of information is introduced on the basis of its accuracy and practicability. Any compromise with accuracy endangers the acceptance of the entire report. Any disregard for practicability creates doubt as to the soundness of the conclusions and the justification for the recommendations.

At times, some of the information does not support the major trends, practices, or deductions. Nevertheless, negative information, when properly introduced and interpreted, often adds to the merit of the report and to the prestige of the writer's integrity. As a rule, completeness in the presentation of information adds to the clearness with which written

Specimen 13.1.

Introduction to a report on illumination of a drafting room

Illumination in the drafting room is inadequate as measured by the lighting standards of today. It is the purpose of this report to determine the condition of the present lighting and to recommend such improvements as will bring the illumination up to the desirable standard of 30 to 50 ft–c.

The drafting room has had heavy usage during the past year and will have for the next few years because of the night shift. The existing fixtures, installed about 15 years ago, were designed mainly for daytime use and are no longer satisfactory because today's standards of illumination are much higher than they were before the fluorescent luminaire became available.

Engineering drawing is exacting work that requires a high level of illumination in order to protect eyesight and in order that a high quality of work can be done. Because it is possible within a reasonable cost to raise the present illumination from its low level of 13.1 ft–c to an acceptable standard of at least 30 ft–c every effort should be made to do so.

An illumination survey of the room was made by standard methods. Besides the generally low level of illumination, it was observed that there are many dark areas which fail to reflect the light and that the widely spaced incandescent luminaires result in a wide variance in illumination throughout the room.

The study carried on to determine how to improve the illumination of the drafting room is presented under the subjects of illumination survey, shortcomings of the present system, requirements of acceptable lighting, corrective measures, and the design of a new system of lighting and its cost.

Specimen 13.2.

Introduction to a report on redesign of a street intersection

The sprawling design of the intersection at Maryville Avenue and Michigan Boulevard combined with four heavy movements of pedestrians a day, at times corresponding with the peaks in vehicular traffic, makes the intersection one of the most potentially dangerous in the city. In fact, its accident history includes an average of two serious accidents a year for the past 10 years.

The intersection can be made safer to pedestrians and vehicles alike through reconstruction according to the design given in this report and by the improvement of Chestnut and Howard Streets so that they will take part of the traffic now using Maryville Avenue.

The investigation reported on herein, which was undertaken for the purpose of determining what should be done to eliminate the traffic hazards at Maryville Avenue and Michigan Boulevard, includes analyses of the volume, speed and character of vehicular traffic and pedestrian counts. Traffic signals are considered, but are not recommended because the conditions at the intersection do not warrant signals on the basis of the minimum standards of the American Association of State Highway Officials and of the National Safety Council.

material is understood. Conciseness is related to the elimination of unessential information and, therefore, to clearness of expression.

Point of View

Since the primary purpose of the report is to gain acceptance of the major proposals or to stimulate action in behalf of a program, the reader's point of view is of paramount importance in guiding the policies and methods of the writer. A report is not an imaginative specimen of writing indulged in to record the undocumented and unsubstantiated ideas of the writer. Neither is it, necessarily, a scholarly document giving a comprehensive treatise on human institutions or scientific and technical phenomena.

Tone and Style

The tone and style of writing are selected in terms of the characteristics of the people who have the power to make decisions and to direct action. To do well in this respect the writer should imagine that the readers of his report are in the same room with him. He should select his facts with the same care, tact, and enthusiasm he would employ were he to present the report orally. Under these circumstances the writer will use diction that is within the understanding of his audience; he will not burden the listener with detailed information, but rather he will select items that drive home the main points to be established. He will anticipate their questions and carefully answer them by so presenting the facts that the listeners will not think of asking certain questions. He will anticipate portions of the discussion that are inherently difficult, and to prevent misunderstanding he will clarify by graphic illustrations or notes these specific items.

The writer can sustain general interest in his report by using dynamic sentences so designed that each one is a stepping stone to the next one, and so designed that the reader senses motion and progress in ideas with as little friction as possible. Short paragraphs with vivid headings will not only hold the attention of the reader but will keep the entire framework of the report clearly before him so that he will know just how far he has progressed and what remains to be covered.

Many words can be saved and clear concepts effectively established by the introduction of numerical tabulations and graphic illustrations according to the accepted practices discussed in Chapters 6 and 7. Long tabulations with detailed items properly belong in the appendix where they are available for careful study. Summarized equivalents of these long tables rightfully belong in the body of the report where they guide the reader's thought. Frequently, a curve will serve the text better than the comprehensive tabulation of the numerical data.

In closing this discussion on the presentation of information, the attitude of the writer may well be that of the designer of modern machinery. Today, streamlining predominates geometric design. Similarly, the presentation of information should discard bulky sentences and relegate to the appendix all computations, detailed drawings, and tabulations that would obstruct the free flow of thought by their inclusion in a forward position.

Analysis of the Data in Relation to the Problem

The process of recognizing the principal elements of a problem is called analysis. The process of explaining or making clear the meaning of terms, ideas, or processes is called interpretation.

To lead the reader logically to acceptance of the solution, conclusions, and recommendations, the writer selects his information carefully. These decisions are the result of working intimately with the data and preparing an outline of the manner in which the report is to be developed. It is only after a problem has been analyzed into its component parts that the law of the association of ideas begins to operate. By this law the writer associates each phase of the problem with some experience or principle known to him.

The reader of the report, being well-trained

in the field, can recognize the soundness of the relationships between the known and unknown elements of the problem. But the reader caused the report to be written because his duties prevented him from making the study in person. Therefore, his delegate, the writer, first conducts as comprehensive a study as the problem warrants. This study results in the collection of a great deal of information, perhaps in excess of that required for a specific assignment. The presentation of only the essential information implies that the writer anticipates the solution and incorporates the minimum amount necessary to support the development. However, he includes an analysis and interpretation of the information in order to save the reader the mental effort and expenditure of time required to arrive at the same viewpoint as that reached by the writer.

The analysis checks the information according to certain criteria. The complete nature of each item of information is revealed by providing answers to as many questions as are suggested by the item. Value of the information is established by comparisons with other related data and by recording the limitations of the data on the basis of physical properties, exposure to chemical or natural processes, and experimental investigations. Calculations often serve to determine the accuracy and even the validity of the information. The merit of some information can be established by statistical methods. Occasionally two sets of data appear to possess conflicting characteristics. This situation calls for a more careful analysis of the causes and effects that control the nature of the information. Finally, the analysis enables the writer to assign to each item of information its particular role in the development of the report.

Interpretation of the Results

Interpretation of the information explains how and why each item is used to sustain the final solution, conclusion, and recommendations. The reader may accept the validity and appropriateness of the information but if he has to clarify the relationship of the information to the solution he may have to spend as much or more time than the writer. Results of an experiment may be clear to the person who performed it, but the reader, not being acquainted with the details and characteristics of the work, needs to have help. The writer who has the special knowledge is in a position to provide the necessary assistance to eliminate the expected difficulties that may be encountered by the reader. By interpretation the writer provides special significance to the information.

The special explanation of facts by the writer often creates viewpoints and interpretations entirely unthought of by the reader, yet these explanations are the basis for making a point, reaching a solution, or arriving at conclusions and recommendations. Interpretation differs from observation in that the influence of the same set of data may be interpreted differently by a group of observers, whereas, each of them would make the same observations of a given scientific phenomenon or group action.

Solution of the Problem

With the presentation of the data as well as its analysis and interpretation completed, the writer is ready to proceed to the solution of the problem. The principal process of obtaining a solution is that of synthesis or of reassembly of information into a new pattern. Judgment and reasoning are the principal mental skills employed in the synthesis of ideas. Judgment may be defined as the power to arrive at a decision or solution directly upon the statement of a problem or its elements. Reasoning may be defined as the logical, systematic, and accepted method for progressing from the statement of the problem to its solution. When several choices need to be made during various stages of reasoning the writer needs to exercise judgment in selection. Judgment is a decision based upon previously acquired experience and knowledge or understanding. The quality of the judgment exercised in any instance depends upon the combined accuracy and practicability of the decision.

Developing the Solution

The usual method of proving theorems in geometry suggests one useful procedure in the development of the solution in a report.

1. The statement of the problem is equivalent to the statement of the theorem.
2. The diagram is a graphical presentation to better illustrate the space relationship of the elements of the problem.
3. Certain information is gathered and assumed to be correct for the sake of argument or verification; this phase corresponds to the hypothesis.
4. The solution is developed by introducing ideas and information in logical sequence until the final statement obviously is the desired solution; this step corresponds to the proof of the theorem.

A more mature concept of reasoning is to consider it a positive process of solving a problem by starting with a known or proved statement of fact or assumption and progressing step by step toward a satisfying conclusion. Actually, the path of reasoning is seldom direct from the statement of a problem to its solution. At each new step a number of related ideas or facts occur to the writer. Each possible suggestion needs to be tried and tested until one of several possibilities is proved to suit the development. In this sense, reasoning is definitely a process of associating established facts with inferences or conclusions which are the result of a series of observed natural phenomena or human behavior traits.

Evidence, Inference, and Analogy

The elements by which facts are established include evidence, inference, and analogy. *Evidence* may be direct in terms of the senses and the conduct of tests, experiments or research, or evidence may be circumstantial because it is based upon one of several possible hypotheses. As reasonable as circumstantial evidence appears to be at times, later facts or happenings sometimes demonstrate the unreliability of this type of evidence. The report becomes convincing in proportion to the amount and dependability of direct evidence. *Inference* involves the deduction of a conclusion, principle, or probability from the evidence available or the assumptions accepted as reasonable. *Analogy* is a form of inference sometimes employed in the reasoning process. Analogy is the process of concluding the similarity of two phenomena which resemble each other closely even though they are different in substance. The analogy of an electric circuit to the flow of water in a pipe is one that is commonly accepted. By their nature, analogies should be used cautiously. The two commonly used forms of inference are the deductive and inductive methods of reasoning.

René Descartes, the well-known mathematician, employed the deductive method of arriving at solutions. He applied his process of reasoning in four steps, taking special care "never in a single instance to fail in observing them."

The following quotation of Descartes' statement of the four steps merits careful consideration by the writer of reports:

> The first of these was to accept nothing as true which I did not clearly recognize to be so, that is to say, carefully to avoid precipitation and prejudice in judgements, and to accept in them nothing more than what was presented to my mind so clearly and distinctly that I could have no occasion to doubt it.
>
> The second was to divide up each of the difficulties which I examined into as many parts as possible, and as seemed requisite in order that it might be resolved in the best manner possible.
>
> The third was to carry on my reflections in due order, commencing with objects that were the most simple and easy to understand, in order to rise little by little, or by degrees, to knowledge of the most complex, assuming an order, even if a fictitious one, among those which do not follow a natural sequence relatively to one another.
>
> The last was in all cases to make enumerations so complete and review so general that I should be certain of having omitted nothing.[1]

The inductive method of inference is employed quite generally to establish scientific

[1] Haldane, Elizabeth S. and Ross, G. R. T., *The Philosophical Works of Descartes.* Vol. 1, p. 92. London, Cambridge University Press. 1931.

facts, theories, and principles. The process of inductive reasoning is based upon the observation of specific instances of behavior either in nature or in experimental procedure. The cumulative evidence of similarity in behavior under identical conditions and circumstances leads the observer to arrive at a generalized statement of fact, theory, concept, or principle.

One must not conclude that inferences, whether they be deductive, or inductive, are infallible. Any human undertaking is subject to the inherent limitations of the human body including the mind. In all phases much depends upon the initial assumption. Certain assumptions in the elastic behavior of beams lead to useful principles. Yet, certain beams made of some materials do not fit the original assumptions and, therefore, the general formulas are not completely applicable throughout a wide range of loading and size. In other words, the investigator and writer must take into account possible shortcomings of the senses and of hasty conclusions based upon too few instances.

THE TERMINAL SECTION

The third section of the body of a report is the *terminal section,* so named, not necessarily because it is placed at the end of the report, but primarily because it is the end result of the discussion. For psychological reasons the terminal section is frequently placed at the beginning of the report. The introduction states the objective and gives reasons for desiring to reach the objective. The discussion presents the facts, makes an analysis and interpretation of them, and arrives at a solution. The terminal section restates the essential findings, conclusions, and recommendations in a concise enumeration. The terminal section is a desirable feature of the letter report and of the periodic and inquiry types of formal reports. A well-written letter report will devote a paragraph or more to a statement of the findings. The periodic type of report and the informational or fact-finding inquiry report lend themselves to the use of the summary type of terminal section, rather than the use of conclusions and recommendations.

Purpose and Content of the Terminal Section

Chief characteristics of reports, as contrasted with general types of expository writing, are the specific purposes for which they are written, and the specific type of readers to which they are directed. Because these specific readers are looking for specific results, the natural plan of the report is one which gives prominence to those results which were sought. The terminal section is the device by which this prominence is obtained. By setting out the findings of the report in a special section, either at the beginning or at the end of the report, the client, executive or administrative officer can locate and read the answers readily. The supporting material and discussion may or may not be read at the moment of receiving the report. If the results are set forth in a terminal section, the details of the report need not be read in order to gain a knowledge of the findings. A second advantage of the terminal section is that, having read the summary or conclusions and recommendations, the reader is in a position to read the discussion sections with greater understanding. Knowing the answer ahead of the reading of the analysis enables the reader to gage the soundness of the analysis as he goes along.

The terminal section is composed wholly of a summary or restatement of facts, findings, answers, conclusions, recommendations, or any combination of these items. The words *summary* and *restatement* are used to indicate that the terminal section is a recapitulation of the significant items developed in the discussion section of the body. The terminal section is not a place in which to present new material nor to develop further the analysis. Statements in the terminal section stand alone. Their support is to be found in the general discussion, though frequently the basic reason for certain conclusions or recommendations may be stated. Content of the terminal section is necessarily co-ordinated with the objectives mentioned in the introduction to the report and with the findings reached in the presentation of the discussion. Tables and diagrams are not usually made a part of the terminal section, though the tables and diagrams given elsewhere in the report may be referred to in setting forth the summary, conclusions, or recommendations.

In form, the terminal section may be written as a series of paragraphs, numbered or not, each paragraph being restricted to a given point of fact or conclusion. The section in its entirety is introduced with an appropriate sentence to indicate the nature of the terminal section, which may or may not be divided into subparts of summary of facts, conclusions, or recommendations.

Position of Terminal Section in Report

The terminal section may appear at the beginning of the report or at the end just following the main discussion. Practice varies in this respect, and justly so, because of the type, length, function, purpose, and character of reports.

Excellent examples of reports are available in which the following positions of the terminal section have been used:

1. As a preliminary part in the place of, or coordinate with, the abstract
2. Ahead of the introduction to the report, but as the first section of the body of the report
3. As the next section following the introduction
4. As the last section of the body

Because of the convenience to the reader there is good reason to place the terminal section forward in the report, particularly so in formal reports of some 25 or more pages. In the short formal report the terminal section may replace the abstract. In such reports the introduction may readily serve the purposes of the abstract. In letter reports a natural position for stating the results is in the second or third paragraph.

The position of the terminal section governs to some extent the contents of the letter of transmittal, abstract, and introduction. When placing a brief terminal section forward, there is little to be gained by stating the results also in the letter of transmittal because the repetition would not be desirable. In writing an abstract to a report in which the terminal section is also to be placed as a preliminary part, it would be unnecessary to give any results in detail. A well-written introduction will give some indication of the results obtained, but no detail. If the terminal section is placed forward, extra care is needed not to repeat much of it in the introduction.

As with other features of reports, the terminal section should be developed to fit the immediate purposes of the report and the length and character of the material to be presented therein.

Specimen letter reports at the end of Chapter 11 state the recommendations and summary, respectively, in the second paragraph. Thus, each of these letters provides the reader with concise and appropriate statements of the findings at practically the beginning of the letter. The specimen tables of contents in Chapter 12 illustrate the placing of the terminal section ahead of the introduction, following the introduction, and at the end of the report. The specimen formal report in the Appendix has its terminal section at the end of the body. This report, *Relocating the Union Bus Terminal in Ames, Iowa,* is an action type of report in which conclusions and recommendations are the natural end point. Fact-finding types of reports easily lend themselves to a terminal section which sets forth in enumerated statements the main numerical or other facts assembled and discussed within the report.

CHAPTER 14

Magazine Feature Articles and Technical Papers

In addition to preparing reports, the engineer, the scientist, and the businessman find it desirable to write for technical periodicals and publications of professional societies. Magazine feature articles and society proceedings and professional papers comprise two general classes of technical writing outside the field of reports.

Although there is no distinct line of demarcation between the magazine feature, the technical paper, and the report, they differ somewhat in their method of preparation, objective, and readership. The close association of these three types of writings and of their readers and authors makes it appropriate to discuss the magazine feature and the technical paper in this book on preparation of reports.

OPPORTUNITIES IN PROFESSIONAL WRITING

Men in technical schools, industry, and business are aware of the many publications devoted to technical and scientific development and business. Each new branch of science and business brings forth new publications. The field of the technical press is large. Table 14.1 lists many of the types of technical publications in circulation. Thousands of pages of copy are written each week for these publications. Obviously, the number of individual authors who supply this copy is several times the number of publications. These authors are mainly professional in their subjects but amateur in their writing. Some authors may write to earn a few dollars or to gain recognition, but mostly they write in the spirit of being helpful to their profession.

The codes of ethics of most scientific groups advise against direct advertising of one's self other than by the display of a simple card or *shingle*. The professions, however, encourage their members to write for publication. The *by-line* on technical writings for the commercial press and professional society publications is an ethical method of securing professional contacts and recognition. Many a successful person gained early opportunities through recognition resulting from publication of his papers. These technical writings bring one in contact with leaders in the field and with prospective employers who are always on the watch for the better-than-average man.

In addition to creating opportunities for advancement, writing for publication provides a natural channel for professional broadening and deepening. The engineer responsible for the design of a new chemical processing plant will gain additional knowledge when he writes a magazine story about the features of his design. Writing about the design calls for a scrutiny of detail that brings forth new ideas and fixes many of the aspects of the job that may have been somewhat hazy before beginning to write. In the writing of many types of articles much new material needs to be read and compared with the author's own experience. The opinions of others are sought, tests are made, and new ideas are analyzed. All of these operations develop in the author new horizons and new ambitions. Examination of the main feature stories in the current magazines and professional society publications will show that the authors must have gained in professional stature during production of their articles.

In addition to the personal gain, writing for the technical press is a means of paying a debt to the profession. The elevation of anyone within a professional field comes about partly because of the work performed by others in the field. If the experiences and successes of others were not made available to the profession through the press, younger and even mature persons would find it difficult to get ahead.

Personal requirements for success in the field of technical writing include the following:

1. Ability to write effectively
2. Willingness to do endless search for information, truth, and accuracy
3. Possession of extensive experience and knowledge in the field
4. Sense of originality and imagination
5. Ability to judge news values
6. Ability to exercise sound judgment applying both to technical subjects and to human relations
7. Ability to gather and classify many facts pertinent to the objective
8. Ability to think clearly and soundly
9. Personality traits conducive to harmonious personal relations
10. Habit of working effectively
11. Ambition to achieve success
12. Habit of being dependable

These qualifications are not unusual; they are common to those personal characteristics on which professional success is based in fields other than writing. Ability to write effectively can be acquired by practice, particularly when a person has had experiences that are worth writing about.

Technical magazines are purchased and society dues are paid for the purpose of gaining information leading to professional development. From every magazine read, the reader hopes to gain at least one idea of direct assistance to him in his work. It behooves every professional man to write for the press whenever he has accomplished a new and difficult job, or a simple job in a new and novel manner.

BUSINESS PAPERS

Business papers consist of innumerable periodicals published primarily for scientific men, technical men, tradesmen, and men of commerce. Incidentally, these magazines are published by their owners to make money. In order to make money, the magazine must have advertising. To hold advertising, circulation must be maintained. Circulation is maintained by giving the readers an editorial content helpful to them. The technical reading must be satisfying, or subscriptions are not renewed.

The nature of business papers (magazines) can be detected by a tabular comparison of the characteristics of their main feature stories with those of the newspaper news story and the technical report. The feature story is presented in Table 14.2 in comparison with the news story and the technical formal report.

Whether a magazine feature story will be purchased by an editor depends primarily upon items 6, 7, and 8 of Table 14.2. The feature story must be written in a style that will entice readers and hold them to the end. Thus, the style must appeal to the readers. The article must provide help and information by giving the readers something new. An old process in new dress, or a new process just developed will meet the requirement of subject. How to get these results in a magazine feature story is examined next.

TABLE 14.1. NUMBER AND CIRCULATION OF SCIENCE, TECHNICAL, TRADE, AND CLASS PUBLICATIONS

Source: N. W. Ayer & Son's *Directory of Newspapers and Periodicals,* pp. 1400–1505. N. W. Ayer & Son, Philadelphia. 1959.

Listing includes all United States publications, free and paid circulation. A few publications are included in more than one group.

Classification Group	Number of Publications	Combined Circulation, One Issue	Classification Group	Number of Publications	Combined Circulation, One Issue
Air conditioning	27	403,954	Metal working, and metal trade	61	1,333,784
Architecture	29	588,889	Mining and minerals	27	552,556
Automatic control systems	6	87,100	Motor bus and taxicab	8	231,421
Automotive trade	56	2,996,146	Motor trucks and transportation	55	702,997
Aviation	37	982,143	Nuclear engineering	10	153,097
Brick, tile, cement, concrete	11	125,338	Petroleum, oil, and gas	69	1,050,943
Ceramics	9	94,583	Physics	8	66,453
Chemistry	48	596,605	Plastic and composition materials	7	130,539
Coal and coke	9	84,102	Power and power plants	14	370,954
Commercial and industrial	146	4,592,404	Radio and television	44	1,602,736
Construction, contracting, building, excavating	102	3,204,059	Railroad	42	1,739,044
Electrical	61	3,512,847	Roads and streets	19	236,873
Electronic engineering	25	1,137,009	Safety	13	311,767
Engineering (various branches)	154	3,058,062	Scientific	28	928,812
Geological	9	69,651	State, municipal, and county	48	459,845
Machinery	14	443,535	Statistical	6	33,677
Mathematics	15	59,367	Water works, wells, sewage	10	80,710

TABLE 14.2. NEWS STORIES, MAGAZINE FEATURES, AND TECHNICAL PAPERS COMPARED

Item	Newspaper News Story	Magazine Feature Article	Technical or Business Report
1. Scope	Single time and place, repeating daily if necessary	Complete, full coverage, applicable to the general situation	Complete, all details covered, applicable to only the specific case
2. Newness	Must be new—today's events	Any date, just so the subject is new to subscribers	Any date, always subject of current importance
3. Seasonableness	Not important	Very important	Not applicable
4. Lead	Orthodox	Unlimited, immediate interest developed	Important to make a strong beginning
5. Body	In order of importance	Most effective manner to maintain interest and understanding	Effective manner, usually from the general to the specific, logical sequence of analysis
6. Author	Unimportant	Important only in giving weight to story if author is an authority	Very important, usually personally in contact with the subject
7. Style of composition	Factual, news only; short sentences and words; impersonal	Borders on literary, may entertain and be somewhat narrative; highly personal and human; high readability	Objective and formal, factual plus interpretation, impersonal, exactness of meaning more important than readability
8. Constructive purpose	None, news only	Helpful, educational, stimulating to thought, applicable to reader's situation	Solution of technical problem, directive, and conclusive
9. Readers	General public	Selected groups of special interest, readership gained through human interest and the technical subject	Limited both in number and interest, readership guaranteed through business responsibility

MAGAZINE FEATURE ARTICLES

Technical and commercial periodicals publish two main classifications of reading matter: First, news stories about people, products, companies, legislation, and the general current activities in the fields of interest to their readers; second, feature articles, usually 1 to 10 pages in length, which are technical expositions of new developments, construction, products, processes, management, or other such activity; and articles about persons, companies, professional matters, and progress having personal interest rather than technical interest. The technical feature article forms the central line of interest to the readers. Feature articles are objective in nature, written to inform and to help the reader rather than to entertain.

Sources of Feature Articles

Copy for the business paper reaches the editor through three primary sources: (1) the magazine staff, (2) free-lance professional writers, and (3) amateur or nonprofessional writers engaged in the practice of their chosen fields. Many magazines maintain a staff of writers who write, assemble, select, and edit the material that makes up the reading sections of each issue. These writers cover many of the important news-features as well as special assignments that require research and field investigation to collect the information on which the story is based. Such staff-written articles may or may not be given a by-line.

Professional writers who free-lance their output, contribute heavily to the general nontechnical periodicals, but less to the business papers. They work on their own and take their chances of selling their output. On occasions, however, they are commissioned by editors to submit a particular article.

The number of articles contributed by men in ordinary practice in the profession is large in percentage of the total number of feature articles in the average technical magazine. These writers, strictly amateur, draw from their own experiences and ideas to produce articles of interest and benefit to their contemporaries. Editors, hearing of an outstanding scientific, engineering, or industrial performance, sometimes solicit an article from the individual responsible.

Many books and many articles have been published on writing for magazines. Would-be journalists, ambitious youngsters with a flair for writing, and students in the writing field combine to furnish a fair-sized market for books on how to write for publication. No attempt is made here to cover completely the field of news and feature writing in the technical field. Nor is there a guarantee that the reading of this chapter will produce a successful writer. A limited amount of background information and a few suggestions on procedure are offered as a limited substitute for a more thorough treatment of the subject, which the reader may find in books listed in Appendix A.

Getting Ideas

Ideas for the technical feature story for magazine publication must come from one's own experience or from an acquaintance with the experience of others. Observation of the events within the scope of daily contacts must be relied upon for these ideas. The prospective author must recognize the news, the event, the situation, or the personality which can be developed into a salable feature article. These events may consist of developments in the field of administration, finance, design, construction, operation, maintenance, sales, research or any of the other phases of industry. A company completes a new departmental organization involving the shifting of responsibilities. A public works department evolves a new system of financing a project. An architect, through a unique arrangement of space, cuts the steel requirement for a building 10 per cent; and a new high-compression engine of unprecedented fuel economy was successful in trial runs. All these and hundreds of similar items become the bases of feature articles. An examination of a few magazines within the field of interest will disclose the general type of articles that are salable.

A good source of feature articles for magazines is found in the periodic and inquiry reports made by various governments and their subdivisions or by private companies. The contents of private reports, however, are usually not available for general release, at least not until the proposals therein are undertaken. Public works activities of municipal, county, and state governments offer rich sources of ideas and information for feature articles. Likewise, federal public works and the many federal activities in agriculture, commerce, public lands, science, and regulation of transportation and commerce furnish almost unlimited possibilities for good feature articles. Information for these articles is to be found in the formal, letter, short, and periodic reports prepared by government agencies.

A successful feature article possesses the direct possibility of bringing improvement or success to the reader. Here is the reason why so many magazine feature articles are written about the success of an individual, an enterprise, a new process, or a new device. A second popular type of feature article is the *how to do it* article in which the reader is shown explicitly how he can adapt a new procedure, organization, or product to his own business. While the types of acceptable stories differ from magazine to magazine, editors agree that the success element and newness are essential. Having discovered these two possibilities in an event, a prospective writer is ready to select the publication most likely to buy the article to be written.

Selecting the Publication

Examination of recent issues of the magazines which are possible outlets for the story will give relatively satisfactory measures of readership, policy, and subject content. This examination is for the purpose of selecting the magazine that is a logical outlet for the story and to determine how the story should be prepared.

Readers are highly important. The first essential to any writing is to know thoroughly those persons to whom the writing is addressed. Readers control the diction, literary style, and the subjects to feature in the article. Six distinctly different stories could be written on the construction of an electric hoist parking garage, depending upon whether the story were to be printed in a magazine read primarily by traffic engineers, city planners, construction contractors, structural designers, investment bankers, or mechanical and electrical designers. Naturally, still different stories would be written for the newspaper, news magazine, popular science magazine, trade paper, or technical monthly.

The policy related to length and literary style and to the type of articles purchased also can be obtained by examining several issues. This study will disclose the general subject matter covered by the publication and whether the particular subject has been covered recently. Editors strive for a variety of subjects. Length of article, handling of illustrations, and styling also should be observed.

Preparation for Writing

The occasional writer of magazine features usually will be writing on a subject or event with which he is familiar. Collecting and preparing information to use in the article will then be an easy task. The job will consist of selecting and organizing the information at hand. For the professional writer not familiar with the subject being written about, collection of the information is a time-consuming task. Only by collecting an excess of material can the author be reasonably certain of having all the facts needed. Gathering the information, its assembly, classification and analysis follow about the same procedure as stated in Chapters 2 and 3 for reports. In selecting material for the article it must be remembered that the readers are not of the same class as the readers of reports.

Because of the attention and interest value of illustrations, magazine editors use well-chosen illustrations. Action pictures and those showing people are usually to be preferred, though not every article can be so illustrated. Diagrams, charts, and plans are highly desirable when they are applicable.

The Process of Writing

After organizing and analyzing the information at hand the author turns to the job of writing. Writing should be preceded by outlining. The discussion on pages 17 to 23 will be helpful in outlining. The formula of good writing holds for magazine feature articles as it does elsewhere. Thorough preparation, rapid writing, and careful revision are desirable. There is no sounder formula. It is the formula of the professionals, long tried and proved.

One who sets out to write a technical or other type of feature article for a magazine will find that the writing procedure will move along easily and that the finished article will be good only if he keeps in mind a specific objective. The objective is a specific accomplishment for a specific group of readers. Readers are to be given help directly or are to be given information that is of immediate or later interest to them. At the outset, the objective should be written down. Frequent reference to this stated objective will be helpful during the course of writing.

Attention of the reader is gained through a good title, unusual illustrations, and attractive typography. Interest may be developed through a series of opening sentences that indicate the character of the subject and how the article can be of help to the reader. Feature articles try to treat their subjects so that the reader can visualize himself experiencing the situation described or applying the same procedures to his own work. Interest, once aroused, can be maintained by unfolding a series of obstacles or developments and telling how they were overcome or achieved. Although the technical article does not usually lead up to a set of conclusions, it does approach a sort of climax — accomplishment of the objective, including satisfying the reader's desire to learn about the subject.

Magazine articles are necessarily shorter than a technical report for management written on the same subject. Brevity is gained by omitting details and background material. Magazine articles drive directly to the heart of the subject. Identical material is seldom presented in both tabular and graphical form. Original data are omitted, and the narrative of the many trials and false starts necessary for accomplishing the technical objectives are briefed to the minimum. Arguments and persuasiveness are usually omitted because there is little attempt to lead up to a set of conclusions or recommendations. The objective is to tell the story so that the reader can grasp at once the lesson, the know-how, the discovery, and the application to his own situation. The reader is given credit for being able to fill in the details himself and for knowing the general processes followed in his field. All he wants is *what's new* or *how it can be done*.

PAPERS FOR TECHNICAL SOCIETIES

Papers presented at meetings of technical societies usually are printed in the official proceedings, journal, or transactions. These papers differ somewhat from the magazine article because of the readership. While magazine articles must appeal to the readers enough to cause them to renew their subscriptions, the technical society paper has no such competition for readers.

Character of Society Papers

Although society papers are frequently thought of as being highly technical and scientific, they do not need to be so. It is true that they may lack the human interest of the magazine article. It is likely that a commercial publisher would go broke if he were to fill the pages of his magazine with the type of papers that appear in society proceedings. Nevertheless, these papers serve an important objective in their respective fields and do reach a critical and appreciative readership. Much of the value of these papers is permanent, and their contents become the basis of later practice. Authors of such papers are frequently professional men who pioneer new theories, techniques, and procedures through research and study. Magazine editors may popularize the subjects of these papers once the developments presented in them reach the stage of being practical or understandable to a majority of the men in the profession.

The writing of scientific papers for technical societies need not be a specialized procedure. All the rules of writing for other types of manuscripts hold. There is a difference in objective and in readership which, when kept in mind by the writer, should present no particular difficulty. These papers usually stand upon their technical content rather than upon the style of writing or their interest-appealing approach. Unfortunately many scientific papers have failed to achieve their maximum readership because they were not written in a readable style. Perhaps there is a tendency on the part of some scientific men to cloud their papers with such technical language that only the highly developed specialist can understand them. Such tendency is to be frowned upon. The society paper is sometimes written in a ponderous style. Because of the necessity for safeguarding the meaning and setting forth the full description of the situation, sentence structure is usually more involved than in the more popular types of writing. This requirement, however, is no excuse for poor writing. In fact it calls for a higher skill in writing.

Society Procedures

Editors of society proceedings usually publish the papers as submitted — little editing is done and no rewriting is attempted. Magazine editors, on the other hand, may do heavy editing and rewriting in order to bring the paper to a suitable length and style of expression the average reader will understand.

Many of the professional societies have a greater number of papers to publish than can be published within their budgets. Selection of the papers, when not the sole responsibility of the editor, is handled by a committee or designated individuals who pass upon the technical merits of the papers. Obviously, the reviewing committee will be prone to recommend only those papers which have technical merit combined with high readability.

When preparing a paper for a society publication, the specifications prescribed by the society should be followed explicitly. Most of the societies have available a booklet setting forth the requirements of length, mechanics of style, illustrations, citations to the literature, and other aspects of papers meeting the publishing requirements of the society.

REPORTS AND OTHER TECHNICAL WRITING

This chapter provides a brief of the essential points of concern in the preparation of articles for the trade and professional business papers and for the technical papers published by professional societies. The writing of these two classes of papers is closely related to that of many reports; frequently, the author of a report may be asked also to prepare an article for a magazine or a society paper covering his report. The material in this chapter should be helpful to the author on such occasions.

Articles written for magazines, as contrasted to those for reports, attract readers strictly on the basis of the subject matter and the manner in which it is developed; thus, writing to attract readers is highly important. The readers of reports are also highly important, but these persons generally read reports as an important phase of their particular job responsibility.

Papers for society proceedings are the outstanding single source of authentic knowledge on technical, scientific and theoretical current developments within the professional fields. Above all else, technical accuracy, complete treatment, and exactness of concept are the prime requisites of society papers. Material so published by societies later becomes the basis of articles for business papers and chapters in texts and reference books. One who has trained himself to be a writer of good reports should experience little difficulty in writing good papers for the business and professional periodicals.

CHAPTER 15

Oral Presentation of Reports and Technical Papers

Language may be spoken or written. The *fundamentals* of combining words to express thoughts are, of course, identical whether one communicates his thoughts by sound or by symbol. The *techniques* differ when one delivers an oral report to supplement or to present a written report. The written report is read or it may be studied by one person at a time; the oral report introduces the essential features of the written report to committees, boards of directors, members of a municipal council, or to public gatherings, any one or all of whom may be in a position to act favorably or unfavorably upon the recommendations. Thus, although this book deals primarily with the preparation of the written report, the preparation and presentation of oral reports serve the important function of selling the product of the written report to those who have the authority to act.

The fundamentals of speech and writing are the same but speech has to be brief, direct, and dynamic. Control of the skills in English is essential because the spoken word must do its work even as it is uttered; it then vanishes forever. The ideas must be chosen and delivered so that the mind of the listener will record the impressions for a long time to come and will urge some form of action.

Certainly, the talents needed to give oral reports and to prepare written reports provide constructive media for the expression of professional talent. The beginner as well as his more experienced associates should welcome the opportunity to make public addresses. Through the experience gained he will acquire the skill, the confidence, the persuasiveness to face hard-headed, practical men of affairs found on committees, councils and boards of directors. He will feel at ease on his feet so that enough fresh blood will rise to his head to enable him to think clearly and talk convincingly and tactfully.

Although few people hesitate to engage in conversation, many dread to face an audience. Comparatively speaking, many prepare convincing reports and excellent technical papers but only a few make effective oral presentations before committees, conferences, technical or business meetings, not to mention more pretentious occasions such as annual conventions, large public gatherings, and governmental bodies. Yet, on his path to ultimate achievement and success a person is called upon more and more to speak before large and small groups to impart information, to create a desired feeling or sentiment, or to motivate positive action. As in all other human endeavor there will always exist a wide margin between the highly competent and those who do reasonably well. However, by mastering the known techniques in oral presentation and by applying these consciously at each opportunity, every person who can prepare a good report or technical paper will also acquire the ability to speak well.

The subject to be discussed is the medium

Fig. 15.1. L. G. Reuss, employee of General Electric, illustrates the need for making an effective oral presentation when he takes over a typical class as conference leader.

that draws together the speaker and the audience. Initiative for the meeting may originate with the audience or with the speaker. But the subject must be of significance, value and interest to both parties or else there is no reason for a meeting.

THE SPEAKER

The success of the speaker hinges upon his ability to attract and hold the attention of the audience. To achieve this the speaker relies upon his grasp of subject matter, his platform technique, and his consideration of the audience.

Oratory, Public Speaking, Conversation

The orator has come to represent a person gifted with the power to arouse the emotions of the multitude. When the emotions cool little substance remains for the help and guidance of the crowd. To sustain interest and action the orator must continue to feed the emotions of his audience. The permanent value and constructive contribution of the orator are very low. He gives little food for thought but much stimulation for emotion.

At the other extreme, the public speaker may assume that his main responsibility is to transmit every bit of minutia to his audience at a professional convention, a service dinner club, or a lecture course. This public speaker forgets that he is still a human being when he faces his audience. After a few memorized stories, humorous but unrelated, he plunges into his manuscript and reads and reads and reads on to the last tabulation, the last slide, and the last memorized paragraph, only to find that one half of his audience has tiptoed out and the remaining half has been lulled into a state of passivity.

Long before boys write their first composition; long before men prepare an essay, business discussion, technical paper, or report, they learn to speak. As soon as two or more persons assemble they participate in conversation. Conversation is natural, spontaneous, and sociable. The conventional speech is prepared and memorized or read. Its relation to oral presentation is about the same as that of a rehearsed stage play to spontaneous conversation.

The Conversational Approach

The basic idea which a person must acquire is that when he makes an oral presentation his main responsibility is to guide the conversation of the group into channels that have been mutually selected for discussion. Thus, the speaker assumes the responsibility of opening the discussion by *talking with* rather than *talking at* his audience.

The speaker probably is or should make himself the master of the subject assigned to him. He should know at least as much about the subject as the members of the audience. Otherwise, he should change place with some member of the audience. In no instance should the speaker read an intricate and lengthy paper, or waste his time memorizing its contents. To keep the attention and interest of his audience, the speaker should think through his sentences and ideas as he is giving his talk. Members of the audience will quickly sense the spontaneity of the speaker, and they will keep alert in thinking with him as he develops his subject. When a person thinks as he speaks, he expresses a sentence or paragraph at a time. Then, he stops or pauses for a brief moment in search of a good word or in search of additional ideas or facts to round out the particular point he wants to make. His face, his hands, and even his body begin to move; he becomes a dynamic personality.

The conversational approach to oral presentation capitalizes on the fact that each person is a distinct and unique individual. The speaker is himself, he does not try to become or to imitate someone else. Thus, his energy and ability are directed toward conversation with his audience, a process which he uses many times each day in normal contacts with his associates. By approaching oral presentation on the conversational basis the speaker has nothing to forget, he has no conventions to restrict him, and he has no acquired mannerisms to embarrass him. In short, he has no reason whatever to become self-conscious or stage-struck. When he converses with the audience, he has confidence in his ability to get his message across. He has confidence in his knowledge of the subject and in his ability to talk about it with his associates whether they happen to be in the audience, in the office, around the conference table, or at a committee meeting. When the speaker employs the conversational method he can develop each topic as the immediate circumstances may require. He is not disturbed by interruptions any more than he would be if he were talking the same subject over with his associate in his private office, or a fellow passenger in a Pullman lounge or transcontinental airplane.

The Oral Presentation

Even though the conversational approach is employed, there are certain techniques which the speaker should use when he talks to an individual in his office, to his associates at a conference, or to members at a committee meeting. By developing and improving these techniques as habits in his private conversations he will apply them automatically and spontaneously when he talks with an audience. These techniques include voice control, gesture, body position, and delivery in conveying the message. Thought should be given daily to these items so that they will become an integral part of the speaker by the time he faces an audience.

A little *thought and consideration about the voice* will result in a noticeable improvement. Breathing should be deep in the diaphragm and controlled by the rib muscles. Pauses for grouping ideas or for giving vocal expression to punctuation, or for allowing the audience to reflect on some important points give the speaker opportunities to replenish his supply of air. To make one's voice carry with resonance, the pharynx, mouth and nasal passages should be clear. Vowels and consonants should be clearly sounded without unnatural affectation. A speaker from the deep South should not try to enunciate like a down-Easter from Maine. The rate of speaking should be varied, now slow, now fast, now deliberate. An even flow of words tends to create monotony, destroys attention, and eventually kills interest. The quality or tone of voice should be comforting and pleasant. Inflect the sentence so that the audience will respond with the impressions desired. The voice can be strengthened when the prevailing idea requires force and conviction. The voice can beseech when the speaker invites co-operation. The voice can be repelling when the prevailing idea should be cast out. The voice can be made to intone any of the prevailing ideas that the speaker wishes to transmit to his audience be it a single person or a thousand.

That person is rare who does not *use some gestures of the hand or arm,* who does not change his *facial expression* whether he is holding a private conference or a committee meeting. Why should gestures be associated only with the professional actor? In fact, why should one painstakingly strive to imitate frozen, pantomime gestures conventionalized for the silent-movie actor? Use gestures, but let those gestures be ones which are natural to the speaker as a unique, and independent individual. Even in the oral presentation of the most intricately technical subject, the hands, arms, and the facial expressions can help considerably to sustain the interest and understanding of the audience. One should learn about the various positions of the hand in order to convey certain thoughts. One should realize that every gesture involves an approach, a stroke, and a return. One should realize that gestures are to be integrated and co-ordinated as well as timed to fit the text. However, the speaker who allows his muscular response to reflect the mental state naturally and spontaneously will use gestures most convincingly and effectively. In short, instead of planned gestures, the speaker will do best when he permits his gestures to function spontaneously. Gestures are a natural means of expression; they should be unrestrained and unaffected. However, the speaker should use them gracefully, subtly, and with discretion.

A healthy person stands erect and walks gracefully. Usually he is unmindful of his arms, hands, and clothing. When he speaks before a group of people he should try to be normal in these respects. His shoes, clothing, and tie should be unnoticed because he has taken care to have them neat and appropriate to his personality and to the occasion. There are a few occasions when the speaker can, to good advantage, move from one spot to another. In this way he can indicate that another major part of his speech is to start. The audience then makes this shift mentally and keeps alert.

In conversing with his audience the speaker should be aware of certain fundamentals of delivery. He should be well-rested and physically fit. The audience responds generously to a speaker who thinks well enough of his subject and of them to be earnest and sincere. The enthusiasm of the speaker should be well-balanced in keeping with the subject as a whole and with the relative importance of different portions of his talk. Above all, his behavior should automatically indicate his desire to communicate with the audience. His actions should not detract the thought and attention of his audience from the principal objectives of the talk. The speaker can develop a constructive attitude in his audience by indicating his belief and competence in the subject he is discussing, and by crediting his audience with good intellect and practical judgment. A speaker can create a destructive attitude in the first few minutes by apologizing for his lack of preparation, brevity of time allotted to him, and by an exhibition of an inferiority complex.

THE SUBJECT

In the case of the oral presentation of a report or technical paper, the speaker has to exercise considerable care to select only those items which are important to convey to the audience and which can be effectively given within the allotted time.

Assuming that the report or paper has been written, the speaker can devote his time and effort to planning and reviewing his talk. He gives thought to the quality of the material to be selected and to the organization he will use when he gives his talk.

Selection of Objectives

The speaker's first concern will be to determine whether the main objective of the audience coincides with the principal objective of his report or technical paper. The speaker then proceeds to outline the principal items he will use in his talk.

1. Co-ordination of the subject of the report or technical paper with the essential purpose of the meeting
2. Statement of the content of the talk in a topic sentence
3. Outline of the main items to be considered in the development of the subject
4. Development of each of the main items
   a. Choice of a few well-selected specific illustrations
   b. Choice of well-selected lantern slides or charts
5. Presentation of the primary conclusions
6. Recommendations for action or further studies
7. Summary and recapitulation of the principal steps by which the original purpose of the talk has been achieved.

Some thought is given to the manner in which the talk may be made satisfying to the speaker and the audience. Keeping in mind that the original report or paper is too long and too detailed to give in its entirety, the speaker selects only those concrete illustrations which are interesting. He will make plans to motivate the talk by including a few personal experiences of an unusual nature, by introducing some new material developed since the original report or article was written, and by calling attention to the special meaning and value of the various topics.

The choice of subject can be difficult when a group invites the speaker and leaves the topic up to him. In these instances the choice is made on the basis of the affiliation of the group and of the particular problems that are under discussion. When the affiliation of the group and the problems with which they are concerned are within the experience of the speaker he can accept the invitation with reasonable expectancy of doing a good job. Otherwise, he should gracefully decline the opportunity.

Preparation of Talk

In preparing his talk, the speaker utilizes the suggestions in Chapters 2 and 3, *Planning the Investigation and Report,* and *Collection of Information.*

How extensively he prepares depends upon his acquaintance with the subject and the length of time allowed for his talk. In any case, the speaker first assembles his information. Then he focuses his thinking by formulating a topic sentence to crystallize the subject of his talk. This topic sentence will make it possible to divide the main theme into its principal parts. Each part can be developed in one of a number of ways as follows:

1. By listing as many parts of the whole subject as the occasion of the talk demands
2. By adopting a time sequence, as for an event or for a manufacturing process
3. By arranging a space relationship, as for a plant layout or for a construction problem
4. By describing the causes and their resulting effects, as for scientific phenomena or economic and historical events
5. By considering the means to an end, as for social, economic, educational, or community goals and objectives.

The speaker has a choice of three ways to prepare himself for delivery of his talk:

1. Write out the talk, double spaced, word for word on letter size or half size sheets
2. Write out the outline in topic sentence or other form on letter size sheets or on 3 x 5-inch cards
3. Make no written notes at all to use during oral delivery

There is no objection from any source to

the use of written aids by a speaker, when such use is casual, natural, and does not draw undue attention from the audience. When a lectern is available on which to lay full size letter sheets, these large sheets will be found to be better than half sheets or cards. The turning over of half sheets or cards is a motion somewhat detracting to the audience. The full size sheet, also, has the advantage of offering to the speaker in one view a larger amount of his talk or outline, which helps him to keep oriented. When the speaker "talks" his speech (as is the best method) he may not follow in exact sequence his prepared outline. Therefore, he has to select his next topic from his paper or cards accordingly.

Advantages of writing out the talk word for word are a better fixation in the mind of the speaker of the talk as a whole, and in the end the talk is immediately available for such uses as may be required. A complete paper can be easily condensed for oral presentation by marking out sections and inserting transitions and remarks to pick up orally. One danger is that some speakers will read word for word a fully developed paper, much to their discredit. When only a topic outline is available the speaker is forced to think on his feet and be more conversational.

With the speech written or outlined in topic form the speaker is ready to practice his delivery. This practice should be vocal, not merely thinking through what he intends to say to his audience. Further, this practice affords opportunity to adjust the talk to fit the audience reaction.

The speaker stands up and talks the subject over just as though he were addressing the audience. At no time does he attempt to memorize a single sentence. When he has close friends, who are interested in the same subject, he may visit them and talk with them about the subject he will present at a formal meeting. He is not likely to talk the subject over twice in the same way. But regardless of what he says, he will be original, creative, inspiring, and interesting to his audience whether it is just his friends or the audience for which he is preparing.

THE AUDIENCE

In this instance the audience is considered from the viewpoint of the speaker. What can the speaker do to make it as convenient and as pleasing as possible for his audience to listen, to understand and to absorb? If the principal object of the talk is to convey information, then clarity, logic, and special relationships assume importance in presentation. If the arousing of certain feeling in the audience is the primary objective of the speaker, he will need to employ group psychology on his audience. If, however, the object of the talk is to incite definite action, he will employ primarily the *cause and effect* reasoning and the *means to an end* psychology to arouse the emotions of his audience to the point of action.

Rhetorical Devices

In developing his theme, the speaker can employ a number of rhetorical devices. First he should define carefully key concepts and key words to be employed throughout his talk. He can always make his ideas real and vivid by citing particular incidents or examples and by giving certain quantitative details. He can clarify some involved concepts by comparing them with those commonly known by the audience. Sometimes the contrast between a new idea and an established one helps to enlighten the audience. Principles are usually abstract and difficult to understand, but a few direct, quantitative applications will bring out the essential nature of a theory. Specific examples are a proved way to establish understanding.

Visual Aids

Some visual aids also are useful. A series of large charts, clearly drawn and easily folded over, help to hold the attention of the audience and provide fixation by sight as well as by hearing. Furthermore, the room does not need to be darkened. Slides projected upon a screen help the speaker to stick to his topic and help the audience to follow the discussion. A darkened room always introduces the possibility of losing a few of the tired ones in the audience. In general, a few slides are better than too many. Colored slides hold attention better than the black and white slides. Motion pictures and sound films are useful when action is an important element in the development of the subject.

Time Allotment

The speaker should be careful to stay within the time allowed for his portion of the program. The platform time is about 33 per cent longer than the time required to read the speech silently. The speaker who prepares a written paper and then carefully plans the oral presentation for the conversational approach has the opportunity to emphasize the important features of his written paper and to stay within his allotted time. In any case a speaker should make every effort to stay within the time assigned to him.

THE SPEAKER IN ACTION

Specific recommendations for improving one's ability to talk before an audience are interestingly portrayed by the following article, "So You're Going to Present a Paper," reprinted from *Civil Engineering,* December, 1946.

So You're Going To Present a Paper—

UNDOUBTEDLY a big moment in any man's life is the occasion when he presents a technical paper before fellow members of his society. Still, despite the fact that all eyes are upon him and he is the center of attraction for the moment, he must be content with second place in the matter of importance. For the audience — the men who come to hear him and to learn what he has discovered in his work — must come first. They must be given every consideration and be assisted in accomplishing just those objectives — hearing the speaker and learning from him.

Not This -

KEEP IT SHORT — A twenty-minute talk is better than one of half an hour's duration. The latter is about as long as you can expect to hold interest. No listener may be expected to absorb your analytical or mathematical data in one reading. Save such supporting matter for the published paper. Present orally only the significant parts, stressing what's NEW and INTERESTING in telling WHAT you did and WHY. Leave the HOW for the studious reader of the published paper.

But This -

Not This -

RELAX — Be friendly, both with your audience and the microphone, if one is provided. Statistics show not one single case of a man having been bitten by a "mike" so don't fight it. A touch of natural humor or human interest will add to your presentation. If there is no microphone, be sure to speak clearly enough so that those in farthest seats will hear you, thus avoiding the ever-present risk of encountering one of those fellows who delights in shouting "louder," just as you think you're getting along so well.

But This -

Not This -

FACE YOUR AUDIENCE — Look at and speak to your audience. Preliminary preparation and familiarization with your paper will enable you to look up from time to time without losing your place, thus giving your audience the impression you are as interested in it as you'd like it to be in you. This will help put across your ideas more effectively. Better yet, have your subject mastered so a few cards containing an outline will be sufficient to guide you through your presentation.

But This -

Not This -

LANTERN SLIDES — It's a sheer waste of your talent, and the audience's time, to address your remarks confidentially to the lantern slides. So keep facing your audience every minute of the time you're talking. If it is absolutely necessary to turn toward the screen to point out some specific item, don't try to continue your talk while doing so. One thing at a time is the best way. The time lost is measurable in seconds. The words lost by the audience can never be recaptured.

But This -

Not This -

TEN THOUSAND WORDS — That's the reputed equivalent of one good picture. But it's not a good picture if it requires a lengthy word-explanation. So express only one idea on a slide, and make it simple and readily understood. Make it the kind of picture you need only name, thus avoiding repetition, in describing the slide, of what you have already presented before the slide came on.

But This -

Not This -

AND IN CONCLUSION — now we're getting somewhere. Have that conclusion ready at all times, so whether you're at a loss for words, or the chairman calls "time" on you (through no fault of yours, of course, but because other speakers have run over and thus prolonged the meeting), you can go right to your conclusion for an effective ending.

But This -

The Result —

This -

Not This -

And Mr. Chairman—

Talk Things Over -

YOURS is an important role in the successful conduct of a technical session. For to you falls the responsibility of making the meeting as interesting and enjoyable and profitable as possible for those who attend. Talk things over with your speakers before the meeting. Emphasize the need for clear, distinctive speaking and the avoidance of monotone; discuss the time to be allotted to each speaker and arrange for unobtrusive signs by which you can keep them posted as to the time still remaining for each to speak.

FURTHER, arrange for someone to be posted in the rear of the meeting to signal you when it becomes difficult to hear the speaker back there, so you, in turn, can inform those on your program that their voices are not carrying their messages adequately. These things, as well as holding speakers to the time allotted, need not be matters of embarrassment if you talk them over in advance with the men on your program and everyone understands the necessity of a well-timed, well-run, smoothly operating meeting.

Reprinted from *Civil Engineering*. 16:548–49. December 1946. Illustrations by Donald D. King. Used by permission.

CHAPTER 16

Copying and Duplicating

The number of copies of technical and business reports needed is usually greater than can be prepared satisfactorily by typewritten carbons. The typing process is good for five to eight carbons at most, so when more copies are wanted, some other process of manifolding must be used. The one who prepares a report usually is not the person who makes the extra copies, nor even the original final form, but he is in a position to facilitate copying or reproducing these copies from the original by attention to the requirements of the process or processes to be used.

DEFINITIONS

The words "copying" and "duplicating" have more or less the same meaning, at least in their general use. In the trade literature, copying equipment is that equipment designed to produce 1 to 25 or so copies of an original and to do so without requiring intermediate master or stencil copies. Duplicating equipment is designed to produce high speed long runs at low cost (less than a cent) per copy. Copying equipment is frequently used to prepare the master or intermediate plate for use on duplicating printers.

Copy, as a verb, means to reproduce or to transcribe. As a noun, *copy* refers to any one separate item of a number of like items. This book on technical and business report preparation is a copy of the several thousand printed.

A *duplicate* is a double or counterpart of an original, usually identical in all aspects. One book from a printing is a duplicate.

Manifold means to multiply. In ordinary office practice a typist manifolds a letter by making carbon copies as she types the ribbon original.

The *original* as used in this chapter means that material — the sheet of paper on which is the *image* of lines, words, numerals, or diagrams — of which more copies are wanted.

A *reproduction* is a close imitation of an original, but the reproduction may differ in size, material, or other physical aspects.

Stock or *paper stock* is the sheet of paper on which the image of the original is to be transferred by one process or another.

In this chapter the words "copy" and "copying" are used to apply generally to all the processes of producing any number of copies, prints, duplicates, or carbons of existing or original material. "Manifolding" includes both "copying" and "duplicating."

USE OF MANIFOLDING WHEN PREPARING REPORTS

During the preparation of a technical or business report the author will frequently find it a saving of labor and time to use copying or duplicating processes. Depending upon the equipment available and its accessibility, the author of a report can utilize manifolding equipment in both his information gathering and writing stages.

Manifolding When Gathering Information and When Writing

When gathering information it may be desirable to have exact copies of certain pages, tabulations, illustrations, or calculations from such sources as books, periodicals, other reports, correspondence, or research notes. With proper regard to use of copyrighted material, machine-made copies of wanted information from these sources offer considerable time saving over hand copying by pen or pencil or by typing. Further, copying errors will not exist. When the copied material is for temporary use or for detailed study, the author has the privilege of writing marginal notes on his copy, which would probably not be permitted on the original source — library book, periodical, or report.

The manifolding processes may also be used to produce copies of forms on which to record data or to summarize data from observations, tests, experiments, or questionnaires in lieu of preparing the necessary number by hand drafting or typing. Similarly, a few or many copies of questionnaires may be produced as needed for the questionnaire process of gathering information.

When writing the early drafts of a report, the author likewise may find many ways to utilize copies of his drafts, in part or in whole. Perhaps the greatest use would be for draft copies when they are needed for others to review. A typed draft, with revisions noted thereon, may be better than a clean copy for the purpose of review by another person whose reactions are wanted or whose approval must be obtained. In this connection, machine copying of pencil or ink outlines, sketches, designs, mathematical derivations, calculations, and tabulations is highly desirable. Such procedure saves time, errors, and the typing labor which would be required if the longhand notes were first to be typed. Complicated and technical material of these types should be copied the minimum number of times in the total process of report preparation to prevent errors, and to save time and labor.

In-process copying of drafts offers a safeguard against transcription errors and saves the labor, yet provides adequate working copies for all persons involved.

The same basic outline, sketch, table of data, or mathematical or chemical expression may have to be used in two or more ways or places in the report. When so required, the additional copies may be made from one carefully prepared original. This process is useful in preparing color overlays, charts of changes with time, land use maps, and before and after studies.

Lastly, in the course of the many steps in preparing a report, preservation and protection of data, working papers, and sketches may become important. When such material needs to be sent by mail or loaned to another person, copies may be made first and placed in a protected file to insure having a copy available.

As pointed out on page 185, one who is preparing a report needs to give continuous attention to the number of copies required of the final report and the copying or duplicating process by which these copies will be produced. The author will do well to consult, at an early stage, with those whose responsibility it is to produce the copies so that he can prepare his material to meet the specifications of the manifolding process to be used.

MANIFOLDING PROCESSES

The writer of reports is primarily concerned with the copying processes during his work of collecting information and the several stages of writing his report in final form. When more than eight or so copies of the final report are needed, the author will be concerned with the duplicating processes. In either case, he will, of necessity, be guided by the processes and equipment available to him.

Factors To Be Considered

Factors to be considered in preparing original material to be copied or duplicated are (1) the original material to be copied or duplicated, (2) the manifolding process to be used, and (3) the final product or duplicated copies. Table 16.1 lists considerations to be kept

TABLE 16.1. Factors To Be Considered In Manifolding Original Copy

Item No.	A. The Original Material To Be Copied or Duplicated	B. The Copying or Duplicating Process	C. The Final Product — Copies or Duplicates of the Original
1	Total number of sheets or pages (size of job)	Number of sheets to be copied	
2		Number of copies required of each sheet or page	Number of complete sets of report required
3	Width and length of sheets	Width and length of paper stock required by machine	Width and length of sheet desired
4		Possible enlargement or reduction in dimensions from original	Enlargement or reduction in dimensions desired
5	Single, loose sheets or pages from bound volume	Ability to handle single sheets and bound volumes	How is report to be bound
6	Adaptable to copy from only one side or from both sides of sheet	Copy from only one side or both sides of original	
7		Print on only one side or both sides of paper stock	Printing desired on only one side or both sides of sheet
8	Color of markings and the material — ink, pencil, crayon — of which they are made	Ability to pick up colors from original (print either black or in color)	
9	Specific colors present	Ability to print in more than one color	Color of ink or inks desired
10	Color of paper or background	Color of paper stock	Color of paper desired — background color
11	Quality of paper — texture, translucency, stiffness	Quality of paper — texture, weight, translucency	Quality of paper desired (must it take pencil or ink marking), folding ability and durability
12		Is a special finished or sensitized paper stock required	
13		Does process require original to be prepared on specially finished paper	
14	Photographs or other shaded material	Will process copy photographs or other shaded material	
15	Mounted or overlay material included	Will process copy mounted or overlaid material	
16	Sharpness of material — will it reproduce in readable image	Sharpness of product	Sharpness desired
17		Brightness of product	Brightness (contrast with background) desired
18		Wet or dry process	Is a dry copy required immediately
19		Length of time to process the order	Time allowable in which to complete the manifolding order
20	Availability for second or later order	Is a reusable master or intermediate sheet produced	Probability of second or later printing (from original, master sheet, or final copy)
21			Permanency required of inks or image

in mind according to these three groups. As to be expected, many of the factors are duplicated within the three groups. By attending to all factors the requirements of the whole process can be met and co-ordinated to minimize the labor and time required as well as to maximize the quality of the final copies.

Availability of Manifolding Equipment

Practically all business offices have one or more processes and machines available for producing copies of all types of correspondence, documents, forms, invoices, reports, and other types of business papers. The copying and duplicating processes and equipment available on the market cover a wide range and meet the many requirements as dictated by types of material to be copied and use of the copies as well as time, cost, space, and convenience. Custom commercial services are available in most cities for those organizations or individuals who desire them rather than the purchase and operation of their own equipment.

The descriptive material[1] presented in the next two sections on copying and duplicating processes is not intended to be used as a guide to selection or purchase of manifolding equipment. It is presented as an aid to those who are preparing reports and who in this work may have opportunity or need for using manifolding processes and equipment.

COPYING PROCESSES

In general, copying processes are those that permit making a few (1 to 25) copies of original material within a few minutes, usually without making an intermediate master, stencil, or other form of the original. The cost per copy (1 to 10 cents) varies not at all or but little with the number of copies produced. Copying processes include diazo, facsimile, photocopy, photography, thermography, typewriting, verifax, and xerography.

Diazo

Diazonium salt, a coupler chemical, a neutralizer (ammonia), and light are the elements used in copying by the diazo process. In these elements the diazo process is similar to the photocopying processes. When the diazonium salt is exposed to light it can no longer combine with the coupler to form a dye.

The original is placed face up over the sensitized stock sheet, also face up. Strong ultraviolet light is passed down through the original. Where there are dark areas on the original, the light is not passed through to the sensitized sheet. On these areas the diazonium remains active and combines with the coupler to form the dark-colored dye. The process is completed when ammonia vapor is passed over the stock sheet to neutralize the reaction and to combine the remaining active diazo with the coupler.

The diazo process requires originals on translucent paper and in good contrast of white and dark. The first and only copy is a positive. For a few copies, the process is fast and low in cost. Offset masters can be prepared by the process.

Facsimile

Photoelectric scanning is used to produce copies by the facsimile process. This process, originally developed for long-distance communication, has been developed for office copy production.

In the facsimile process, the original is scanned completely and continuously by a narrow light beam which reflects into a photoelectric cell. In this cell, electrical current is generated in direct proportion to the strength of the reflected light from the original. The light areas on the original reflect more light than do the dark areas. This generated current is then passed to a receiving unit which has a stylus. The stylus passes over a sensitized stock sheet where the electrical current "burns" the image into the sheet, producing dark areas in exact conformity to the dark areas of the original.

Some of the facsimile equipment will copy photographs and other shaded material. The machine is used to transfer copy to stencils

---

[1] Much of the technical description of the processes described is based upon the article "Tools of the Office – Copying and Duplicating Equipment." *Office Management.* 20:5:38–84. March, 1959. This article gives the manufacturers' names, trade names, and descriptions of the models of the several machines on the market. A second article in the January, 1961, issue. pages 76–87, summarizes and updates the 1959 article. An article by Lawrence Victor, "Choosing the Right Copying Machine." *Administrative Management.* March, 1962, pages 35–55, presents a comprehensive discussion.

THE SIX BASIC

WHICH METHOD OR COMBINATION OF METHODS IS

Diffusion Transfer

The diffusion transfer method is the most widely used office copying process today. It depends on the transfer (by diffusion) of silver-halide salts to à chemically treated surface where they are reduced to a silver (black) image. The process takes place as follows:

1. The original copy and a sheet of paper with a light-sensitive, silver-halide surface are placed face-to-face and exposed to light which passes first through the sensitized sheet (called the negative) then to the original. The light is reflected from the un-printed area of the original (such reflex exposure makes possible the copying of two-sided originals on opaque stock), bounces back to the negative and makes insoluble whatever silver-halides it strikes. The printed area of the original absorbs the light leaving the corresponding area on the negative soluble and ready for diffusion.

2. The original is layed aside and the negative is placed face-to-face with a chemically-treated sheet of positive paper. Both are passed through a solution of developer and silver-halide solvent. The soluble silver-halide salts on the negative (corresponding to the copy on the original) are diffused to the positive sheet where they are reduced to silver to form a black image.

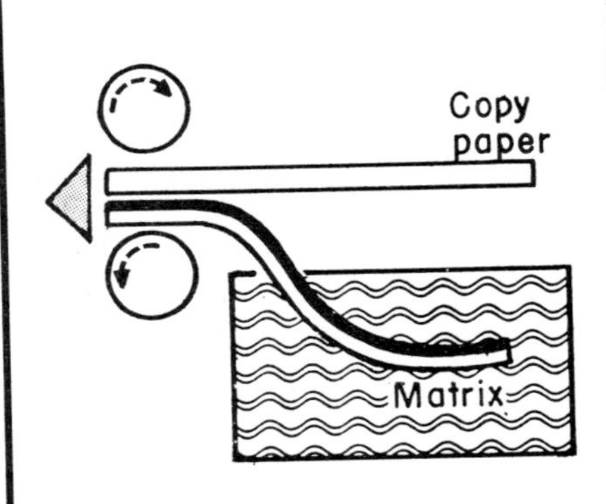

Dye Transfer

The dye transfer process is similar to the diffusion-transfer method and is often confused with it. The basic concept of using reflected light to expose certain areas of the negative is the same; only in this case, the exposed areas become non-transferable through hardening rather than insolubility. The final image-fixing and the making of extra copies is also different.

1. The original is placed face-to-face with the negative whose surface is coated with silver-halides in a gelatin matrix (carrier). As in the diffusion transfer method, both sheets are exposed to light and the non-image area of the original becomes the exposed area of the negative.

2. The negative is fed through a solution as before. The non-image area is developed but the gelatin turns hard preventing transfer. The image area also turns dark, forming a dye. Here the gelatin remains soft permitting the dye to be transferred to another sheet as a positive image.

Making extra copies is done simply by pressing additional sheets of ordinary paper against the negative and peeling them apart. As many as five or six good copies can be made before the dye is exhausted.

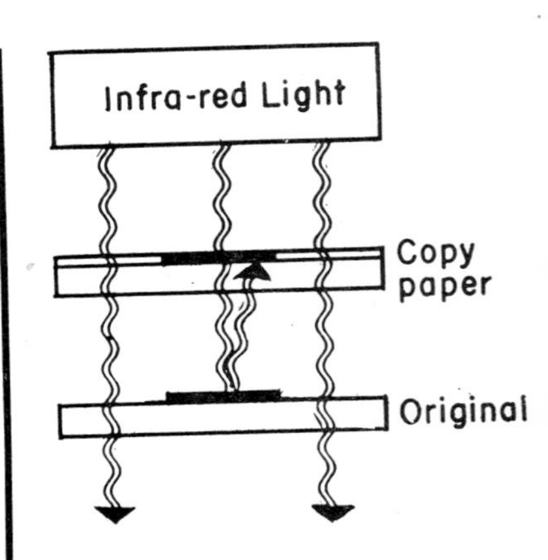

Thermographic

The thermographic method, as its name implies, uses heat to form an image. The process is fast and simple.

1. A heat-sensitive copy sheet is placed face up over the original.

2. Both are fed simultaneously int the unit where they are exposed t heat-bearing infra-red light whic passes through the copy sheet ont the original.

3. The heat absorbed and held b the background area on the origina is insufficient to cause a reaction o the copy sheet, but that held by th image area is enough to cause th corresponding area on the copy shee to turn dark, forming a duplicat image.

The great advantages of this met od are speed, simplicity and clean ness. Thermographic units can tu out about seven copies per minut The machine can be used by even t most inexperienced personnel a there are no liquid developers to m or pour.

The thermographic process do have its drawbacks, though. The fide ty of reproduction is not as high in other methods. and some types colored pen and pencil markings sist reproduction. But where spe and ease of use are more importa than the absolute fidelity of the co the thermographic method sho prove entirely satisfactory.

COPY PROCESSES

BEST FOR YOU DEPENDS ON YOUR COPYING GOALS

Electrostatic

The electrostatic method of office copying is based on the well-known theory that opposite electrical charges attract. The process, also called "xerography," is carried out in five basic steps:

1. A photoconductive plate is electrically charged.

2. The image to be copied is projected onto the plate. Where light rays strike the plate's surface, the electrical charge is dissipated; where the rays are blocked by the copy, the electrical charge is retained. In other words, we have a latent electrical "photograph." (Since the degree of dissipation is proportionate to the amount of light, variations in tone can be achieved permitting accurate copying of photographs and drawings.)

3. Powder carrying an opposite charge is flowed over the plate. It adheres to the charged areas of the plate making the latent image visible though in reverse.

4. A sheet of copy paper is placed over the plate and both are passed under charging wires where the copy sheet is given an electrical charge opposite to that of the plate causing the powder image to leave the plate and adhere to the copy sheet.

5. The powder image is permanently affixed to the copy sheet by heat or a powder solvent.

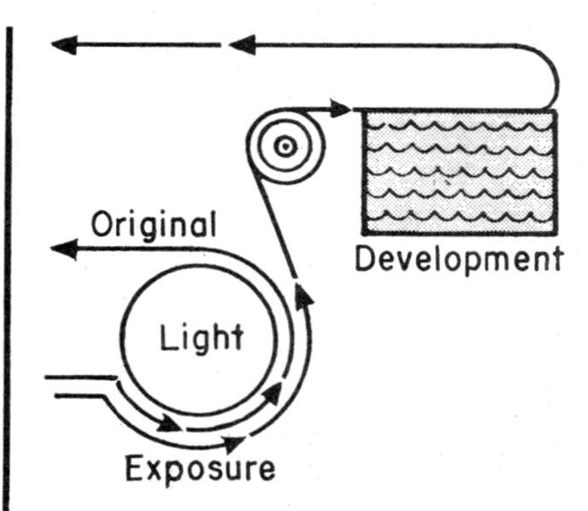

Diazo

The necessary materials are: a translucent original (master) to permit the passage of light; a copy sheet coated with light-sensitive diazonium salts (hence the name "diazo"); a source of ultra-violet light to de-activate or "kill" those salts contacted; and a coupler to react with the remaining "live" salts to form a visible dye.

Here's what happens:

1. The translucent master is placed face up over the copy sheet.

2. The two sheets are exposed simultaneously to ultra-violet rays which pass through the translucent master striking the copy sheet surface. Where the rays strike, the diazonium salts are de-activated; where the rays are blocked (i.e. the text area on the master), the salts remain "alive" ready to form a visible dye on contact with the coupler.

3. With the dry developing method, the copy sheet is coated with both the diazonium salts and the coupler, but any reaction is prevented by a chemical "stabilizer." When the exposed copy sheet is brought into contact with ammonia vapor, this stabilizer is destroyed and the dye forming process is free to take place.

With the moist method, the copy sheet holds the diazonium salts only, and after exposure, the sheet is moistened with a liquid coupler resulting in the same dye formation.

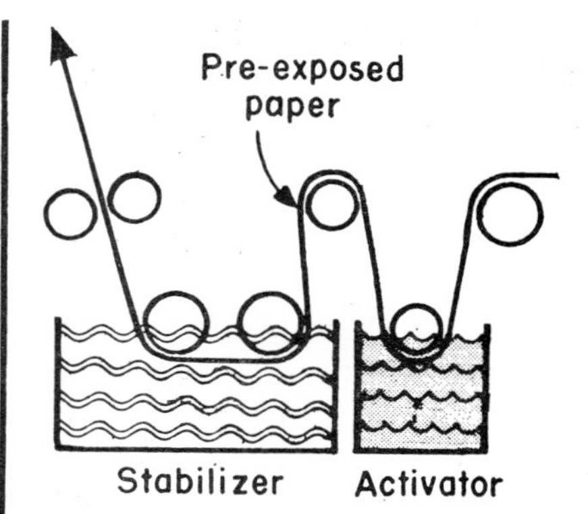

Quick Stabilization

In photography, the print is made permanent after development by being "fixed" in a solution of thiosulfate known as hypo. This converts the unexposed silver halide to a soluble salt which can be removed by washing in water.

The quick stabilization process uses a sheet covered with a silver sensitive emulsion combined with a developing agent. The original copy is exposed to this sheet which is then run through a solution which activates the developing agent. The resultant image is then fixed by running it through a stabilizer. Actually, it accomplishes the familiar photographic process but without the need for further processing.

The image obtained may be a reverse negative, a right reading negative, or it can be a black-on-white print. Reverse negatives must be rerun through the machines with a second copy sheet for a positive copy.

The principle advantages of this process are the need for only one sheet for either the negative or positive, its ability to copy tone values faithfully, and the longevity of the negative which can be stored indefinitely for making future copies. The disadvantages, if they can be called such, are the need for chemicals and the necessity of going through a negative stage in order to get a positive copy.

Reprinted from "Choosing the Right Copying Machine"
by Lawrence Victor, *Administrative Management*, March 1962.

and masters for other duplicating processes as well as for single copies.

Photocopy

The chemistry of photography is applied in different ways to produce the several variations of the photocopying process. But compared to the usual lens optical system of the camera, photocopy equipment prints in direct contact with the material to be copied on sensitized paper.

The ordinary transfer process prints a negative when light is passed through the sensitized sheet to the original material. The original is in contact with the sensitized side of the paper stock placed in the printing compartment of the machine. The dark areas of the original absorb the light. The light areas reflect the light to the sensitized surface thus causing a chemical reaction. Upon developing the sheet, the areas receiving the reflected light come out dark, the dark areas of the original develop light, thus a negative is made.

This negative is then placed face to face with another sensitized sheet and the two sheets placed in the processing compartment. In this compartment, a chemical solution (developer) produces a dye while the sheets are in contact. The two sheets are left together for about 15 seconds after they emerge from the machine to give time for the dye to transfer. The sheets are then peeled apart, the dark dye leaving its print on the sensitized sheet in the exact form of the light areas on the negative and dark areas on the original.

In a variation of this basic process, similar results are obtained without producing a negative. In this autopositive method the light is passed through the original copy, which is face up on the sensitized sheet. In this direct printing process, the original must be blank on its back side and translucent enough to permit light to pass through to the sensitized sheet.

Other variations of the photocopying method are in use, including one that produces a mirror-image reading right to left. This image is reversed to read left to right in the second step.

The photocopy method is good and fast for 1 to 20 or so copies, but too slow and expensive for long runs. The continuous feed equipment will not copy from bound volumes, but flat bed models of the equipment are available that will copy from both single sheets and bound volumes.

Photography

The well-known process of photography by use of a lens system, light, and sensitized film is not adaptable to ordinary office copy work because of the time and expense required. The process, however, is valuable for high precision work and originals of considerable shading. The process has the advantage of enabling enlargement or reduction from the original. In reproduction work, engraving plates or printing masters are made from photographs.

Thermography

As may be judged from the name, the thermography process utilizes heat in effecting a transfer of the image on the original to the stock sheet. This process, popularly known by the trade name Thermo-Fax, produces a dry sheet final copy in a single direct step.

The heat-sensitive stock paper is placed sensitive-side up on top of the original, also face up. An infrared light is then passed up through the original and through the stock to the sensitized coating. This substance is activated by the heat which is formed when the dark areas on the original absorb the light and transmit heat thereby. The white areas of the original do not absorb the light, so therefore do not transmit heat to "burn" the sensitizing substance on the top surface of the stock sheet.

The Thermo-Fax machine is fast — only four to five seconds to produce a copy. It works best on heat-absorbing dark inks and carbon (pencil) markings. The paper stock is waxlike and not too durable.

Typewriting

Typewriting is a universally familiar form of relief printing used extensively for copying as well as in making masters for other processes.

By use of carbon sheets, up to five to eight carbon copies can be made at one time in addition to the original, or ribbon copy. Since the introduction of the quick copy machines and processes, typewriters are used less and less in making extra copies of letters and other materials. Typing has the disadvantage that only words and numerals can be typed.

Verifax

The reflected light principle of the photocopy method is used in the Verifax process. The original and a sheet of sensitized paper are placed face to face in the machine. The light is passed through the sensitized stock sheet or matrix. The light reflected from white areas on the original to the matrix causes these areas to develop white while the dark areas not reflected develop dark on the matrix.

The two sheets are removed from the machine after exposure. The matrix is then placed in the developing compartment. The developer leaves a deposit of a dark dye image corresponding to the original. This deposit is transferred to the final copy in the third step which consists of a face to face transfer from the developed matrix to a second sensitized sheet. These sheets are pressed together by rollers as they leave the printing compartment of the machine. The final copy is produced dry.

Since not all the dye is transferred in the first printing, four or five good, dark copies may be made from one matrix. The Verifax process will copy from a wide variety of materials, including two-sided originals, just as long as the material to be copied will not reflect light from the image and will reflect light from the background areas. Blue, and other nonlight-absorbing colors cannot be copied.

Xerography

The principle of electricity that like charges repel each other and unlike charges attract each other is used in the xerographic process of copying. By using a copying camera, light is reflected from the original to a plate coated with a positive electrical charge. The reflected light from the light areas of the original cancels the positive charge. But the dark areas of the original do not reflect the light, so these corresponding areas on the plate remain with their positive charge.

In the second, or developing step, a dark resinous powder electrically charged in the negative is passed over the exposed plate, which attracts and holds the dark powder on the positive-charged areas (dark areas of the original). The third step is to place over this plate, now visibly showing the original material, a sheet of positively-charged stock paper. Some of the negatively charged dark powder is transferred to the stock sheet by electrical attraction. In the final step, this transferred powder is fused by heat into the stock paper to fix a permanent image.

The xerographic process is adaptable to two-sided opaque originals, but the image must be in black or other light-absorbing colors. Some equipment will permit enlarging or reducing in size. The process takes about three minutes. It is used also for producing intermediate, or masters, for some of the duplicating processes.

DUPLICATING PROCESSES

Duplicating processes are those that provide for making up to many thousands of copies, usually by use of a master, stencil, or other intermediate form of the original. The cost of the first copy produced is high, but the unit cost decreases as the number produced increases. The main duplicating processes are gelatin, letterpress printing, offset printing, relief printing, spirit and special liquid, and stencil.

Gelatin

Hectograph is another name for the gelatin process which makes use of aniline dyes. The process is a contact transfer using specially coated paper stock.

The original work is typed or drawn on a hectograph carbon paper placed face down on top of the master sheet. This step produces a right to left reading image of aniline dye on the master. The image is then transferred to the bed of gelatin by placing the master face down on it. This process completes the transfer of the original to the printing gelatin, but in reversed form. The final step is to press against the gelatin the special high-finished stock paper, a sheet at a time. During the contact, aniline dye is transferred to the stock to produce a final copy.

Since only a thin layer of the dye is transferred to the stock sheet at each printing, some 50 to 100 printings can be made from the one master. The final copy is usually of purple ink (dye) on white paper. Both flat bed and cylinder machines are available.

Letterpress Printing

The standard process of letterpress printing from printers' type, a form of relief duplicating, produces high quality, artistic work. In combination with engravings, it is available for any duplicating work, including process colors. This printing process is too time consuming and too expensive for ordinary office use and for runs of less than 500 copies. Letterpress printing is used for reports, however, when the circulation is large. Annual reports of agencies and corporations frequently are produced by this standard printing process.

Offset Printing

For many years the printing industry has used the process known as photo-offset lithography, in which the printing is done from a flat surface. The process is possible because the nonprinting area of the printing plate is water-moistened to prevent the greasy ink from adhering to the plate except on the image to be transferred. The offset process gets its name from the fact that the image is offset from a normal reading master to a reversed reading image on a cylinder of the machine. Stock paper then comes in contact with the reversed image on the offset cylinder and picks up the image in normal form.

The master sheet, or plate, is prepared photographically, or by another copying process, on a sheet of paper, thin metal, or thin plastic. The master image must be of greasy texture so that moisture will not adhere to the image, but will to the background areas. The master is then fastened to the drum of the duplicator or printing press.

In the duplicating process the first step consists of applying a light film of water to the master by a roller. This moisture does not adhere to the lines of the image, but does to the background areas. In the second step, inked rollers pass over the master and deposit a somewhat greasy ink to the image areas. The moist background repels the ink. Thirdly, the master cylinder revolves against a second cylinder, or blanket, of firm rubber and transfers (offsets) the image to this blanket cylinder. Lastly, the blanket cylinder is rotated against an impression cylinder over which is the stock sheet. The impression cylinder thus transfers the image to the paper to make the final copy.

In spite of the many steps to the offset process, and particularly the offsetting step, the offset printing process produces highly accurate results. The process is adapted to color work and long runs at high speeds—4,000 to 9,000 copies per hour. Once the equipment is available, short runs, 10 to 100, are economical when low cost masters are used.

Relief Printing

The office typewriter is the most common process of printing from relief; the letterpress printing from type is another well-known method; and a third is the commonly used office rubber stamp. Inking of the type is done by an inked ribbon or carbon tape, as in the typewriter, or by applying ink to the raised type as in the rubber stamp or letterpress process.

Office printing equipment is designed to hold metal or rubber type in slots on a rotating drum, or is locked up in a form or in slots on a flat printing head.

The machines are most commonly designed so that the paper stock is fed mechanically to the printing drum. The type is inked from rollers or from ribbons. Impression of the image is made when the paper stock is pressed between the inked type and an impression surface, a cylinder in a rotary machine.

The relief method is suited to long runs, varied colors of ink and paper. Speeds up to 6,000 sheets an hour are available.

Spirit and Special Liquid

The spirit process is chemically similar to the gelatin process. The essential difference is in the mechanical handling. This process is also called the liquid hectograph process, because it uses alcohol as the solvent for the printing medium — aniline dye.

A master is prepared in the same manner as in the gelatin process. The special paper is placed on a faced-up special carbon and the original typed or drawn on this paper. The result is a transfer of the original in reversed form to the back of the sheet. The dye in the carbon forms the printing ink.

The master is placed around the drum of the duplicating machine. When operating, the machine feeds to the printing cylinder sheets of paper stock which are moistened with alcohol just as they pass to the cylinder. This moist alcohol dissolves off a thin layer of the aniline dye from the image on the master to transfer a normal reading image to the paper stock. With each sheet printed, the supply of dye is slightly reduced. But even so, when all factors are favorable, perhaps 400 copies can be obtained from one master. Printing speeds vary from 40 to 120 copies per minute. The cost per sheet is low. The ink (dye) color is usually purple, but other colors may be had by using a carbon of the desired color.

A variation of the spirit process has been developed by some companies to avoid staining the operator's hands. These processes withhold making an active dye until the paper stock is fed to the machine. The master is a specially treated sheet which does not expose its dye color until moistened within the machine.

These special liquid processes will not reduce the length of runs obtainable from the spirit process. About 100 copies is the limit. Otherwise the processes are comparable. There is a certain interchangeability of the processes and equipment.

Stencil

The well-known mimeograph stencil process has been in popular use for years in offices. The stencil process is a simple and inexpensive one. A master or stencil is prepared on paper, plastic, metal, or other material in which fine holes can be made. These holes, made in the form of the image, allow ink to pass through to the paper stock.

Generally, the stencil material is so designed that the cutting process does not cut out the whole form of letters, lines, or symbols, but leaves some fibers intact. Cutting away of the waxy stencil (the most commonly used material) is sufficient, however, to allow passage of the ink; where the stencil is uncut, the waxy surface prevents the ink from passing through to the paper stock. Art work, drafting, and design can be cut into the stencil by hand, typewriter, die, or other methods.

The completed stencil is wrapped around the printing drum, which contains the ink. As the drum revolves, paper stock is fed into the machine and comes in contact with the stencil. Ink is absorbed by the paper stock at the points where it emerges through the cuttings in the stencil.

The copy paper is usually somewhat rough in order to possess high absorbent qualities, so that offsetting will not occur from a freshly printed sheet to the back of the sheet above it as the printed sheets pile up. Smooth papers can be used by slip-sheeting (inserting a dry sheet above each sheet as it is printed). In some instances quick drying ink can be used.

Speeds are 60 to 100 copies per minute for manual operation and 180 to 240 per minute for motor driven machines. Runs of many thousands can be made from one stencil.

CHAPTER 17

Editing, Copyreading, and Proofreading

Many inquiry and periodic reports are duplicated by one process or another for circulation to a greater readership than can be reached economically with typescript carbon copies. The process of manifolding may involve editing by other than the author. Careful copyreading and proofreading are usually necessary regardless of the process adopted for making copies of the report. However, whether or not the report is to be duplicated, the writer has the responsibility of preparing his manuscript for final typing and of proofing the typescript copy before releasing the report. There is a close similarity in objective and procedure between copyreading (preparing copy for final typing or for typesetting) and proofreading (checking final typing or printer's proof for errors) done by the writer and that done by an editor. In fact, if the author's work is done properly and completely, an editor's work would consist only of marking instructions for typesetting or other process of manifolding.

THE WRITER'S COPYREADING

During the process of writing, revising, and rewriting as discussed in Chapter 9, a manuscript may become somewhat heavily marked with pencil changes, corrections, and interlining. It is the author's responsibility (1) to make the manuscript free from all errors and discrepancies, (2) to see that all corrections are legible, understandable, and positive as to their application, and (3) to indicate instructions governing typography and page format.

Inconsistencies in references to tables, illustrations, footnotes, and pages, inaccuracies in arithmetic, and inconsistencies in mechanics of style should have been removed during the several steps in revising. A final review of the manuscript is desirable to make certain that the typist will have no difficulty in interpreting the markings and that copy can be followed explicitly. A typist cannot be expected to recognize errors and inconsistencies in copy.

Margins, spacing of headings, use of capital and lower-case letters in headings, placing of illustrations and tables, and other mechanical details affecting the typist's work should be clearly designated by the writer on his manuscript. Only by designating these items clearly and completely can the writer expect to get back from the typist the finished manuscript in the format, style, and arrangement he desires.

Whether the final form of the report is to be in typescript or in printer's type, the writer's procedure is about the same. He has the responsibility of copyreading his manuscript before it passes to final typing, and then of proofreading it after the final typing and before the sheets are assembled in their proper order. When the report is to be printed the same two steps are taken, but usually by an editor or someone designated to handle the publishing procedures. Even if the report is to be published, the author should exercise the same care in achieving excellence as he would for a report to be submitted in typescript. Thus, copyreading and proofreading are important steps in the preparation of every report.

In copyreading, the writer will save time and achieve good results if he will follow the standard methods and principles used in marking copy for the printer. A typist, however, may not be familiar with the special marks used in copyreading in the printing process, although most of the marks are self-explanatory. The marking of printer's proof for corrections follows a similar process. Both copyreading and proofreading marks are illustrated at the end of this chapter. By custom these marks and practices are practically the same in all editorial offices and printing shops. They are also followed in many business offices in the ordinary routine of typing reports, papers, or other typescript. A correctly and clearly marked manuscript enables the typist to complete the final typescript with speed and with a minimum of errors.

THE WRITER'S PROOFREADING

If the manuscript turned over to the typist were free from all errors by the writer, if the writer had given the typist full and understandable instructions, and if the typist made no errors in typing, there would be no need for proofreading the final typing. Such is not the case, however, so an author will do well to proof carefully the final typing. In doing so he will look particularly for typing errors, since theoretically there should be no other errors to be found. On the contrary, however, he will probably find other errors; if not errors, a few places where he decides to make a change in the interest of clarity or consistency. How far he will go in making changes will depend upon the time available, the nature and importance of the changes, and how meticulous he needs to be for that particular report.

The printer's proofreading marks are not practical for marking typescript for corrections. When changes are extensive enough to warrant recopying of the whole page, the changes may be marked in accordance with the procedure for copyreading. When the corrections may be made without retyping, the indicated operation should be made in easily erasable marks placed in the binding margin.

THE EDITOR'S WORK

Reports or technical papers to be published by the printing process are handled in a manner not unlike that just described for original manuscripts, but in a varying degree of intensiveness depending upon the publisher. Reports, technical papers, scientific papers, and books are published by the firm or consultant preparing the report, by business papers (magazines), scientific societies, and book publishers. The editing process is the same for all these publishers, though the editor's responsibility varies accordingly.

A report published by the firm or consultant preparing the report will undergo a minimum of editing. Essentially all that will be done is to give the printer the necessary instructions covering the page size, binding, and general typography. The editors of professional societies who are responsible for the proceedings of the society frequently do little more editing[1] than to mark the manuscript for typography, indicate the size of the illustrations, and check the manuscript for gross errors in grammar and styling. Book editors process the manuscript with considerable care, though usually do not edit wording and arrangement heavily. They usually purchase only manuscripts that are free from wordiness and loose statements and which are consistent in mechanics. The editors of trade, class, commercial, and professional magazines are highly reader conscious and economy minded. Their editing is heavy when necessary, and, while they do accord the author certain considerations, their chief concern is to produce an article that is high in reader

[1] These editors usually send the technical papers to qualified reviewers who check the theoretical or practical soundness of the text, the clearness of presentation and the general quality of writing in addition to the originality of the paper.

interest and short in length. It is to the work of the magazine editor that most of the following discussion applies.

The Editor's Responsibilities

The technical editor serves five masters: the reader, the author, the publisher, the printer, and himself. The editor's job is to see that each of these five parties is treated fairly and kept satisfied as far as can be done within the scope of his five-fold obligation.

For the reader, the editor selects only pertinent material of high interest and high value. He has to choose for each issue a variety of subjects dealing with items of current importance. No field can be overlooked, yet no one field must be overworked. The editor must see that all manuscripts are edited so that the meaning is direct and clear. In this respect the editor has full liberty to rearrange the manuscript as he desires in order to achieve his objective. The language is made to agree with that familiar to the readers. The editor, rather than the author, is responsible for the final wording and thus the readability of the printed article. To accomplish selection of articles and news that fulfill the wants of the readers, the editors must have a broad background in the general subject field of his publication, a progressive outlook toward future developments, and a close contact with events of the day.

For the author of a technical article accepted for publication, the editor endeavors to preserve style of expression and objective, while at the same time recasting the manuscript to fit the needs of his readers whenever the author fails to do so. Although the author is expected to submit a manuscript free from errors of fact, grammar, and arithmetic, the editor carefully checks such material in order to save both the author and himself embarrassment resulting from mistakes. In editing a manuscript, the editor is particularly careful to eliminate possible double meanings in an effort to make certain that readers will interpret the meaning in the light the author intends. He further guards against unreasonable or illogical conclusions on the part of the readers. All in all, the editor acts as the agent of the author to make certain that he is understood and accorded the respect due him.

For the publisher, the editor endeavors to protect publication policies and to increase readership through selection and treatment of reading material. The editor strives for low-cost production, consistent with the development of interesting and valuable reading content. He accomplishes this objective by condensing articles to a minimum, making economical layouts of type and illustrations, holding corrections in proof to a minimum and by handling efficiently all production processes.

For the printer, the editor strives to submit clean copy with exact instructions. Illustrative and tabular matter is carefully planned so that the printer has no difficulty in obtaining the arrangements of type desired. In order to specify typographical arrangements of pleasing character and of economical design, the editor needs a thorough knowledge of printing practices and of the artistic qualities of type.

For himself, the editor strives to preserve his good reputation by issuing only the highest class of publication both in subject matter and typography. He strives to maintain friendly and co-operative relations with authors, publisher, and printer, while adhering to principles of good editing.

The Editor's Procedure

A systematic procedure in preparing a manuscript for printing is necessary if the editor's responsibilities are to be carefully fulfilled. A series of steps are desirable similar in purpose to those recommended in Chapter 9 for revising manuscript. These readings or steps may be as follows:

1. An appraisal reading to get in mind the author's general treatment as a basis for deciding whether the manuscript is worthy of acceptance and, if so, whether it needs heavy or only minor editing and reorganization

2. Reorganization of the manuscript, when necessary, to achieve the best sequence and choice of subject matter
3. Editing of the composition to achieve clearness of expression, correctness of grammar, positiveness of meaning, and accuracy
4. Editing of tables and illustrations
5. Styling of manuscript
6. Marking of manuscript for typography and other instructions for the print shop

An editor evaluates each article submitted to him in terms of subject matter, specific objective developed by the author, readability, technical slant, quality of English, and length. From this evaluation the editor formulates in his mind what needs to be done to the article to make it meet his specifications. Steps 2,3,4, and 5 are then carried out in accordance with this decision, similar to the manner stated on pages 175 to 185 for the writer's revisions leading to his final draft.

Tables and illustrations require special handling. The mechanical limitations of characters per inch of line and lines of type per inch necessitate detailed checking of all tables to determine the size, face, and arrangement of type to be used. The typescript tables may need some reorganization to permit a satisfactory and economical type layout. Likewise, the size and page position of illustrations and form of legend are determined in the editing process. Illustrations are marked for kind and size of engraving to fit the page layout planned for the article.

The final step is to mark the manuscript with all necessary instructions for the print shop. The type is designated by name, face, size, leading, and length of line.

Editing is a comparatively easy job for articles written by good authors who took care to prepare their manuscript for the particular publication and to follow the specifications required by that publication. Regardless of the quality of the article, the editor follows the usual steps, but while the poorly-written article may require hours to edit, the well-written one will require only minutes.

PROOFREADING OF PRINTER'S PROOF

Manuscript (copy) for newspapers, magazines, proceedings, books, and most bulletins and reports, once edited and marked for the printer, usually is set in type by the use of typesetting machines. Of recent years, however, a photo-offset printing process has come into usage by which typescript sheets are photographed on sensitized thin metal sheets which become the printing surface. This offset process requires that the typed copy be letter perfect and arranged on the page exactly as desired when printed. The copy typed for photographic processing must be proofread carefully. Special typewriters have been developed for typing offset copy.

In the typesetting process, two proofreadings are required: first, the printer's galley proof, and second, the page proof. A galley in printer's lexicon is an oblong metal tray with three upright sides in which type is held. Thus, a galley proof is taken from type as set and before line and head spacing material is added or illustrations supplied. Galley proof is read carefully so that necessary corrections in page form may be kept at a minimum. After the galleys have been proofread and corrected, the type, including tabular material and illustrations, is assembled in page form exactly as desired in the completed magazine, book, report, or bulletin. From this type page form a proof is taken. Page proof is carefully read and marked by the editor or his proofreader or author, or by all of them. Corrections are then made in the type pages as the last step prior to locking up the forms for press work.

From the time the writer prepares his first draft to the lockup on the printing press, author, editor, and proofreader (frequently the editor, or both author and editor) strive to eliminate errors and to improve wording. There seems to be no end to changes that could be made because each reading suggests additional changes. Up to the stage of proofreading the printer's galley proofs there is no reason to withhold changes in the copy. On printer's proof, however, there is both a cost and a time restriction on changes.

Changes in proof should be held to a minimum. There will be changes, however, in spite of the efforts of the author and editor to make the manuscript correct and acceptable.

Strictly speaking, proofreading is the process of marking printer's proof to correspond to the copy from which the type was set. Therefore, only typographical errors are expected in proof; actually, the author or editor frequently indicates corrections of errors overlooked in the copy and corrections which are changes from copy. Changes of mind and new interpretations result from each reading of the manuscript and proof, especially so when days have passed since the previous reading.

From a cost and production viewpoint all changes in proof are undesirable, so the proofreader must weigh the cost and delay of making changes in proof against editorial quality. No author, editor, or printer wants to see printing with obvious errors in it. On the other hand, there are many changes in wording and punctuation that could be made, but which, if made, may not be worth the cost. Those changes in proof which require setting of additional lines are particularly costly. A good proofreader, in such cases, will strive for some change in wording which will retain the sense of the copy, but which will exactly fit the type space available. Copy, before it is set in type, may be reworded and revised to any extent; proof, on the other hand, should not be subjected to a process of rewriting.

Copy is edited; proof is corrected and made to agree with edited copy. When authors and editors are meticulous and final with their work on the copy, proofreading becomes in reality just proofreading, not rewriting. Typesetters are trained to follow copy. A good operator will follow copy with a high degree of accuracy when copy is clean and instructions clear and complete.

MARKING OF COPY AND PROOF

The marks used in editing, copyreading, and proofreading are illustrated on the following pages. The marks used vary slightly from office to office and shop to shop, but once the marks are learned individual variations are easily recognized.

The essential difference in marking copy for either the typist or the printer and in marking printer's proof is that in copy corrections are marked directly at the point of correction within the lines, while printer's proof is marked on the margins of the proof sheet. Should printer's type be set with widely spaced lines as is double-spaced typescript copy, the corrections could be marked within the lines as is done on the copy.

COPYREADING SYMBOLS

	HOW THEY ARE USED	WHAT THEY MEAN	HOW TYPE IS SET
TYPE SIZE and STYLE	Lansing, mich.--	Capitalize.	LANSING, Mich.—
	College Herald	Small caps.	COLLEGE HERALD
	the Senator from Ohio	Change to lower case.	the senator from Ohio
	By Alvin Jones	Bold face.	**By Alvin Jones**
	Saturday Evening Post	Italicize.	*Saturday Evening Post*
PUNCTUATION and SPELLING	"The Spy"	Emphasize quotes.	"The Spy"
	Northwestern U.	Emphasize periods.	Northwestern U.
	said, "I must . . .	Emphasize comma.	said, "I must . . .
	Johnsons'	Emphasize apostrophe.	Johnsons'
	picnicing	Insert letter or word.	picnicking
	theatre	Transpose letters.	theater
	Henry Cook, principal	Transpose words.	Principal Henry Cook
	days	Delete letter.	day
	judgement	Delete letter and bridge over.	judgment
	allright	Insert space.	all right
	th ose	Close up space.	those
	Geo Brown	Spell out.	George Brown
	100 or more	Spell out.	one hundred or more
	Doctor S. E. Smith	Abbreviate.	Dr. S. E. Smith
	Six North Street	Use numerals.	6 North Street
	Marion Smythe	Spell as written.	Marion Smythe
POSITION	Madison, Wis.--	Indent for paragraph.	Madison, Wis.—
	today. ¶ Tomorrow he	New paragraph.	today. Tomorrow he
	considered serious. Visitors are not	No paragraph. Run in with preceding matter.	considered serious. Visitors are not
	No ¶ But he called last night and said that he	No paragraph.	But he called last night and said that he
	]Jones To Conduct[or <Jones To Conduct>	Center subheads.	**Jones To Conduct**
MISCELLANEOUS	He was not unmindful	Bridge over material omitted.	He was mindful
	one student came (stet)	Kill corrections.	one student came
	or more	Story unfinished.	
	30 or #	End of story.	———

From **SCHOLASTIC JOURNALISM,** by Earl English and Clarence Hach, revised 3rd edition, © 1962, Iowa State University Press, Ames, Iowa.

PROOFREADING SYMBOLS

	SYMBOL	EXPLANATION	EXAMPLE: MARGINAL MARKS	EXAMPLE: ERRORS MARKED
TYPE SIZE and STYLE	wf	Wrong font.	wf	He marked the proof.
	x	Burred or broken letter. Clean or replace.	x	He marked the proof.
	ital	Reset in italic type the matter indicated.	ital	He marked the proof.
	rom	Reset in roman (regular) type, matter indicated.	rom	He marked *the* proof.
	bf	Reset in bold face type, word or words indicated.	bf	He marked the proof.
	≡	Replace with a capital the letter indicated.	H	he marked the proof.
	lc	Set in lower case type.	lc	He Marked the proof.
	sc	Use small capitals instead of the type now used.	sc	He marked the proof.
	9	Turn inverted letter indicated.	9	He maɹked the proof.
PUNCTUATION and SPELLING		Take out letter, letters, or words indicated.		He marked the prooof.
	#	Insert space where indicated.	#	He marked theproof.
	r	Insert letter as indicated.	r	He maked the proof.
	⊙	Insert period where indicated.	⊙	He marked the proof
	^	Insert comma where indicated.	^	Yes he marked the proof.
	ⅴ	Insert apostrophe where indicated.	ⅴ	Mark the boys proof.
	/=/	Insert hyphen where indicated.	/=/	It was a cureall.
	?/	Insert question mark where indicated.	?/	Who marked the proof
	em	Insert em dash, implying break in continuity or sentence structure.	em	Should we can we comply?
	n	Insert en dash, implying the word "to."	n	See pages 278 93.
	" / "	Enclose in quotation marks as indicated.	" "	He marked it proof.
	spell out	Spell out all words marked with a circle.	spell out	He marked the 2nd proof.
	out, see copy	Used when words left out are to be set from copy and inserted as indicated.	out, see copy	He proof.
	stet...	Let it stand. Disregard all marks above the dots.	stet	He ~~marked~~ the proof.
	⌒	Draw the word together.	⌒	He ma rked the proof.
	tr	Transpose letters or words as indicated.	tr	He the proof marked
	?	Query to author. Encircled in red.	? was	The proof read by
POSITION	¶	Start a new paragraph as indicated.	¶	reading The boy marked
	No ¶	Should not be a separate paragraph. Run in.	No ¶	marked. The proof was read by
	=	Out of alignment. Straighten.	=	He marked the proof.
	□	Indent 1 em.		□ He marked the proof.
	□□	Indent 2 ems.		□□ He marked the proof.
	□□□	Indent 3 ems.		□□□ He marked the proof.
	eq. #	Equalize spacing.	eq. #	He marked the proof.
	⊥	Push down space which is showing up.	⊥	He marked the proof.
	[or]	Move over to the point indicated. [If to the left; if to the right]	[	He marked the proof.
	⊔	Lower to the point indicated.	⊔	He marked the proof.
	⊓	Raise to the point indicated.	⊓	He marked the proof.
	∪	Less space.	∪	looks better

From **SCHOLASTIC JOURNALISM**, by Earl English and Clarence Hach, revised 3rd edition, © 1962, Iowa State University Press, Ames, Iowa.

COPY MARKED FOR TYPIST OR TYPESETTER

Copy marking
Specimen 7.1.

Caps **Marking of Copy**

Copy is prepared for the typist or type setter by marking all co(r)rections entirely within the lines wherever room permits, rather than in the margins. Long passages ~~that are~~ to be inserted may be written in the margin. Material ~~which is~~ to be deleted is marked out solid.

Either ink or a medium soft pencil may be used. The harder pencils do not make a black enough line, and real soft lead smudges too much. When the inter-changing of words, sentences, or paragraphs is complicated, the sections should be retyped or cut out and pasted in their proper sequence. As a rule, typists and type-setters "follow copy" and are not expected to follow the sense of what is being typed or set. ~~copied~~. All marks, therefore, are so placed that they will be seen by the operator in time to comply there with. For this reason, markings ~~are~~ usually placed, above the line rather than below. ~~the line.~~ At places where words are inserted or deleted, leaders are used to direct the eye from the end of a correct word to the next.

¶ A ring around a numeral (or an abbreviation,) in the copy is an instruction to spell out the encircled material. If the words abbreviated may not be known to the typist they should be spelled out above the abbreviation and the abbreviation crossed out. The reverse indication does not generally apply; cross out the number in words or the spelled out

out words and write in the numerals or the abbreviations. Example: a pressure of 9 psi ~~nine pounds per square inch~~ was observed in the (8) tests completed in (Jan.)

MARKING OF PROOF

The Proof reader reads to find mistakes; he is not concerned with the gaining of information. Nevertheless, he must be continually aware of the thought expressed in order to catch omission of words, wrong derivatives of words, and errors of grammar. He reads each letter of each word in order to prove spelling. This method is in contrast with ordinary reading for pleasure or for information in which whole words or word groups are recognized without individual reading of the letters.

Printer's proof is marked in much the same way that copy is marked for typing or printing, except that corrections are marked on the margins rather than within the lines. Corrections in proof-reading are indicated either with leaders from the point of correction to the margin, or by indicating the point of correction with caret or other suitable indicator and placing the markings at either end of the line. correction marks at the end of a line are separated by stop signs as shown in the sample proof which follows.

GALLEY PROOF MARKED FOR CORRECTIONS

Specimen 17.2.
Proofreading

MARKING OF COPY

Copy is prepared for the typist or typesetter by marking all coections entirely with in the lines wherever room permits, rather than in the margins. Long passages to be inserted may be written in the margin Material to be deleted is marked out solid. Either ink or a medilum soft pencil may be used. The harder pen cils donot make a black enough line and real soft lead smudes to much.

When the inter changing of words sentences or paragraphs is complicated, the sections should be retyped or cut out and pasted in their proper sepuence. As a rule, typists and typesetters "follow copy and are not expected to follow the sence of what is being copied All mirks, therefore, are placed so that they will be seen by the operator in time to comply therewith. For this reason, markings are usually placed above the line than below. At places where words are inserted or deleted, leaders are used to direct the eye from the end of a correct wod to thenext. A RING around a numbperal or an abbreviation in the copy is an instruction to spell out the material encircled. If the words abbr eviated may not be known to the typist they should be sped out above the abbreviation and the abbreviation crossed out. the reverse indication doesnot apply; Cross generally out the number in words or the spelled out words and write in the numerals or the abbreviations. Example: a pressure of nine psi/was observed in the 8 tests completed in Jan.

Marking of Proof

Theproof reader reads to find mistakes; he is concerned not with the gaining of information. Nevertheless he must continually be aware of the thought expressed in order to catch omission of words, wrong derivatives of words, and errors of grammar. He reads deach letter of each word in oer to prove spellng. This method is in contrast with ordinary reading for pleasure or for information in which whole words or word groups are recognized with out out individual reading of letters.

Printers proof is marked in much the same way that copy is marked for typing or printing, except that corrections are marked on the margins rather than within the lines. Corrections in proofreading are indicated either with leaders from the point of correction to the margin, or by indicating the point of markings at either end of the line. Correction marks at the end lf a line are separated by stop signes as shown in th sample proof which follows.

GALLEY PROOF CORRECTED

Specimen 17.3.
Corrected galley proof

MARKING OF COPY

Copy is prepared for the typist or typesetter by marking all corrections entirely within the lines wherever room permits, rather than in the margins. Long passages to be inserted may be written in the margin. Material to be deleted is marked out solid. Either ink or a medium soft pencil may be used. The harder pencils do not make a black enough line, and real soft lead smudges too much.

When the interchanging of words, sentences or paragraphs is complicated, the sections should be retyped or cut out and pasted in their proper sequence. As a rule, typists and typesetters "follow copy" and are not expected to follow the sense of what is being copied. All marks, therefore, are placed so that they will be seen by the operator in time to comply therewith. For this reason, markings are usually placed above the line rather than below. At places where words are inserted or deleted, leaders are used to direct the eye from the end of a correct word to the next.

A ring around a numeral or an abbreviation in the copy is an instruction to spell out the material encircled. If the words abbreviated may not be known to the typist they should be spelled out above the abbreviation and the abbreviation crossed out. The reverse indication does not generally apply; cross out the number in words or the spelled out words and write in the numerals or the abbreviations. Example: A pressure of 9 psi was observed in the eight tests completed in January.

MARKING OF PROOF

The proofreader reads to find mistakes; he is not concerned with the gaining of information. Nevertheless, he must continually be aware of the thought expressed in order to catch omission of words, wrong derivatives of words, and errors of grammar. He reads each letter of each word in order to prove spelling. This method is in contrast with ordinary reading for pleasure or for information in which whole words or word groups are recognized without individual reading of the letters.

Printer's proof is marked in much the same way that copy is marked for typing or printing, except that corrections are marked on the margins rather than within the lines. Corrections in proofreading are indicated either with leaders from the point of correction to the margin, or by indicating the point of correction with a caret or other suitable indicator and placing the markings at either end of the line. Correction marks at the end of a line are separated by stop signs as shown in the sample proof which follows.

APPENDIX A

References for Collateral Reading

American Standards Association, 70 East 45th Street, New York 17, N.Y. The following American Standards:

Y14.1 — 1957. American Drafting Standards Manual, Section 1, Size and Format.

Y14.2 — 1957. American Drafting Standards Manual, Section 2, Line Conventions, Sectioning, and Lettering.

Y14.3 — 1957. American Drafting Standards Manual, Section 3, Projections.

Y14.4 — 1957. American Drafting Standards Manual, Section 4, Pictorial Drawing.

Y14.5 — 1957. American Drafting Standards Manual, Section 5, Dimensioning and Notes.

Y15.1 — 1959. Illustrations for Publication and Projection.

Note: The above series is published by the American Society of Mechanical Engineers, 345 East 47th Street, New York 17, N.Y.

Z10.1 — 1941. Abbreviations for Scientific and Engineering Terms.

Z15.2 — 1938. Time Series Charts.

Z32.13 — 1950. American Standard Abbreviations for Use on Drawings.

Anderson, Chester Reed, and others. Business Reports: Investigation and Presentation. 3rd ed. New York, McGraw-Hill Book Co. 1957.

Angoff, Charles. Handbook of Libel. New York, Duell, Sloan and Pearce. 1946.

Arkin, Herbert, and Colton, Raymond R. Graphs — How to Make and Use Them. Rev. ed. New York, Harper and Brothers. 1940.

Babenroth, A. C. Babenroths Modern Business Communication. Ed. by Charles C. Parkhurst. Englewood Cliffs, N.J., Prentice-Hall, Inc. 1955.

Ball, J., and Williams, C. B. Report Writing. New York, Ronald Press Co. 1955.

Bickle, Margaret D., and Houp, Kenneth W. Reports for Science and Industry. New York, Henry Holt and Co. 1958.

Billett, Roy O. Preparing Theses and Other Typed Manuscripts. Paterson, N.J., Littlefield, Adams & Co. 1956.

Bingham, Walter V. D., and Moore, Bruce V. How to Interview, 3rd rev. ed. New York, Harper and Brothers. 1941.

Bird, George L. Article Writing and Marketing. Rev. ed. New York, Rinehart & Co. 1956.

Birk, W. Otto. Structural Grammar for Building Sentences. Boston, D. C. Health and Co. 1949.

Brown, Leland. Effective Business Report Writing. Englewood Cliffs, N.J., Prentice-Hall, Inc. 1955.

Carnegie, Dale. Public Speaking and Influencing Men in Business. New York, Association Press, 1955.

Corbin, Richard K., and Perrin, Porter G. Guide to Modern English. Chicago, Scott, Foresman and Co. 1955.

Crocker, Lionel G. Public Speaking for College Students. 3rd ed. New York, American Book Company. 1956.

Douglass, Paul. Communication Through Reports. Englewood Cliffs, N.J., Prentice-Hall, Inc. 1957.

Elfenbein, Julien. Business Journalism. Its Function and Future. Rev. ed. New York, Harper and Brothers. 1947.

Flesch, Rudolph. The Art of Plain Talk. New York, Harper and Brothers. 1946.

———. The Art of Readable Writing. New York, Harper and Brothers. 1949.

———. How to Make Sense. New York, Harper and Brothers. 1954.

———. How to Test Readability. New York, Harper and Brothers. 1951.

———. New Way to Better English. New York, Harper and Brothers. 1958.

Flesch, Rudolf, and Lass, A. H. Way to Write. 2nd ed. New York, McGraw:Hill Book Co. 1955.

Gamble, Charles W. Modern Illustration Process. 3rd ed. New York, Pitman Publishing Corp. 1953.

Gaum, Carl G., Graves, Harold F., and Hoffman, Lyne S. S. Report Writing. 3rd ed. Englewood Cliffs, N. J., Prentice-Hall, Inc. 1950.

Gehman, Richard. How to Write and Sell Magazine Articles. New York, Harper and Brothers. 1958.

Gray, William S., and Leary, Bernice E. What Makes a Book Readable. Chicago, The University of Chicago Press. 1935.

Gundell, Glenn. Writing – From Idea to the Printed Page; Case Histories of Articles in the Saturday Evening Post. Garden City, N.Y., Doubleday & Co. 1949.

Gunning, Robert. How to Take the Fog Out of Writing. Chicago, Dartnell Corp. 1956.

———. Technique of Clear Writing. New York, McGraw-Hill Book Co. 1953.

Hall, Ray Ovid. Handbook of Tabular Presentation. New York, The Ronald Press Co. 1943

Handy, R. S., and Cliffton, Katherine. Business English in Practice. 2nd ed. New York, Pitman Publishing Corp. 1956.

Harwell, George C. Technical Communication. New York, The Macmillan Co. 1960.

Hay, Robert D., and Lesikar, Raymond D. Business Report Writing. Homewood, Ill., Richard D. Irwin. 1957.

Hodges, John C., and Connolly, Francis X. Harbrace College Handbook (English). 4th ed. New York, Harcourt, Brace and Co. 1956.

Hoffman, William George. How to Make Better Speeches. New York, Funk & Wagnalls Co. 1948.

Hogan, Homer. Dictionary of American Synonyms. New York, Philosophical Library Publisher. 1956.

Howell, Almonte C. Handbook of English in Engineering Usage. 2nd ed. New York, John Wiley & Sons, Inc. 1940.

———. Military Correspondence and Reports. New York, McGraw-Hill Book Co. 1943.

Howell, Herbert A. The Copyright Law. Washington, D.C., The Bureau of National Affairs. 1942.

Hutchinson, Lois I. Standard Handbook for Secretaries. 7th ed. New York, McGraw-Hill Book Co. 1956.

Ivins, William M., Jr. Prints and Visual Communication. Cambridge, Mass., Harvard University Press. 1953.

Jenkinson, Bruce L. Bureau of the Census Manual of Tabular Presentation. Washington, D.C., U.S. Government Printing Office. 1949.

Jones, W. Paul. Essays on Thinking and Writing. Rev. ed. Dubuque, Iowa, Wm. C. Brown Co. 1955.

———. Writing Scientific Papers and Reports. 4th ed. Dubuque, Iowa, Wm. C. Brown Co. 1959.

Kierzek, John M. and Gibson, Walker. The Macmillan Handbook of English. 4th ed. New York, The Macmillan Co. 1960.

Lasky, Joseph. Proofreading and Copy-preparation. New York, Mentor Press. 1954.

Leggett, Glen, Mead, C. D., and Charvat, William. Handbook for Writers. Englewood Cliffs, N.J., Prentice-Hall, Inc. 1954.

McCrimmon, J. M. Writing With a Purpose. 2nd ed. Boston, Houghton Mifflin Co. 1957.

McDonald, Philip B. Personality and English in Technical Personnel. New York, D. Van Nostrand Co. 1946.

McGraw-Hill Publishing Co., Inc. Typographical Stylebook. New York, McGraw-Hill Publishing Co. 1940.

McPeek, James A. S., and Wright, A. Handbook of English. New York, Ronald Press Co. 1956.

Marder, Daniel. The Craft of Technical Writing. New York, The Macmillan Co. 1960.

Mawson, C. O. Sylvester (editor). Roget's International Thesaurus. New ed. rev. New York, Thomas Y. Crowell Co. 1946.

Moore, R. H. Effective Writing. New York, Rinehart and Co. 1955.

Morgan, William S. Writing and Revising. New York, The Macmillan Co. 1957.

Nelson, J. Raleigh. Writing the Technical Report. 3rd ed. New York, McGraw-Hill Book Co. 1952.

Nicholson, Margaret. A Dictionary of American-English Usage. New York, Oxford University Press. 1957.

Oliver, Robert T., and Cortright, Rupert. New Training for Effective Speech. 3rd ed. New York, Henry Holt and Co. (Dryden). 1951.

Opdycke, John Baker. Say What You Mean; Everyman's Guide to Diction and Grammar. New York, Funk & Wagnalls Co. 1944.

———. Take a Letter Please! Rev. ed. New York, Funk & Wagnalls Co. 1944.

Parkhurst, Charles C. English for Business. 3rd ed. Englewood Cliffs, N. J., Prentice-Hall, Inc. 1958.

Patterson, Helen M. Writing and Selling Feature Articles. 3rd ed. Englewood Cliffs, N.J., Prentice-Hall, Inc. 1956.

Perrin, Porter G. Writer's Guide and Index to English. 3rd ed. Chicago, Scott, Foresman and Co. 1959.

Perrin, Porter G., and Smith, George H. Handbook of Current English. Chicago, Scott, Foresman and Co. 1955.

Racker, Joseph. Technical Writing Techniques for Engineers. Englewood Cliffs, N.J., Prentice-Hall, Inc. 1960.

Robertson, Horace O., and Carmichael, Vernal. Business Letter English. 2nd ed. New York, McGraw-Hill Book Co. 1957.
Sandford, William P. Speak Well—and Win! A Short Cut to Results. New York, Whittlesey House (McGraw-Hill Book Co.). 1944.
Schmitz, Robert Morell. Preparing the Research Paper. 4th ed. New York, Rinehart & Co. 1957.
Shaw, Harry. Writing and Rewriting. 4th ed. New York, Harper and Brothers. 1955.
Skillin, Marjorie, Gay, Robert M., and others. Words Into Type. New York, Appleton-Century-Crofts, Inc. 1948.
Smart, Walter K., and McKelvey, Louis W. Business Letters. 4th ed. New York, Harper and Brothers. 1957.
Souther, James W. Technical Report Writing. New York, John Wiley & Sons, Inc. 1957.
Summey, George. American Punctuation. New York, The Ronald Press Co. 1949.
Sypherd, W. O., Fountain, Alvin M., and Brown, Sharon. The Engineer's Manual of English. Rev. ed. Chicago, Scott, Foresman and Co. 1943.
Taintor, Sarah A., and Munro, Kate M. The Secretary's Handbook; A Manual of Correct Usage. 7th ed. New York, The Macmillan Co. 1949.
Thomas, Payne E. L. Guide for Authors: Manuscript, Proof, and Illustrations. Springfield, Ill., Charles C. Thomas. 1958.
Thompson, Alan R. Handbook of Public Speaking. Rev. ed. New York, Harper and Brothers. 1949.
Thorndike, Clarence L. (editor). Thorndike-Barnhart Concise Dictionary. Rev. ed. New York, Doubleday & Co. 1958.
Trelease, Sam F. Scientific Paper: How to Write Scientific and Technical Papers. 3rd ed. Baltimore, Md., Williams & Wilkins Co. 1958.
Tucker, S. Marion. Public Speaking for Technical Men. New York, McGraw-Hill Book Co. 1939.
U.S. Army Service Forces. Standards of Presentation. 3rd printing. Washington, D.C., War Department. May 1946.
U.S. Government Printing Office. Style Manual. Rev. ed. Washington, D.C., U.S. Government Printing Office. 1959.
University of Chicago Press. A Manual of Style. 11th ed. Chicago, The University of Chicago Press. 1949.
Waldo, Willis H. Better Report Writing. New York, Reinhold Publishing Corp. 1958.
Walters, Margaret. Basic Guide to Clear and Correct Writing. Chicago, Scott, Foresman and Co. 1958.
Warriner, John E., and Griffith, Francis. English Grammar and Composition: A Complete Handbook. New York, Harcourt, Brace and Co. 1957.
Watt, W. W. An American Rhetoric. 2nd ed. New York, Rinehart and Co. 1957.
Webster, Noah. Webster's Dictionary of Synonyms. 1st ed. Springfield, Mass., G. and C. Merriam Co. 1942.
Weil, Benjamin H. (editor). Technical Editing. New York, Reinhold Publishing Corp. 1958.
———. Technical Report; Its Preparation, Processing, and Use in Industry and Government. New York, Reinhold Publishing Corp. 1954.
Williams, Cecil B., and Ball, J. Effective Business Writing. 2nd ed. New York, The Ronald Press Co. 1953.

APPENDIX B

Specimen Formal Report—Relocating the Union Bus Station in Ames, Iowa

The following formal report is presented exactly as it was originally prepared in double-spaced typewritten form, except that in this book it is printed on both sides of the sheet to conserve space.

Preliminary Proposals For

RELOCATING THE UNION BUS STATION IN AMES, IOWA

by

Edwin R. Overborn
Senior Civil Engineering Student

to

Loren R. Heiple
Assistant Professor of Civil Engineering
Iowa State University

Ames, Iowa
December 5, 19..

327 Welch Avenue
Ames, Iowa
December 5, 19..

Loren R. Heiple
Assistant Professor
Civil Engineering Department
Iowa State University
Ames, Iowa

Dear Professor Heiple:

The report which you requested September 27 on moving the intercity bus station of Ames from the Sheldon-Munn Hotel is submitted herewith.

Because certain desirable information upon which to base a decision to relocate the station was not available to me, I suggest that a more thorough study be made before anyone is induced to construct the new station. However, the results herein given are reliable in pointing out that a new station is highly desirable and that a separate station at a new location can be operated with reasonable assurance of financial success.

While this report is submitted as one of the requirements of C. E. 484, Engineering Reports, it has been a realistic assignment, and I appreciate having had the opportunity to prepare the report.

Very truly yours,

Edwin R. Overborn

Edwin R. Overborn
Senior Civil Engineering
Student

TABLE OF CONTENTS

ABSTRACT

The motor vehicle and pedestrian traffic around the intercity bus station at the Sheldon-Munn Hotel of Ames, Iowa, and the passenger facilities within the hotel are now so unsatisfactory that for reasons of traffic safety and convenience to the public immediate improvement of the bus station services is desirable.

The purpose of this report is to inquire into the existing conditions as a basis for determining what facilities should be provided in a new station, and then to propose arrangements which will relieve the congestion and provide the city of Ames with convenient and satisfactory bus station services.

The investigation results indicate that the present location cannot be remodeled to produce a satisfactory station and that an ideal location is available at the vacant southeast corner of Main Street and Clark Avenue, two blocks west of the present bus station.

A preliminary analysis of the financial considerations shows that a station can be developed at the proposed location which will provide the normal facilities required by intercity bus passengers and off-street loading space for six buses. The development is estimated to cost $87,000 and to produce a revenue sufficient to earn 5 to 18 per cent annual return on the investment over a period of 30 years.

PRELIMINARY PROPOSALS FOR RELOCATING THE UNION BUS STATION IN AMES, IOWA

INTRODUCTION

The over-all passenger and vehicle facilities at the Sheldon-Munn Hotel are no longer adequate to care for the intercity bus traffic of Ames, Iowa. For reasons of safety to traffic and convenience to passengers, it is desirable to move the bus station to a location which will provide adequate room for both passengers and buses without interfering with regular city traffic. This report shows that a separate union bus station can be made a sound financial venture and that a separate bus station is the preferred method of improving the intercity bus traffic facilities in Ames.

No attempt is made in this report to develop final plans for a bus station with exact costs of investment and operation. This preliminary report shows that a complete investigation and final design should be made because there is need for improved bus facilities in Ames and that it is economically profitable to operate a separate station. While the exact records of bus traffic to and from Ames were not available to the author, the data used in this report are indicative of the existing situation and are reliable for purposes of this preliminary report.

That a new bus depot is desirable is made apparent by the unsatisfactory conditions at the present hotel location, and that a new station is a possibility is indicated by the action of the Ames City Council in endeavoring to bring about a new location. Officials of the two main bus lines serving Ames, the Interstate Transit Lines and the Jefferson Transportation Company, have indicated their willingness to relocate their main stop provided suitable facilities are found. Thus, if a separate location and building can be provided, the bus companies, the traveling public, and the city of Ames will each benefit because the loading and handling of passengers will be easier, accommodations for passengers will become adequate, and traffic congestion around the hotel will be relieved.

In order to determine whether a new bus station is economically feasible for Ames, this report will discuss the existing facilities and conditions, the available sites for a new station, the cost of construction, and the probable financial return from the operation of a new station.

CONDITIONS AT THE HOTEL STATION

A description of the unfavorable conditions at the hotel station indicates that this location (Fig. 1) is not adequate and that it cannot be improved. Principally, the objections are lack of building facilities to accommodate the passengers and their friends, and traffic congestion on Kellogg Avenue.

In the early 1920's the Sheldon-Munn Hotel was a logical location for the bus traffic because the facilities available there were adequate

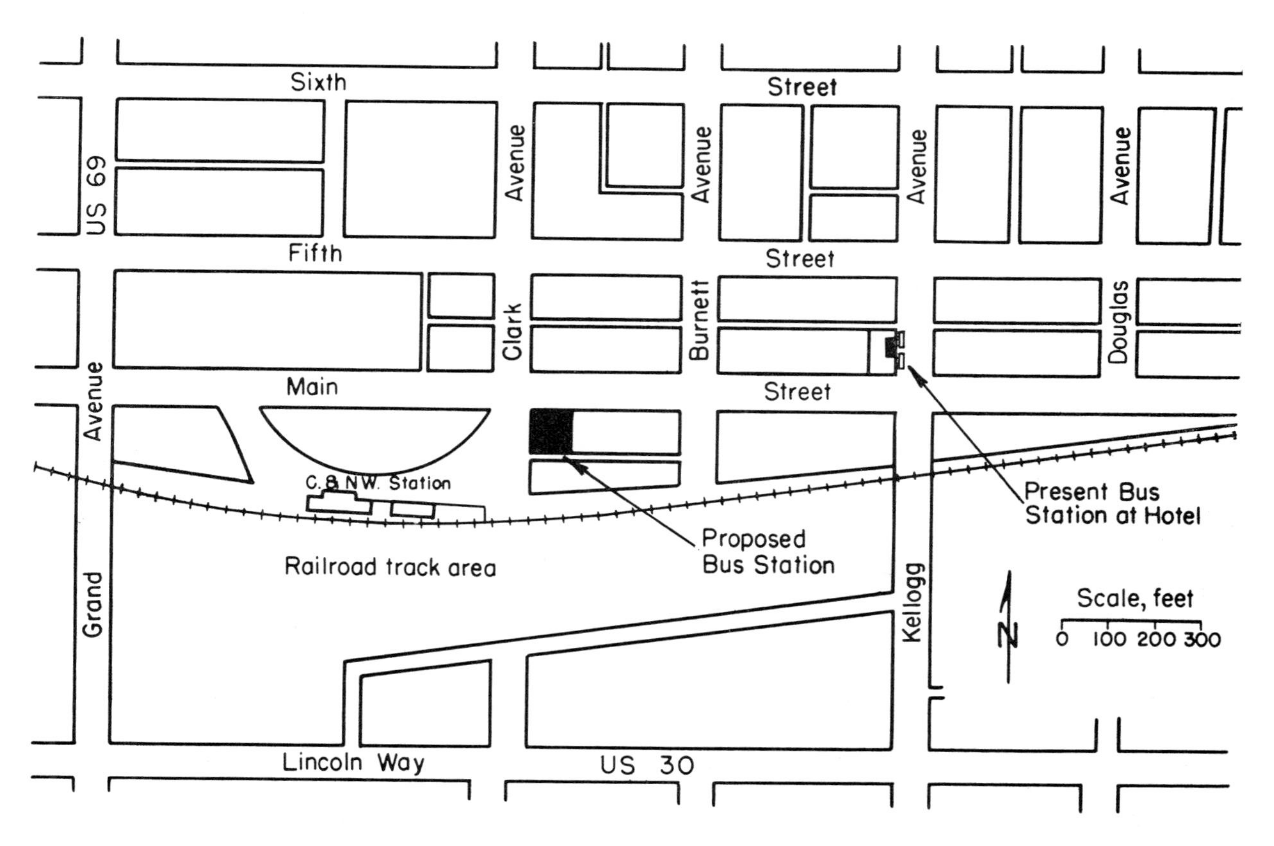

Fig. 1. Location of present and proposed bus stations.

to handle the relatively light volume of bus traffic and the business would not support a separate station. Today, however, the hotel has inadequate waiting room capacity, lunch room space, and rest room accommodations. Kellogg Avenue, along the east side of the hotel where the buses stop, is not wide enough to handle the four to six buses which are at the station at one time. The resulting congestion within the block has been the cause of about 16 vehicle accidents a year. Because of the blocking of the sidewalk by bus passengers and their nonpassenger friends, pedestrians cross the street in the middle of the block which further contributes to the traffic hazards on Kellogg Avenue north of Main Street.

A typical peak day, this fall, Saturday, October 11, was chosen for making passenger and traffic counts. Between 5:00 and 5:30 p. m., there were 75 passengers awaiting transportation. The hotel lobby seats only 33, so the half of the passengers who were unable to find seats concentrated around the doorway and out on the sidewalk. This action blocked the doorway for both hotel guests and others desiring to enter or leave the hotel by the east door, and made it difficult for anyone to walk along the sidewalk outside the hotel. During this same half hour there were about 148 passengers-in-transit who endeavored to use the rest rooms and coffee shop. These crowded conditions are undesirable for the passengers, hotel guests and passers-by. The congestion is likewise objectionable in case of fire because of suitcases and traveling gear which are scattered about. The doorway and entry hall through which the passengers move in and out of the hotel are narrow. During inclement weather the congestion inside the hotel is particularly bad.

The motor vehicle traffic count which was taken 5:00 to 5:30 p. m. on October 11 was 96 vehicles south and 149 north on Kellogg Avenue past the hotel. Parking of private vehicles is allowed on the east side of the street and on the west side north of the alley, except when buses are there. The street is barely wide enough for four lanes of traffic; the in and out maneuvering of these wide buses creates poor visibility, and the south-bound vehicle traffic, particularly, must exercise the utmost caution to prevent accidents. Pedestrians are prone to cross the street at the alley because of the difficulty of getting through on the west sidewalk during the hours of heavy bus traffic.

From the observation of these congested conditions, which occur every weekend and holiday throughout the year and many times during week days, it is evident that improved facilities are highly desirable. In order to achieve acceptable facilities, the bus station will need to be moved to another location because there is no space available at the hotel for additional passenger waiting room space and general facilities, and the street is not wide enough to construct bus loading space off the regular traveled way. The new buildings north of the hotel, now used for a grocery store and a bank, are too costly to even consider remodeling for a new bus depot.

SPACE REQUIREMENTS

Since passenger waiting space and bus loading space are the two chief considerations in arranging new accommodations, it is in order to determine how much space is needed. The combined resident and student population of Ames is about 27,000. About 160 bus tickets are sold on ordinary week days and 650 on holidays and other peak days. From the meager records available, it is found that the bus traffic has increased somewhat faster than the increase in population of Ames. The bus traffic has increased about 70 per cent in the past 10 years, and will likely increase 25 per cent within the next 10 years, or to 200 tickets on average week days and 800 on peak days. The combined population of Ames in another 10 years is estimated at 31,000.

The bus depot facilities will need to be large enough to care for a crowd of 150 people, with adequate cafe and rest room facilities for the passengers of six to eight buses at the station at one time. Figure 2 shows the number of buses at the present station through the day. In addition to a normal week-end peak of about six buses in the station at one time, loading space for three additional buses should be provided for student traffic at the end of school terms and for vacations at Iowa State University. Ames is not likely to become a division point, so space for mechanical shops and bus servicing need not be provided.

The other important requirement is a location where the bus and pedestrian traffic will not interfere with the normal city traffic. Loading space for the buses should be entirely off the street and sidewalk areas.

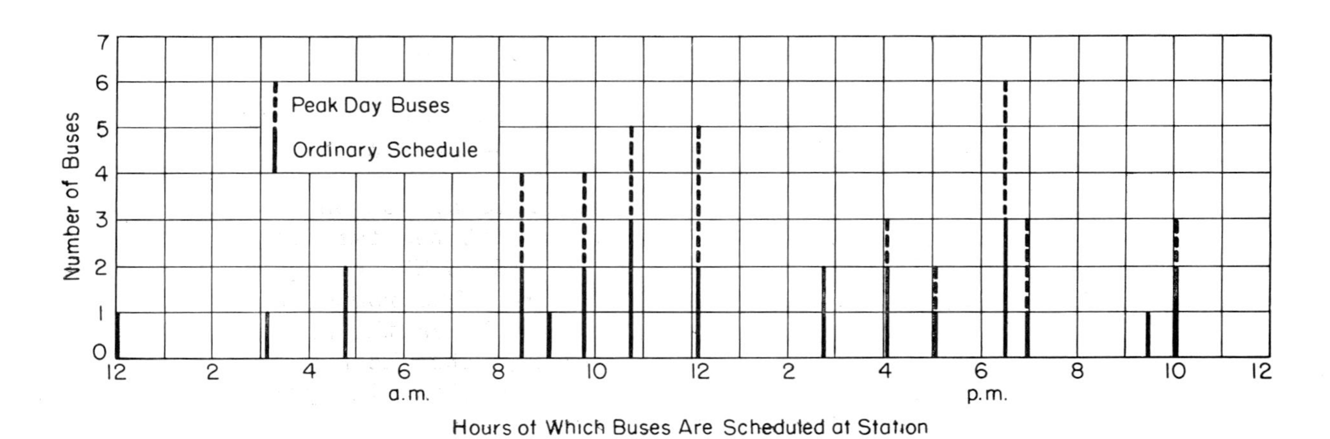

Fig. 2. Number of buses scheduled at the hotel station for typical days in October.

SELECTION OF BUILDING SITE

The requirements of a lot for the bus station are briefly stated:

Size--About 75 by 100 feet or larger

Topography--Nearly level and at street grade

Improvements--Preferably a vacant lot on a street fully improved with utility services and paving

Location--Near the business center of town, not on a street of heavy normal traffic, not too far off the main highway routes US 69 and US 30 through town, reasonably close to the city bus route, so located that buses may enter and leave the bus loading area without interfering with the movement of other vehicles, and a location with private car parking areas close by.

The requirements of location limit the generally accepted areas to Sixth Street near Kellogg, Fifth Street, and the western portion of Main Street. See Fig. 1. Lincoln Way, although convenient to the bus routes, is not considered because of its heavy traffic and distance from the business district. Kellogg Avenue, a convenient location, is not desirable because of the now crowded traffic conditions between Lincoln Way and Sixth Street. Suitable locations are to be had on Fifth Street west of Clark Avenue and on Sixth Street, but in both areas houses would need to be moved at a considerable extra expense over what a vacant lot would cost. Vacant lots at Fifth and Kellogg, Fifth and Burnett and Fifth and Grand are suitably located and improved, but in each case the lots are unavailable because the owners are planning other developments.

The most desirable location for the bus station is the area at the southeast corner of Main Street and Clark Avenue (Fig. 1). The four lots, each 24 by 100 feet, form an area adjacent to the Prehm Transfer and Storage Company, and are now used for general parking of vehicles. E. W. Lackore, executive secretary of the Ames Chamber of Commerce, stated that the Chicago and North Western Railway Company has indicated a willingness to sell the lots for use as a bus station.

Because this corner at Main and Clark fully meets the requirements for a bus station and is available, other locations were not investigated in detail. The area, 96 by 100 feet, is at street grade on all three sides, and is of ample size, particularly so because it is bounded on the south by a lightly used paved alley and on the west by the wide stub-end of Clark Avenue which is the east entrance to the Chicago and North Western Railway Station area. Main Street traffic along the north side of the lot is not too heavy, because it is at the edge of the business district and beyond most of the cruising-for-parking-space traffic. City traffic regulations should be changed to prohibit U-turns at this intersection. Parking for vehicles is available around the railway station grounds and on Main Street to the west, where traffic is usually light. This location is adjacent to the railway station, only two blocks west of the present hotel station, and one block south of the present city-bus route.

Buses arriving or departing from Ames may reach the station without driving through any main business street. Buses from the north, and to the southeast and west, will follow Main Street from and to Grand

Avenue; buses to the north and from the south, east and west will follow Fifth Street. Thus, all the bus travel within Ames will be confined to US 30, US 69, Clark Avenue between Main and Fifth Streets, and Main and Fifth Streets between Clark and Grand Avenues. There will be no bus traffic within the business area east of Clark Avenue.

A plan for the development and operation of a bus station at the southeast corner of Main Street and Clark Avenue is next presented, before the financial aspects are considered.

STATION REQUIREMENTS

For the purposes of this report the general layout of the station and its approximate size are all that are required; no attempt is made to develop the structural or architectural details. The usual features of waiting room, rest rooms, food service, newsstand, baggage checking and ticket purchasing are provided in the general plan shown in Fig. 3.

Other bus stations were studied in arriving at the preliminary plan. There is a waiting room seating capacity of 75 persons, lunch room seats for 20, and sufficient additional floor space to accommodate 150 people within the station building, as shown by the preliminary plan in Fig. 3. Because the lot is relatively small, the rest rooms for both employees and passengers are placed on the lower floor, which also houses all the mechanical equipment and general storage for the restaurant.

A wide concourse, or loading platform, on the west, runs the length of the 53- by 86-foot building. A large doorway opens between the waiting room and this loading area. The three north-south loading lanes

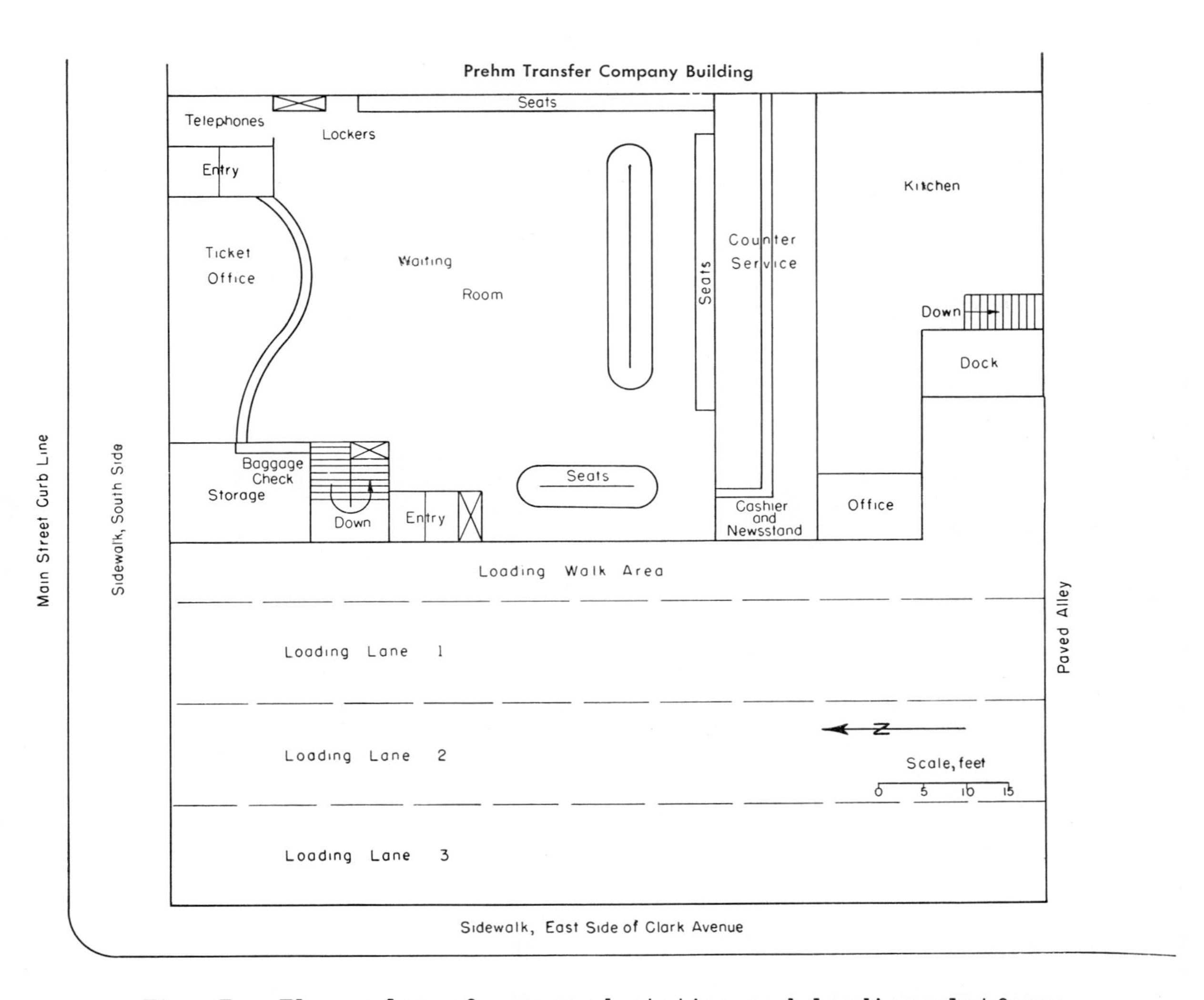

Fig. 3. Floor plan of proposed station and loading platform.

provide for six buses at a time; additional buses may be stopped to the south or in a fourth lane along the east side of Clark Avenue.

FINANCIAL CONSIDERATIONS

Because records of the exact bus traffic and costs of operating the present station are not available, the financial analysis to be presented should be regarded as preliminary and subject to adjustment in a final report. Further, because the proposed station building is not detailed, the estimated costs are also approximate.

Whether or not a separate bus station can be operated in Ames at a profit may be determined by an analysis of the cost of construction of the station building and loading areas, the cost of operation of the station and the revenue to be derived therefrom through the sale of tickets, food and other services incident to the use of the station. Estimates of these costs and incomes are given in Table 1, together with some detail as to the basis of the estimates.

The net return of $4,070 indicated in Table 1 provides an annual return of 4.7 per cent on the initial investment or about 9 per cent on the average investment over the 30-year period used in estimating the depreciation of the entire facilities. These rates of return are not sufficient to justify the investment because the risk involved is great enough to justify a rate of 10 to 12 per cent. On the other hand, the income from ticket sales is estimated in Table 1 on the basis of present traffic and rates of fare, while an increase of 25 per cent in traffic

TABLE 1. CONSTRUCTION AND OPERATING COSTS AND REVENUES

A. Construction Cost (exclusive of restaurant equipment)	
1. Purchase price of lots 11, 12, 13, and 14	$12,000
2. Building construction	70,000
3. Paving of loading area 43 by 100 ft	2,000
4. Seats, lockers and office furniture	3,000
5. Total investment in station	$87,000
B. Annual Operating Expense	
6. Manager's salary	$3,000
7. Clerk hire, 3 at $2,000	6,000
8. Janitor services	1,500
9. Fuel, maintenance and general operation	1,200
10. Taxes, insurance and licenses	1,800
11. Total annual operating expense	$13,500
C. Annual Revenue	
12. Commission on ticket sales (10% of gross)	
310 days, 160 tickets at 20 cents each	$9,920
55 days, 650 tickets at 20 cents each	7,150
13. Commission on newsstand and tobacco sales	1,500
14. Lease on restaurant	1,500
15. Total annual gross revenue	$20,070
D. Analysis of return	
16. Return, exclusive of depreciation	$6,570
17. Annual depreciation, 30-year life	2,500
18. Estimated annual net return	$4,070

is expected within 10 years. Increase in revenue from this increase in traffic would double the net return and make the rate of return over the period of operation sufficient to justify the investment.

CONCLUSIONS AND RECOMMENDATIONS

An analysis of the operation and facilities of the intercity bus traffic for Ames, Iowa, clearly indicates that the existing arrangements at the bus station at the Sheldon-Munn Hotel are no longer adequate and that unwarranted traffic hazards are created on the streets near the hotel. Examination of possibilities for improving the facilities and relieving the traffic congestion at the bus station further indicates that the only solution is to establish a union bus station at a more desirable location.

The southeast corner of Main Street and Clark Avenue is recommended as the ideal location for a new bus station. At this location, a new building can be constructed and ample off-street loading space provided for six buses, and for additional buses on the little-used south end of Clark Avenue.

An analysis of the financial aspects indicates that there is sufficient possible net return, 5 to 18 per cent, to warrant an investment of $87,000, the estimated cost of the new station. Because the financial analysis has been made without full information and without a detailed design for the station building, it is recommended that the bus companies cause a final analysis to be made with the full and complete information which they alone can furnish.

Because of the dangers to traffic, and resulting congestion around the hotel, it is recommended that the City Council of Ames serve notice on the bus companies concerned that their station is to be moved from the hotel before the end of next year.

Index

D

E

F

G

H

I